PRAISE FOR I'LL BE RIGHT THERE

I have always held in the back of my mind an uneasy to-do list as it relates to caring for my mom, especially now that my dad has passed. After reading this book, I know I can take this on. Today that means that I can take inventory of all the paperwork in my safe (which I have been avoiding) and that I can be better plugged in to what my mom may need help with at home (but won't ask for). Tomorrow that might mean knowing how to deal with a medical situation…or something more serious.

—**Heather**, caregiver

I'll Be Right There is from the heart. Chock full of detail, humor, compassion, and love. Fern has captured the essence of being a caregiver, and we know the best advice comes from having lived that role. The book is an easy read, not a classic Rx, and Fern's style and comic relief allow one to say, "OMG—that's my parent(s)!"

—**Judy Simon**, geriatric expert; creator of T.A.P.—The Alzheimer Project
(movement program based on ballroom dance) and The Parkinson's Choir;
Former owner A&J Home Care

After more than 15 years of caring for my disabled father—leading up to his passing—I thought I knew everything an adult child caring for an aging parent needed to know. I'm happy to say that *I'll Be Right There* proved me wrong in the best way possible. This book is a wonderfully comprehensive resource. Fern manages to present an amazing amount of information in an engaging yet realistic way. She doesn't shy from the difficult or sensitive topics and uses her compassion and experiences to guide a reader through what can be a very hard process and major life event. I'm reassured that I'm now better prepared to help care for my aging mother.

—**Karen**, caregiver

This book provides an amazing road map for the reader. You can choose what chapters you need to visit and spend time reviewing. The guidance is clear and relatable along with recommendations and valuable resources in one comprehensive location. Congratulations, Fern, on taking this journey with your parents and procuring all the expertise along the way for the benefit of others.

—**Marie Duquette**, Atria @ Villages of Windsor, Community Sales Director

Fern has a nice way of relating difficult concepts into digestible sections. I particularly like the way she addresses driving. Driving while incapacitated (the real DWI) is a major problem, especially in cities without a good public transit infrastructure. It is an issue that must be approached with understanding and respect. The tools provided in *I'll Be Right There* should help readers on this and many other issues. Fern approached these types of difficult topics with sensitivity and insight.

—**Scott Solkoff**, Elder Law Attorney

I particularly liked reading about your journey and about dealing with anger. I thought it was only my situation that my husband was so very angry and hostile.

—**Barbara**, caregiver

I would have bought *I'll Be Right There* for the title alone, but as an adult who has cared for grandparents and is now sharing care for my parents along with my siblings, I am very aware of the need for great resources along the way. This guidebook is practical and compassionate, helping us avoid panic and assuring us that we will have what we need to navigate these uncertain times. Empowered with the information Fern has generously shared in this book, we can care for our parents and also care for ourselves. We can do this!

—**Connie M. Baker**
Executive Director, Wong-Baker FACES Foundation
Co-creator of the Wong-Baker FACES® Pain Rating Scale

In the 23 years since I gave up managing the books for my parents' retail business and founded Judith Heft & Associates, I have seen so much. I've watched less-than-honorable people insinuate themselves into the Wills of elderly people; grandchildren smooth talk their way into taking tens of thousands of dollars from their grandparents' checking accounts; charities harass people until someone keeps giving (even after they had just made a donation); identity theft perpetrated by strangers, families, and care-workers, and so on. My goal is to keep an eye out for my clients, handling the day-to-day money management issues that arise, while educating them on how to avoid repeats of similar situations. Working with adult children who have found themselves in the caregiving role for their aging parents, I know how overwhelming it can be to manage things that keep popping up all the time. People have their own lives and then suddenly they're managing another whole set of finances, legal issues, property concerns, health changes, and possibly mental capacity decline for the people who raised them! It's a complicated situation. Assistance to make the situation manageable can be a huge relief.

I found Fern's book to be very well written and comprehensive. She didn't leave anything out and it is easy to read. She makes the sometimes difficult topics so easy to understand. I love that Fern injected humor into some places even when the situation she was describing was dire. I think readers will really appreciate the personal touch it all seems to have. In the end, a caregiver child will be able to create a plan, develop steps to execute that plan, and gain confidence to know that things are being covered, whether local or long-distance. That's a gift!

—**Judy Heft CMC®**
Certified Money Coach

I'LL BE RIGHT THERE

I'LL BE RIGHT THERE

—— *A Guidebook for* ——
ADULTS CARING FOR
THEIR AGING PARENTS

FERN PESSIN

PUBLISH
YOUR
PURPOSE
PRESS

For permission requests, write to the publisher, addressed "Attention: Permissions Coordinator," at the address below.

Publish Your Purpose Press
141 Weston Street, #155
Hartford, CT, 06141

The opinions expressed by the Author are not necessarily those held by Publish Your Purpose Press.

Ordering Information: Quantity sales and special discounts are available on quantity purchases by corporations, associations, and others. For details, contact the publisher at the address above.

Edited by: Heather B. Habelka
Cover design by: Alex Valchev
Typeset by: Medlar Publishing Solutions Pvt Ltd., India

Printed in the United States of America.
ISBN: 978-1-946384-69-0 (print)
ISBN: 978-1-946384-70-6 (ebook)

Library of Congress Control Number: 2019939184

First edition, July 2019.

The information in this book is for educational purposes only.

This publication contains the opinions and ideas of its author. It is intended to provide helpful and informative material on the subjects addressed in the publication. It is sold with the understanding that the author and publisher are not engaged in rendering medical, health, financial, legal, or any other kind of personal professional services in the book. The material may include information, products, or services by third parties. As such, the author and publisher do not assume responsibility or liability for any third-party material or opinions. Readers are advised to do their own due diligence when it comes to making decisions. The author and publisher specifically disclaim all responsibility for any liability, loss, or risk, personal or otherwise, which is incurred as a consequence, directly or indirectly, of the use and application of any of the information contained in this book.

Neither the author nor the publisher shall be liable or responsible for any loss or damage allegedly arising from any information included in this book. Nothing contained in this book is intended to be instructional for medical diagnosis or treatment. Nothing contained in this book is intended to be legal or financial advice for your personal situation. The information should not be considered complete, nor should it be relied on to suggest a course of treatment or actions for a particular individual. It should not be used in place of a visit, call, consultation, or the advice of your physician or other qualified healthcare provider, legal counsel, or financial advisor. Neither the author or the publisher directly or indirectly practice medicine, therapy, dispense medical services, financial advising, or legal counsel as part of this book.

At the time of writing, all the URL, addresses, phone numbers, and statistics are current. Please note that over time, information and/or access to certain pages may change.

Data and organizations mentioned within this book are primarily US-based. Financial and legal terms are based on author's local knowledge and may be different in other countries and in different municipalities throughout the United States.

Some names and locations were changed to respect privacy.

Publish Your Purpose Press works with authors, and aspiring authors, who have a story to tell and a brand to build. Do you have a book idea you would like us to consider publishing? Please visit PublishYourPurposePress.com for more information.

For my family (birth and chosen)

HOW TO USE THIS BOOK...

Wait! Don't panic. You've picked up this book and you're looking at how much information there is and you're thinking, "OMG!!!" Don't worry.

The goal of this book is to give you a heads-up on what will be coming, so that you can consolidate your efforts, make lists, and do things calmly and economically *before* you are actually crushed for time and/or money.

Several things:

a)   A lot of pages are worksheets to be filled in.

b)   You won't need to follow everything in this book! Everyone's situation is different, and there are several options to help you find what works for you.

c)   You will only need some new things as your parents reach new levels of required care, so you're going to go through this book—like life—in phases.

Here's the optimal way to use this book:

1)   Take a quick look through the Table of Contents to get a sense of what's included.

2)   Read through the book once and make note of things you want/need to come back to right away.

3)   Make a list of things you want to do NOW, Soon, and Later

4)   Over time, when you're ready at each phase of your parent's aging, you can come back and find what you need in the Table of Contents, and then go through those sections in depth as you need them.

TABLE OF CONTENTS

People talk about the serenity prayer and, while I always loved it, I never really personally connected with it until I became a caregiver.

"God grant me the serenity to accept the things I cannot change,
the courage to change the things I can,
and the wisdom to know the difference."

FOREWORD

At the Louis and Anne Green Memory & Wellness Center we are dedicated to serving the aging population through a holistic approach, grounded in the Christine E. Lynn College of Nursing's Philosophy of Caring. Our expert interprofessional team provides clinical evaluations that address the nature, extent, and causes of memory disorders and other health concerns. Our goal is to reach beyond the medical diagnoses to provide education, ongoing support, and improve the quality of life of the person experiencing health challenges and their loved ones who are often referred to as *caregivers*.

Supporting the caregivers is essential to achieve our mission. My daughter Patricia is one of the facilitators for our adult child caregiver support group. Patricia told me about a group member, Fern, who had evolved from being exhausted and discouraged to someone sharing advice and peer support with new group members. One thing led to another, and Fern (being a writer) wrote everything down for her fellow caregivers, and I was honored when she asked me to read her manuscript and write this foreword.

For the first time in many years, I saw, heard, felt, and read what I had been wishing for. For the first time, someone presented caregiving as a positive, cheerful action. Thank you, Fern!

Fern takes very difficult and emotional topics and shares her lived experience and stories of her fellow caregivers to reduce the burden and stress of caregiving. Her stories are funny, honest, helpful, and hopeful. When reading this book, you feel as if a friend is with you, having a conversation about something that happened today. Caregivers need that kind of support!

I like that Fern did not start this manuscript as a professional expert. She did get her Home Health Aide certification, but mostly it's been learn-as-you-go, which is how most caregivers manage their responsibilities. There are lots of books written by trained experts in the field, but sometimes practical advice from someone living the experience moment to moment can be reassuring and useful: It makes it real. Using tips and techniques learned by trial and error, filling in the worksheets with important information, and making use of resources and contacts will help any caregiver manage the work that needs to be done with confidence and efficiency. It's much less stressful if you can be ahead of the game by preparing and will be less costly if things aren't handled at the last minute, when your options might be limited. Fern's lived experience is brought to you with joy, passion, and hope.

Whether you live in the same house, down the block, across the city, or out of the country a world away from your loved ones, *I'll Be Right There* is a valuable addition to any caregiver's library, an enchanting and enriching tool to guide you, support you, and cheer you up through the caregiving journey. Thank you, Fern!

María de los Ángeles Ordóñez, DNP, APRN, GNP-BC, PMHNP-BC, FAAN
Director, Louis and Anne Green Memory & Wellness Center
FAU Memory Disorder Clinic Coordinator, Alzheimer's Disease Initiative
Associate Professor of the Christine E. Lynn College of Nursing
Assistant Professor of Clinical Biomedical Science (Secondary)
Charles E. Schmidt College of Medicine
Florida Atlantic University

PREFACE

I moved to Florida to help my parents age with grace. I moved to provide support. Of course, I didn't mind moving to warmer weather, far away from the Northeast's snowy winters. I was proud to be the family representative on-site for my parents so my siblings could remain in New York with their families and careers. I came to Florida open to whatever would come.

I didn't arrive in Florida with a degree in nursing. I'm not a lawyer or financial planner. I've never worked in assisted living. I am just a regular person, like all the other people I've been meeting who are going through the same thing with their own parents. It has taken a lot of research, patience, and advocacy detective work to figure out what exactly I needed to do to accomplish my mission of helping my parents.

I am not alone. There are over 34 million unpaid caregivers in the United States! When I talk with people beginning their own parent-caring journey and I share some tips and tell them what I've done so far, they ask me, "How the he** did you know to do all that? Where did you find that information? Why can't someone just give me a list of everything I need to do?" And then they say, "You should write a book!"

I searched and found that the information I needed to steer my parents' aging years was scattered, but available. There are some fantastic resources in book and web formats. There are organizations with experts and tools to help. There are businesses designed to reduce your burdens and make it all go smoothly. There are devices galore that make life easier. But it takes time to source all this, and most people I meet are smack-dab in the middle of their own lives and already too busy to add research to the to-do list.

I gathered what I could, researched late into many nights—until my eyes turned red from staring at computer screens—and I started attending local caregiver events where I found resources. I read what experts had to say. Then I interviewed local experts in various specialties, got certified as a professional Home Health Aide from a nursing school, and participated in caregiver tools programs. I attend support groups every week.

It is my hope to provide for you, the reader, all the "Things You Didn't Know You Need to Know" stuff. I've compiled everything I've learned into this guidebook to help you manage the different stages of your parents' aging challenges; understand when to focus on what; and offer guiding questions to help you figure out what to look for in your own situation.

Support is available. It is my hope that this material helps you figure out what you need to make the journey ahead less stressful. If you feel that you can take on this responsibility with confidence, then I've accomplished my goal. Feeling recognized and appreciated may not be voiced by your family and those around your parents but please know that you are, and we (your fellow caregivers) are here to listen and help!

Welcome to the club!

PARENTING MY PARENTS

"I'll be right there," I said, putting the laptop aside while rising from my chair. I disconnected the call, grabbed my keys and purse, and ran out the door. Ran back in the door because I forgot my sunglasses. Double-checked to make sure I had my cell phone (because half the time I forget it!) and went back out the door again. This lifestyle of being on call can make a gal a little ditzy!

The cell phone call had been from Mom. Aargh! "Where does she need a ride to now?" I had grumbled under my breath as I answered the phone. With a lump in her throat, she creaked out that Dad was "feeling like he's going to die." Translation: Dad's daily light-headedness is worse today. And my athletic, manly dad does not like being out of control—not of his body, certainly not of his mind, not of his life, managing his family, nor his finances. And here he is…85 years old…gradually losing his abilities to manage anything.

Of course Dad is angry and wants to rage against the world. Of course he's scared. So now my usually lighthearted, always smiling when he sees his family, secret-keeper for friends, generous and loving dad lashes out verbally or becomes petulant. Knowing these changes are happening, I'm running out on my life and dropping my work to go to my parents' to assess the situation. To provide any support I can.

Mom called me from her bathroom so Dad wouldn't hear her calling me. Normally, Dad would say, "Don't bother Fern." My mother whispered worriedly into her cell phone, "Is this the time he's really going to die? Or is it the same as last time and he'll feel better in a few hours?" When Dad has a day when he feels like the end is near, you never know what he wants. Will his machismo override his fear today? Since we don't know, I'm on the way.

Just my walking in the front door calms my mother, who is anxious and frightened about taking care of Dad. She doesn't know how to handle him when he gets like this. When Dad is scared, Mom is terrified. My parents have been married for over 60 years and Mom has always been protected from the world.

I walked in calmly, went straight to Dad, sat down in the cream-colored leather swivel armchair, turned to face him—my concerned eyes locked onto his teary, cataract-cloudy-blue eyes, and empathetically said, "Dad, it's okay. I'm here. What's going on? Tell me how you feel."

My dad looked back at me and said, "It's worse today. I don't know what's happening. I feel like I'm going to die."

"Why, Dad? What's different today?"

"I don't know. I just feel different. I'm more lightheaded. I'm not walking that well."

"Okay. How long have you felt like this?"

And the conversation continued until I figured out what was happening. In this moment, Dad's distress was because he had found himself unexpectedly face-planted on the floor when he tried to get out of his power recliner. He didn't put the leg extension down before trying to stand up. He had lain dazed on the thick, blue pile carpet in front of the chair in the bedroom trying to remember how to stand up. This scared him to bits.

The chair has a remote function that can guide him up without any struggle, but he simply forgot to push the button to return the leg extender before trying to stand up.

On a similar "I'm going to die" day in the past, he was upset because, despite his clothing hanging on the door handle of his armoire, he didn't know how to get dressed that morning. Another day he was ping-ponging down the hallway getting to the bathroom and knocked artwork off the wall. Glass was everywhere.

Before that, there was the day he tried to stand up, slipped off a metal terrace armchair, wound up with his butt on the hard tile floor, and was not able to remember how to get up by himself. This scared him so much that he became terrified it would happen again and asked me to teach him how to get off the floor. We practiced!

The worst time was when he literally lost his crap because he was taking drugs for bronchitis, didn't realize he had to go to the bathroom, and just didn't make it there on time. That "real shitty experience" as my dad jokes, is on the top of his "most terrifying things I don't want to ever happen again" list.

People talk about their Bucket List of things they want to do or experience before they die. What about the list of things we DON'T want to happen? What is that list called? The UN-Bucket List maybe? The Anti-Bucket List?

The lists of things that are bothersome for my dad grows daily. He's always been an athlete. He still walks 2.5 to 3 miles a day. "How," he wonders aloud, "can I be having these issues? I'm strong! Doc says I'm in great shape!" And it's true, he is. But his brain is becoming like Swiss cheese, and it's not something he can control, fix, or change. Nor can I do anything to help stop that process. I am not the super human I think my parents want me to be.

Dad's worried that he's going to totally lose his mind and sit drooling and staring off into space. Or that he'll fall and Mom won't be able to help him or care for him if something serious happens. Or that he'll be a burden on the family.

Dad notices changes in Mom's cognition and says to me, "That wasn't the deal." She was supposed to start taking care of him! He took care of Mom during the year and a half she battled a rare bone cancer. Her job was to take care of him in his declining years. It doesn't work if Mom is getting worse at the same time Dad needs her.

Dad's nervous that he won't be able to take care of my mother if she falls and, with newly diagnosed osteoporosis, fractures something. He has ALWAYS taken care of her. There's a lot of ego caught up in caring for a family for almost 60 years.

Every day I am now privy to personal things that my parents feel and do. I hadn't thought about that when I agreed to move to Florida.

I never thought my parents were invincible or infallible, but I was always the child and they were the parents and, via experience, they knew things that I didn't. Now, the roles are flipping and I'm teaching and using parenting skills to guide my parents. Listening to he said/she said arguments like they're siblings complaining about each other. Nope. That wasn't on the list of expected responsibilities.

On a daily basis, Dad gets agitated when my mother doesn't talk to him face-to-face, which means he can't hear her because he doesn't wear his hearing aids in the house (long story); or she walks away while still talking to him; or she mumbles; or she talks on the phone set to speakerphone; or tears newspaper articles while he's trying to watch television and he *is* wearing his hearing aids...a myriad of small things set him off now.

Dad gets angry that Mom says, "In a minute..." when he asks her to look at something or bring something to him since she's standing already. He believes she's disrespecting him. And that hurts now, more than when he was younger and totally self-reliant. He doesn't understand that Mom also has dementia issues and can't focus on more than one thing and she knows she'll forget what she's doing if she doesn't finish it. But practical tools—like write things down, put them on a whiteboard, keep all the papers in one place—don't apply when the brain is playing games with cognition.

The physical changes in Dad's body are the stated reason he gets upset. Angry that his body is betraying him. The loss of hearing. Rheumy eyes with occasional floaters. Being off balance. Constant light-headedness. Persistent tinnitus. He has a pacemaker. His legs swell. His hands lock up. Every time a new sign of aging and changing pops up, he becomes agitated and anxious. But the deepest fear is that his mind is going. He does his checkbook every day—balancing against the bank to the penny. He was a tax man, so money and numbers are safety. When the ability to manage numbers goes, he will get further depressed. I know this.

Physically, for an 85-year-old, my dad and his pacemaker-ed heart are going well. The pieces of the brain decaying are what make me nervous—and it is so unpredictable that I'm on call, on demand, 24/7/365. And that is where things get tough. If I can't hold it together, who is going to take on this caregiving role with my parents?

If Mom was able to handle Dad, that would be okay. But my issues are not only with my father. My mom is a proud bone cancer survivor, is a hoarding clutterer, has neuropathy in one foot, has osteoporosis, takes cholesterol medication, and is on an antidepressant. She takes a cocktail of drugs and supplements to prevent her from getting too upset when Dad yells at her. This means she looks at me blankly when I ask her questions. It also means that she walks around Costco telling people on the checkout line that she's a cancer survivor, so she gets hugs and sympathy! I spend time returning things to the store when she buys another load of "but it's only $2! A bargain!" items that are not needed.

I am not alone. I know this because my friend Rosemarie, visiting her cognitively impaired mother (Marie), found her mother had purchased 62 wallets in one shopping trip! Why would anyone need 62 wallets? Marie couldn't explain it. Back they went. There are millions of us going through this. YOU are not alone!

On more interesting days, when Mom's mind seems to be fully open, she shares whatever's in there—without filters. Mom once told me that she thinks I am trying to get rid of her so I can marry my father! My therapist and I spent a lot of time on that little nugget!

Recently, Mom started recalling childhood trauma of sexual advances by a man working on my grandparents' house. Seems like I'm hearing all kinds of new stories. Are they imagined or real?

Tell me—do you also feel like you've acquired a whole new list of job skills? I have. I'm suddenly a psychiatrist, social worker, physical therapist, home health aide, marriage counselor, nurse, hostage negotiator, family counselor, legal expert, doctor, financial planner, chauffeur, errand girl, chef, companion, friend, and confidante...and my skills grow daily. I should be able to get one heck of a job when I have time again!! Occasionally, I'm still just one of the kids. But more often, I'm a parent of my parents.

Do you also find yourself saying, "I'll be right there!" or "I'm on the way!" more often than in the past? Have you tried to offer logical advice to your parents and had it rejected? Made suggestions to siblings about possible improvements to a parent's lifestyle for better wellness and had it rejected as "You're worrying too much!" or been told to stop spending Mom's money? Welcome to the role of a caregiver.

After my first two years in Florida, my parents and siblings started seeing what I was seeing and we made the logical (though very, very difficult) step of moving my parents to an independent living residential setting where everything is at their fingertips and help is a cord pull or button push away.

I tell people my parents now live on a cruise ship that never leaves port. Many of the challenges that faced them in their snowbird Boca Raton condo are now gone. The calls to me for daily assistance have not totally vanished, but I can direct my parents to resources right in their own building, which makes my life a bit easier. But naturally, different challenges appear because my parents are in a newly constructed and unfamiliar environment.

My nature is to control what I can, plan for everything I can anticipate, and find support to help me. My goal is to get through helping my parents enjoy their last years in the most effortless way possible.

I participated in three caregiver groups until I found the right fit—one specifically for children caring for parents. I've taken caregiving education classes, attended Alzheimer's education programs, and worked with aides and nurses. I was in the fitness business for 15 years, where I attended conferences, workshops, and classes, and was a consultant on motivation. This should all be easy for me, right? NOPE. Anyone in the field will tell you that, even though they help others all day long, when it comes to their own parents, it is way different!

To paraphrase Bette Davis in *All About Eve*, "Fasten your seat-belts, it's going to be a bumpy ride!" In taking on this caregiver challenge, you will find blessings, joy, and enlightenment along with tears, resentment, loneliness, anger, frustration, and feelings of being overwhelmed. And there's quite a bit of guilt that weaves in and out of every week. Don't feel you need to repress it—we all go through it. How much or how little you want to be involved in your parents' care, how much is too much before you run into your own health issues, is ultimately only up to you to determine.

I wish you a smooth ride and internal peace! As my support system keeps reminding me, I pass to you:

You are remarkable to take on this challenge. Your family is lucky to have you.

And when your family members don't remember or acknowledge that, I am here, along with my friends and other caregivers, to reassure you! You are not alone. My contact info is at the back of this book!

YOU KNOW IT'S TIME

Just when you start feeling like you're getting your own life back—perhaps your kids are out of the house, the mortgage is paid off, or you've got business worked out so you can get away—it's time for you to discover what you love to do. It's the Bucket List check-off time! You believe this is YOUR time. HAH! Not so much. If you're reading this book, chances are you're in transition to a caregiver role.

Suddenly, the trips to visit your parents become more frequent. One parent passes away and the other is now alone. The phone calls from neighbors start coming, "I haven't seen your mother taking her morning walk, you might want to check on her." or "Your father locked himself out of the house again, just thought you should know."

Perhaps your generous parents start hoarding their money because somehow (they don't understand how) their financial accounts are diminishing quickly. It takes three hours for a parent to get home from a place they visit all the time that is 10 minutes away because they can't remember the route back home. Or one of your parents slips, trips, falls, has a heart or brain incident, or a worsening of a health condition, and being completely on their own is not advisable anymore.

This is when you knock your head against the wall, cry into a pillow, and silently (or maybe not so silently) scream, "WHY NOW? WHY ME?" And then the "guilts" arrive. Uninvited and unwelcome. You shove that feeling of frustration way down deep and become the responsible person who you are. Time to step up and take care of your parents. Maybe you have the support of your whole family and your siblings. Maybe you don't. Maybe, like me, you're the "logical" one to take on this role.

As I write this, I am feeling huge guilt. I am taking time to write this book instead of being with my parents. I have trouble accepting that taking time to do something that is important to me is okay. How do I manage feelings of not being my usual business leader self? My creative self? My romantic self? I'm easily lost these days. You might be too when you take on the caregiver role.

You know you could just ignore what's happening. You could let your parents fend for themselves. Many people do. But if you're reading this book, you're the one who has likely realized that someone has to fill this caregiver/protector/advocate role because this person—these people—gave birth, adopted, and/or raised you, and you'd want someone to make sure you headed into the golden light of the sunset ahead, with grace and dignity intact.

If you live far away from your parents, you start to worry all the time. You call, they don't answer. Where are they? What happened? How can I check on them from here? Call the neighbor? Wait, do I have that number? Call the fire department? Can't. What if they just went to get the mail? The fire department will be pissed off! And your brain starts to spin. You never feel comfortable. You just worry. All the time. Well, we all know that's not healthy!

Decision made—you know you need to take care of this—but what next? What comes first? Who can help? Do I even know what I'm supposed to do?

It can become overwhelming and confusing. There are so many options for every decision, so how do you know you made the right choices? You hear stories of fraud, deceit, abuse, and start to worry about that too.

Or hey (love this one), your parents don't want your help. Oh yeah! That's pretty darn common. "We are the parents!" they might protest. "Stop telling us what to do!" or "Who made you king?" And my favorite: "You are not the boss of us!" What? Now my parents have moved into the teenager role. They (and, therefore, I) are going backward!!!! It's a daymare.

You still have your own life to live and now you are making lifestyle recommendations to your own parents? The psychological and emotional toll on you is as devastating as the physical and financial issues. How are you supposed to manage everything that you expect of yourself and everything others have come to expect from you?

Most of all…how do you know what to do and when?

ROUGH WATERS AHEAD

Have you ever gone whitewater rafting or tubing on a river? Imagine parental caregiving as a river. You're in a raft with your family and you're drifting down the gentle river. Every now and then, there's a turn or an obstacle and you make your way around it. No problem. You, together with your parents', siblings, relatives, and family friends, can loll around letting your hands trail in the water as you enjoy the view and the sun above.

But then the wind picks up and the water becomes more turbulent. If you keep paddling alone to avoid the obstacles, the raft could start spinning in 360-degree turns because you can't paddle on both sides simultaneously. You need help. You need to wake up everyone in the raft and have them paddle too. With everyone synchronized, you get back to a nice ride. Heading down the river toward that campsite party and big barbecue! Now we're having some fun.

When the powers that be decide to release the dam water...whoo hoo...it's a wild ride now! Well-managed, with everyone pitching in, guided by one leader, the ride can be exhilarating and exciting and uplifting. WOW! If someone slacks off, if someone falls off the raft, then it becomes nerve-racking and gut-wrenching "I can't wait to get out of here alive!" stress and prayers.

Fall out of the raft? Maybe you are bobbing in and out of water and can barely breathe—choking and gasping for air and clearing your lungs of water? Your instructor at the start of your adventure will have taught you to get into Down River Swimmers Position. This is on your back, nose and toes to the sky, with your head up so you can see where you are going. Feet pointing downstream with your knees slightly bent. This way, if you come in contact with a rock you can use your feet and legs as shock absorbers and push off the rock. Arms should be out to your sides to help keep yourself in control.

If and when you fall out of the raft (it happens), grab onto the outside safety (OS) line and wait for someone to help you back in. If you can't make it to the OS line, look for someone to offer you a paddle or toss you the throw bag. (A throw bag is a rescue device with a rope attached to it that can be thrown to an overboard rafter.)

Likewise, you should also know what to do if someone else falls out of the raft. Throw them the OS line or give them a paddle to grab on to. Toss them the throw bag. Are you with me?

When you first realize there are some issues with your parents' ability to be fully independent, it's like a lazy river raft trip. Your parents can handle the river just fine and when there's an obstacle, you can manage the situation and keep them heading toward smoothly running life. Get things back on track, if you will.

When the rough waters pick up and challenges start coming at your parents on a regular basis, you're called in (or perhaps you recognize some help is needed). It becomes clear that someone needs to take over at the helm because the situation at hand is beyond your parents' abilities or resources. Then it's time to bring in help. If your parents don't want you to take over, this becomes much more difficult to navigate.

Perhaps they only want you to help where they want you to help. Also difficult, but at least they're open to your guidance.

If you just try to manage everything as it comes up, like the river, eventually it will be coming at you so fast you won't be able to get to the surface and breathe. You need to kick onto your back, feet leading in front to feel for danger ahead, and have a plan. Contingencies and options anticipated in advance will allow you to be cost-effective and reduce emergency or last-minute decisions that can cost more and ultimately prove to be the least desirable choice.

Answering the questions in each section of this book will help clarify for yourself what you already know and what you still might want to know and what you absolutely need to know to help you create a map to get you through the rough waters.

Once you understand the different components of your parents' care, you will be better able to divide responsibilities with anyone else able to help: friends, family (your siblings, for example), neighbors, professionals, etc. With everyone paddling together toward the same destination, the raft stays afloat, people have a great time, and the end of the journey comes without incident.

This is what I wish for you, and for your parents.

GETTING STARTED

It's best to start organizing and collecting information while your parents can communicate and are still able to help, identify, and advise.

Scott Solkoff, nationally recognized Elder Law specialist with over 20 years' experience, said the one thing he wished people knew was "you should start working on all this before incapacity." Solkoff said the reality is that people mostly wait until there is a diagnosis before coming to see him (or his colleagues) and, at that point, it might be too late to take advantage of money-saving or protecting options.

Once you know that your parents are mobility impaired, slipping into dementia, or have an illness that will progress in a way that will make it difficult for them to live independently, things will start accelerating at a rapid pace, and you're likely to feel like you're drowning.

"I wish someone would have told me all this six months ago, while Mom could have been able to answer those questions!" or "I'm stuck in a paperwork/legal nightmare. Why didn't anyone tell me to get this done?" So here I am, offering you what I have learned.

My goal is to provide you with a plan, the to-do list, an order/schedule to help get you through this very complex part of your life. I'm offering to you what I've learned as just a regular daughter called into service by her family.

IMPORTANT: The titles, language, names of things I describe are how they were told to me, but be aware that you should check with your local experts to find out what is proper in your market. What worked for me in New York City and Boca Raton, Florida, may not be called the same thing or work the same way in your town. I am not a lawyer, doctor, or financial expert. Please take what you read here as my story, which will serve to inform you on what kinds of things you might find helpful in your own situation.

The information is organized in chronological-ish sequence.

Phase I begins with things you can start doing while your parents are aging at home, living independently.

Phase II covers what you can do to make managing oncoming physical and mental changes less frustrating and overwhelming. Perhaps you'll be able to keep your parents living independently for a while longer.

Phase III addresses what to do once permanent impairments set in and outside assistance is needed. We'll review what to do when you notice advancing decline, determine that your parents cannot live alone any longer, and need constant and skilled supervision and support. We'll also review options for end-of-life care.

In each section, details are provided, resources are identified, and tips are offered from people who have gone through it.

Part IV is about you! It's meant to guide the caregiver on ways to cruise through this rough journey with the finesse of a seasoned adventurer.

At the end of the book, you'll find resources and information that I expect will be as helpful for you as they are for me. Should you be interested, there's also information about how to contact me and my network of willing-to-listen parental caregivers. My true goal here is to let you know that you are not alone! Let's laugh and de-stress through this journey together! YOU are a gift to your family.

HOW TO KNOW WHAT YOU NEED TO KNOW

Every person I've spoken to who has become a caregiver (willing or unwilling) has said that the hardest part is knowing what they will need to do. It can feel like you're always starting from scratch. Things come upon you and you suddenly realize that if you knew you were going to have to do this/that/other thing, you could have combined it with the something you did three weeks ago, or you could have bought it all in one place, or you could have asked the expert you already talked to about that topic before, etc. Constantly playing catch-up makes you feel like you're always falling behind, taking two steps forward and one step back, over and over.

Completing the information in this book will enable you to keep everything centrally located. Feel free to use additional sheets where needed. There are blank pages at the back of the book.

Place this book and/or your completed information somewhere easily accessible for yourself, so you can oversee your parents' household free from stress. Keep the book in a place that's visible for someone else if they take over your caregiving role, whether it's for a day, a week, or ongoing. Alternatively, you might consider setting up a digital version of this important information. Then, if necessary, you can find it or share it from wherever you are without carrying a paper copy of info with you. You know—if you win the lottery and run off to take a world cruise and your sister is taking over for now. Hey, it could happen!

10 STEPS TO CAREGIVING

These basic 10 steps can be reviewed and applied to each and every situation that arises when you are caregiving.

Step 1:
Know that if you don't take care of yourself, you won't have the strength to take care of your parents. Remind yourself to take deep breaths and inhale. Breathe out slowly. Repeat often.

Step 2:
Every time the phone rings with a call from your parents: Scrunch your shoulders up to your ears, tightly. Now blow out through your mouth and let your shoulders fall. Relax. Repeat.

Step 3:
Assess your parents' situation.
How far on the spectrum are your parents?
What is needed?
What resources do you have at your disposal?
What support do you have in your network/family?

Step 4:
Make a plan for going forward:

- ❖ Financial
- ❖ Legal
- ❖ Health
- ❖ In the Home
- ❖ Choosing Where to Live

Finding Help:

- ❖ For you
- ❖ For parents

Step 5:

Put your plan into a calendar, a master to-do list.

Step 6:

Identify the contacts and resources you need to execute your plan.

Collect all the contact information, account numbers, costs, etc.

Gather all the paperwork.

Step 7:

Create a budget to figure out what options will work best and what you and your parents/family can afford.

Step 8:

Implement your plan.

Step 9:

Revise, redo, refocus (because things will continually change!).

Step 10:

Take care of yourself!

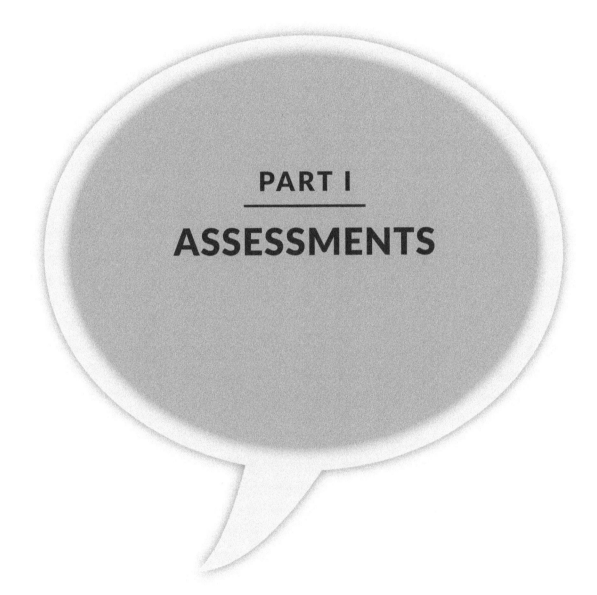

NOTES

AM I WORRYING TOO MUCH?

Mom's always been a little flaky, but now she wears her slippers to the supermarket. Dad's always had a joke for everything, but it feels like something is being hidden or avoided with his humor now. Your "feeling" that something is off seems too vague to start worrying about caregiving, right? But then the egg carton is in the oven and the telephone is in the washing machine. Dad is walking along fine, but suddenly stops at a dark tile on the floor and won't go forward.

Residential facilities recommend looking for signs of needing help with ADLs (Activities of Daily Living—toileting, cooking and eating, driving, dressing, grooming, etc.) to know when your parent needs more assistance and/or supervision.

So, absent a life-changing health incident (a stroke, heart attack, cancer, Parkinson's, Multiple Sclerosis, diabetes side effects, etc.) or an accident, what concrete signs should you look for to know that you might be stepping into a caregiver role soon?

I've created the following checklists for you to assess where your parents fall on the spectrum of aging in various segments of life. The assessments are a compilation of what I've learned from several sources and from my own experiences. Once you check off the things you or your siblings have noticed, it's time to begin getting things in order. After the assessments, you will find more concrete steps for ways you can help, resources you should line up, and suggestions on when to do what.

Behavioral Assessment

Behavior	Category	Area of concern
☐ Taking too long to drive a familiar route	Auto	Mental
☐ Can't find the car	Auto	Mental
☐ Shopping excess (repeatedly buying items not needed or bulk purchases)	Financial	Emotional
☐ Trouble paying bills	Financial	Mental
☐ Money disappearing	Financial	Mental
☐ Giving donations to the same charities over and over (forgot they already gave)	Financial	Mental
☐ Dressing in the same clothing from day to day	Grooming	Mental
☐ Dressing in clothing that smells or is dirty	Grooming	Mental
☐ Stained clothing	Grooming	Mental/Physical
☐ General grooming issues	Grooming	Mental/Physical
☐ General self-care issues	Grooming	Mental/Physical
☐ Changes in mood	Health	Emotional
☐ Increased anxiety	Health	Emotional
☐ Malaise	Health	Emotional
☐ Stressing about daily activities	Health	Emotional
☐ Depression	Health	Emotional
☐ Expressing loneliness (calling more, requesting visits)	Health	Emotional
☐ Skipping hobbies and passion	Health	Emotional
☐ Making inappropriate sexual advances (perhaps flirting more than usual or trying to touch, hug, kiss)	Health	Emotional
☐ Making excuses to hide changes in behavior	Health	Emotional
☐ Moldy food in refrigerator	Health	Mental/Physical
☐ Eating only junk—nothing healthy	Health	Mental/Physical
☐ Always eating—forgot they had already eaten	Health	Mental/Physical
☐ Skipping medication	Health	Mental/Physical
☐ Taking the wrong medications	Health	Mental/Physical
☐ Taking excess medications (Rx or OTC)	Health	Mental/Physical

Behavior	Category	Area of concern
☐ Not eating	Health	Physical
☐ Hospital or Urgent Care visits for cuts, bruises, falling, etc.	Health	Physical
☐ Lots of black and blue marks or cuts and scrapes	Health	Physical
☐ Losing things	Household	Mental
☐ House becoming dirty and untidy	Household	Mental
☐ Suddenly hoarding and hiding things	Household	Mental
☐ Ignoring mail and bills	Household/Financial	Mental
☐ Joking to minimize problematic situations to hide the truth	Memory	Emotional
☐ Forgetting people, places, things	Memory	Mental
☐ Repetitive storytelling	Memory	Mental
☐ Unable to tell you what happened yesterday or last week, not understanding current events or television shows	Memory	Mental
☐ Burning food and/or pots, microwaving unusual things, forgetting to turn off the stove.	Safety	Mental
☐ Trash overflowing	Safety	Mental
☐ Getting lost in the neighborhood	Safety	Mental
☐ Wandering out of the house (Fully dressed? Naked?)	Safety	Mental/Physical
☐ Falling/Tripping	Safety	Physical
☐ Wobbling when walking	Safety	Physical
☐ Can't get out of a chair or off a toilet without falling backward/forward	Safety	Physical
☐ Never leaving house	Socialization	Emotional
☐ Socialization with friends and family changing	Socialization	Emotional
☐ Fear of doctor visits	Socialization	Emotional
☐ Missing appointments	Time/Calendar	Mental

How many of these signs have you noticed? _____

How many were emotional issues? _____

How many were physical issues? _____

How many were mental cognition issues? _____

Sometimes, when people do this kind of assessment, they find themselves surprised by what they uncover. If there are more than three or four discoveries, or if any of them seem much different than "normal" for your parent, then the next step would be to take Mom or Dad to the doctor for a professional assessment. If all works out to be fine, you will feel better. If not, then you're ahead of the game and can take action. If nothing popped up now, I would suggest you redo the assessment in a few months to stay cognizant of any oncoming challenges.

Rachel, feeling that her father was covering up that he was forgetting conversations, told her father a story about a man who dyed his cat pink and they discussed this at length. What a funny story! Ten to 15 minutes later, Rachel asked her father a question about the pink cat. He couldn't recall the story and was trying to cover it up by making Rachel feel guilty for questioning him because *of course* he remembered what she said! Rachel took her father to see a neurologist.

A neurologist will do tests to see if your loved one has cognitive decline. The neurologist may ask your loved one to count backward, remember random items in a list a few minutes after hearing them, touch their fingers to their nose with closed eyes, walk straight, pick out shapes or colors, etc.

The primary care physician will check for bacterial and viral causes of symptoms. If there's something noticeable in a different realm, a referral to a specialist might be recommended.

Between a neurologist and your primary care physician, you can determine if there are physical causes for the signs you checked off. If so, there may be medical or physical remediation that can help. For example, sometimes a UTI (Urinary Tract Infection) will present itself as signs that resemble mental issues, delirium, or physical symptoms of aging. An antibiotic could take care of that and then you're done! Bruises may come from walking into furniture just because Mom or Dad needs new glasses. A loss of appetite could be because of depression or loss of taste buds, or a cold, mouth sores, etc. The critical thing is to be aware and pay attention to the behaviors and evidence you can see or hear that are different for *your* parents.

For example, cluttering and collecting/saving things is normal for my mother. Thus, finding five years' worth of sugar packets from restaurants is not something I would find questionable. But if your parent never did that before, then something might have been triggered.

Paying bills when they come in is my father's pride, so when I find unpaid bills, I know things are off.

I can't count backward in increments of seven *now* without using my fingers! Someday, a neurologist is going to ask me to count backward and they will say my brain is gone because I can't!!! I'm putting this deficit on my record now, so I don't get an early dementia diagnosis and moved into assisted living! LOL

Follow your instincts and intuition. Know your parents' "normal" so you can tell when there's something to note.

Health Assessment

As part of the assessment process for your parents, collecting data on general health issues is going to provide a baseline so you'll know what to look for when talking or visiting with your parents' physicians at whatever point that happens.

My mother forgets that she already had a CT scan a month ago in a similar area of her body. Why should she have to go through that again? She asks EVERY doctor about her "champagne bottle legs" and the white bump on the roof of her mouth. They look at me and I just give them the update and what's been done by the physician who really needs to be concerned about those issues. When something changes, and I think there may be a reason to be concerned, then at least I have the history.

Every doctor asks for the same lists and history. If you can collect it and type it all up, you'll save your parent a lot of time and embarrassment when they can't remember, you'll know the info is correct and current, and the doctors can make the best decisions based on full information.

If your parent is typically private about personal health, remind them of when you were a child and they knew all your health issues and how handy that was. "If," you say nicely, "something was to happen and you were unable to speak (a car accident, a stroke, fainting, etc.) to the doctor or EMS, wouldn't you want me to have the information to ensure you get the best care?"

If your parent is concerned that you are going to declare them incompetent or try to steal their money or kill them off, then you are going to have an uphill battle getting this info. The next best thing is to observe where you can. Ask your parent to carry a flash drive with updated medical info perhaps? Or at least give you the names of their doctors and medications that you can give to the emergency room staff to call to get an updated medical history if the situation calls for it.

Here's a worksheet to help you compile the basics:

Medical History

What conditions does your parent have now?

Brain: _____

Dental: _____

Energy: _____

Eyes: _____

Hearing: _____

Heart related: _____

Immune: _____

Mobility: _____

Muscle: _____

Other: _____

_____

Check conditions parent has been treated for in the past:

Allergies:_____

> ❖ Food: _____

> ❖ Latex: _____

> ❖ Medicine: _____

> ❖ Other: _____

Anemia: _____

Arthritis: _____

Asthma: _____

Blood Pressure Issues/Stroke: _____

Cancer: _____

Diabetes (insulin?): _____

Epilepsy: _____

Glaucoma: _____

Hay Fever: _____

Heart Condition: _____

Hepatitis: _____

HIV: _____

Jaundice: _____

Sinus: _____

Tuberculosis: _____

Ulcers: _____

Parent's Wellness Activities

How often does parent exercise?

Cardio _____ × per week

Strength _____ × per week

Flexibility _____ × per week

Balance _____ × per week

Does your parent use an exercise facility in their community/building/home, attend classes, go to the pool, etc.?   ☐ Yes   ☐ No

Does your parent play racquet sports (tennis, paddleball, squash, racquetball?)   ☐ Yes   ☐ No

Does your parent play golf?   ☐ Yes   ☐ No

Does your parent have a person or people to exercise with? Someone who might hold them accountable for showing up and going for a walk around the neighborhood or at the local mall?   ☐ Yes   ☐ No

Other: _____

_____

What does your parent do to challenge his/her brain? How often?

Board Games _____ × per week

Jigsaw or other physical puzzles _____ × per week

Reading (books, newspapers, etc.) _____ × per week

Game shows (answering the questions) _____ × per week

Computer Games _____ × per week

Lectures/Classes _____ × per month

Travel—how often? _____

Meet new people _____ × per month

Gather with friends _____

Card games _____

Competition games (mahjong, bridge, dominoes, chess, checkers, etc.) _____

Other: _____

_____

Driving Assessment

Take a ride with your parent while they are still driving. Keep an eye on their ability to focus, lane adherence, turn signal usage, finding locations, speed, safety, stop time at lights and/or behind someone stopping ahead on the road. Reaction time to other drivers and people, animals, or bicycles, etc. on street is important to track and notice.

How many of these signs do you observe with your parents?

- ☐ Forgetting how to locate familiar places
- ☐ Failing to observe traffic signals
- ☐ Making slow or poor decisions
- ☐ Driving at inappropriate speeds
- ☐ Becoming angry and confused while driving
- ☐ Hitting curbs
- ☐ Using poor lane control
- ☐ Making errors at intersections
- ☐ Confusing the brake and gas pedals
- ☐ Returning from a routine drive later than usual
- ☐ Forgetting where he or she has been
- ☐ Distracted by signs or buildings/stores along the side of the road
- ☐ Startled by or unaware of quick movements outside of the car
- ☐ Distracted by things in the car (how do I work the lights/radio/GPS/turn signal, where is my change/tissues/eye glass case?) while driving
- ☐ Not noticing things in peripheral vision (a pedestrian walking off the curb, a cyclist in a bike lane, a car turning at right on red ahead)
- ☐ Unaware of emergency vehicles approaching (lights and/or sirens)

Ask your parent these questions:

- ❖ Have you gotten lost going someplace familiar?
- ❖ Has anyone told you that you should stop driving?
- ❖ Have any of your friends told you they don't want to be in the car if you're driving?
- ❖ Have you gone through a red light or stop sign without realizing it?
- ❖ Have you ever confused the brake and the gas pedal or had trouble deciding which one to use?
- ❖ Have you hit or nearly hit someone or something?
- ❖ Have you heard or felt someone smack your car because you were backing up and they were behind you?
- ❖ Have you recently been stopped by an officer who questioned how you were driving?
- ❖ Have you ever thought or been told that you shouldn't drive with your grandchildren in the car?

If the answer to any of these questions is yes, then it is time to have "the talk." In the Communication section of this book, you'll find suggestions on how to approach this topic with your parents, siblings, and other family members.

Another option to consider is scheduling your parent for a driving evaluation. These can be arranged at the Department of Motor Vehicles, driver's ed schools, and private and/or nonprofit cognitive functioning/memory testing centers. Ask your local Area Agency on Aging, a neurologist, or elder advisory center for recommendations.

Remember—driving is not just about the person behind the wheel being able to start and drive the car. Driving ability is impacted by all the other people driving on the road, people and animals walking, cyclists, motorcyclists, driving conditions (weather, traffic, road conditions [pot holes, cracks, rocks, etc.]), as well as car maintenance.

Distracted driving comes in three different forms according to Esurance[1]:

❖ Cognitive distraction: When a driver's mind isn't focused on driving.
❖ Visual distraction: When a driver looks at anything other than the road ahead.
❖ Manual distraction: When the driver takes one or both hands off the wheel.

Driving with even mild cognitive impairment is the same as driving while texting, drunk, or physically exhausted. None of these are legitimate excuses when someone gets hurt or killed, or when property has been destroyed.

---

[1] http://www.Esurance.com

Home Life Assessment

When you're visiting your parents, start to observe or ask questions to help you assess the viability of your parents remaining at home and independent. If the answers reflect a need for more support, at least you'll know what kind of support you want to seek.

- ❖ Can your parents still use the telephone? □ Yes □ No
- ❖ Can your parents use remote controls? □ Yes □ No
- ❖ Do your parents have support? Friends or groups to go to/talk to if you're not available? □ Yes □ No
- ❖ Are there nonperishable supplies in case of a power outage (soup, canned fish, peanut butter, water, etc.) □ Yes □ No

Daily Upkeep

- ❖ How often do your parents do laundry? _____ × per week _____ × per month
- ❖ Is the home clean? □ Yes □ No
- ❖ Is there food in the refrigerator and pantry? □ Yes □ No
- ❖ How often do your parents grocery shop? _____ × per week _____ × per month
- ❖ How often is linen changed on the beds? _____ × per week _____ × per month
- ❖ Have you ever seen rodents, bugs, spiders, etc. in your parents' home? □ Yes □ No

Wander around the house. Take the long way to the bathroom with a few detours and pretend you're looking for something you know "is here somewhere, Mom." During this inspection of the home, do you notice any of the following? Put a check next to things you will need to address:

- ❖ Things that need repair?
- ❖ Trip hazards that should be removed?
- ❖ Problems with appliances?
- ❖ Light bulbs that need replacing?
- ❖ Electrical hazards? (e.g., too many things plugged into one outlet or extension cord, frayed cords)
- ❖ Plumbing issues?

Fire hazards:

- ❖ Has anyone checked filters on heating or a/c units to see if they need replacing or cleaning?
- ❖ Do the carbon monoxide and smoke detectors need new batteries? Do they work?
- ❖ Appliances overheating (going on or off on their own?)
- ❖ Knobs/buttons for stove/oven loose or broken

- ❖ Metal dishes or foil in microwave
- ❖ Matches close to flame
- ❖ Candles exposed (not in glass containers)
- ❖ Burn marks on surfaces
- ❖ Overstuffed closets

Safety Issues:

- ❖ Clutter
- ❖ Too much paper
- ❖ Tilting or over-packed shelves
- ❖ Tilting or over-stacked boxes

Money Issues:
- ❖ Are bills being paid?
- ❖ Any sign of power, heat, water, or phones being cut off?
- ❖ Is there a tracking system for money paid to charities (perhaps to track for taxes) to avoid duplication?

Auto Related:

- ❖ Is the car in good condition inside and out?
- ❖ Notice any scratches? Dents? Cracks?
- ❖ Tearing in upholstery or carpets?
- ❖ Maintenance schedule adhered to?
- ❖ Oil changes current?

Perimeter of The Home:

- ❖ Are steps painted with anti-slip paint?
- ❖ Are there railings on both sides of any stairs? Railings along walkways?
- ❖ Is there a clear path between garage/car port/sidewalk to the door of the home?
- ❖ Is there a clear and safe path between the mailbox and the door of the home?
- ❖ Do stairs or walkways need repairs?
- ❖ Are all garden items and tools well away from walkways?
- ❖ Are plants, bushes, and trees clear of walkways?
- ❖ Are movement-sensor lights functioning?
- ❖ Are there any exposed wires or electric shock risks?
- ❖ Is the garden free of poisonous berries, plants, and mushrooms?
- ❖ Are any toxic chemicals being used in or near the garden?

- ❖   Are bird seed dispensers well back and away from walking paths?
- ❖   Is there a contract for snow shoveling and leaf raking to keep paths clear?
- ❖   How is ice removed from walkways during cold days?

Pets: If animals are in the home

- ❖   Are they fed, groomed, and exercised properly?
- ❖   Are the animal areas clean?
- ❖   Are there signs in the home of urine or excrement accidents?
- ❖   Are the animals healthy?
- ❖   Do the animals seem animated and happy?

Results: Areas of Concern

Based on the lists you checked off in this assessment section (Behavioral, Health, Driving, Home) what are the areas causing the most concern?

- ☐ Physical
- ☐ Emotional
- ☐ Mental
- ☐ Other:

Self-Care

Do you believe your parent(s) can still:

Feed themselves	☐ Yes	☐ No
Clothe themselves	☐ Yes	☐ No
Groom themselves	☐ Yes	☐ No

Physical Safety

Are you concerned for their physical safety?	☐ Yes	☐ No

Are your parents:

Eating properly	☐ Yes	☐ No
Managing medications	☐ Yes	☐ No
Seeing okay	☐ Yes	☐ No
Hearing okay	☐ Yes	☐ No
Walking straight	☐ Yes	☐ No
At risk of tripping/stumbling	☐ Yes	☐ No
In a home safe and free of impediments	☐ Yes	☐ No

Independent Living

Do you believe your parents can handle these independent living skills? Do they need assistance?

Can your parents still handle their own errands?	☐ Yes	☐ No
Drive a car on their own?	☐ Yes	☐ No
Do they still own a car?	☐ Yes	☐ No
And can they take care of it?	☐ Yes	☐ No

Take public transportation?	☐ Yes	☐ No
Have friends drive with them?	☐ Yes	☐ No
Know how to hire drivers? (taxi, Uber/Lyft, personal driver)	☐ Yes	☐ No

Financial Safety

Can your parents manage their own money and banking? Do they:

Pay credit card bills?	☐ Yes	☐ No
Balance checkbook?	☐ Yes	☐ No
Use technology to transfer, withdraw money, or view statements, or do they need to visit a bank?	☐ Yes	☐ No
Transfer funds?	☐ Yes	☐ No
Use credit cards and pay the bills?	☐ Yes	☐ No
Use a debit card?	☐ Yes	☐ No
Use an ATM?	☐ Yes	☐ No

Are you parents at risk for fraud or abuse by a con man, scheming organizations, or internet/phone phishing scams?

Are they financially secure?	☐ Yes	☐ No
Are they able to grasp money issues?	☐ Yes	☐ No

Emotional Stability

Are your parents emotionally secure?

Do they need/want more visitors?	☐ Yes	☐ No
Do they have someone to talk to?	☐ Yes	☐ No
Would they benefit from an animal to love?	☐ Yes	☐ No

By analyzing the results, you'll know if it is time to talk to your parents about driving (or *not* driving), staying in their home (or moving or bringing in help), finding financial checks and balance systems or resources to avoid losing assets, or scheduling doctor appointments.

Based on your yes/no answers, you will know where to focus remediation. Make notes here of the steps you'd like to take to work on any issues: _____

_____

In Part II on Communication, strategies and suggestions for how to approach these conversations will help smooth the way for nonconfrontational and productive dialogue.

In Part III, you will find guidance for taking the next steps in supporting your parent, whether issues are mental or physical—or a combination of the two—and whether they are at the beginning or late stages of aging.

PART II

COMMUNICATION

NOTES

TALKING WITH YOUR PARENT

Clear communication with your parents as they age is essential to creating and maintaining harmony among all of you and in the home. We'll begin with tips on how to communicate directly with your aging parent in general.

Communicating with Your Parent: One-to-One Strategies

My mother has a habit of talking to my father as she's walking from room to room. She starts asking a question as she's approaching him and finishes it with her head in the refrigerator or sitting on the toilet in the bathroom. (TMI?) My father hears, "Honey, would you like mmghphon?" And he gets agitated. She may have been asking if he wants his favorite shrimp cocktail appetizer or if he wants a prostate exam—my dad doesn't know! So, he gets angry. And Mom wants to know why he never answers her questions! Communication can be simply about making a connection.

More complicated communication comes when you want your parent to do something they stubbornly do not want to do. Like take a shower. Rosemarie learned that if she asks her mother, "You said you wanted to take a shower. Do you want to do that now or after lunch?" instead of, "Mom, you need to take a shower," the decision-making has changed and the behavior is no longer *if* but *when*, which makes a big difference in caregiving.

The Louis and Anne Green Memory & Wellness Center recommends the following for clear communication:

❖ Do not talk until you are face-to-face
❖ Speak clearly and in concise, simple, short sentences
❖ Allow your parent time to respond, as it may take them longer to process information
❖ Use gestures when appropriate
❖ Give your parents every opportunity to express themselves
❖ Be a creative listener; listen to the meaning behind words
❖ Do not argue over the correct answer
❖ Use "I" statements instead of "you" statements when/if you do become angry
❖ Continue talking about things that were important to your parents
❖ Monitor and modify your tone of voice, body language, and other ways of communicating

If you see your parent often, at some point you may find yourself in a conversational dark hole. What do I talk about now? We've run out of chit chat.

21

You can have great conversations with your parents early on about their history, collecting and storing factoids and most-loved stories, to be able to prompt discussions later when a parent seems despondent or lonely, has lost energy, or is trying to converse with a grandchild. If a parent has mental cognition and memory issues, allowing your parents to tell stories they would most likely love to share can bring them out of their shell.

Naturally, you know how many children your parent has and the names of grandchildren and great grandchildren, but you might want to gather more details—a favorite activity with a grandchild, best memories with family, lessons he or she wants to teach children and grandchildren. What about favorite recipes that could be fun to pass down through generations? Maybe even writing them down together in a journal or memory book. Or writing letters (even decorating the envelopes) to children and grandchildren to be read at significant birthdays or events (wedding day, graduation days, birth of a child, etc.). Help your parent feel like, even though they are aging, it is possible to remain part of family life.

- ❖ Where did you grow up?
- ❖ Who were your neighbors?
- ❖ Did you have a best friend?
- ❖ Did you have a nickname?
- ❖ What jobs did you have in your life?
- ❖ How long were you married?
- ❖ Where else have you lived?
- ❖ What are you most proud of in your life?
- ❖ What do you like to watch on TV? Sports? Movies? Cop shows? Documentaries?
- ❖ What are your favorite shows?
- ❖ Did you have a favorite radio show?
- ❖ What kind of music do you like?
- ❖ Who is your favorite singer?
- ❖ Who is your favorite movie star?
- ❖ What is your favorite movie?
- ❖ What books changed your life?
- ❖ What kind of books do you enjoy?
- ❖ What are your favorite hobbies?
- ❖ What kind of games do you like?
- ❖ Where was your most favorite place to travel?
- ❖ Where have you traveled?
- ❖ Where do you wish you could go?
- ❖ What was your experience in the military like?
- ❖ What charities do you contribute to? Why?
- ❖ Have you ever belonged to any clubs?

- ❖ What is your favorite holiday? Why?
- ❖ Who was your favorite pet? Can you name your pets?
- ❖ What is/was your favorite sport to play? Watch?
- ❖ What are your favorite foods?
- ❖ What is your favorite food to cook?
- ❖ Where do you like to go to relax? (In the house, community, city, etc.)

READING BEHAVIORS AS CLUES FOR INFORMATION[2]

As your parents age, you might see behaviors that seem different than their norm. Try looking at all behaviors as a form of communication. Understand that "acting out" may not be personally directed at you, but actually a call for attention to something your parent is trying to tell you.

New behaviors you might see your parents exhibit include giddiness, aggression, withdrawal, anxiety, agitation, confusion, paranoia, repetition, trouble with sleep, wandering off, forgetfulness, depression, inappropriate sexual advances, hallucinating, or hiding things, and so on.

Any new behaviors may simply be a sign your parent is trying to tell you something but can't find the words. So, behaviors just mean you need to investigate. Perhaps he has to go to the bathroom, has a tummy ache, is hungry. She is tired and wants to go to bed, wants something to drink, has an itch, needs a hug, etc.

Causes and Response

Jordana's father suddenly began cursing at her, telling her she was a horrible daughter, pointing out every flaw, demanding attention and immediate gratification for food and snacks—all unlike his usual grateful self. Jordana took her dad to the doctor and, many tests, later discovered that her father had a brain tumor.

At a doctor's office one day, in the waiting room, Maddie's mother reached out and banged the side of her hand against Maddie's arm—*chop, chop, chop*—repeatedly, violently, causing pain. Maddie couldn't get her mother to stop hitting her. Maddie gave one chop back on her mother's arm, the same strength her mother was using, and her mother retreated and yelped, "Ouch!" Maddie said, "That's what you're doing to me! Stop it! It hurts!" Her mother looked at her with sad eyes and said, "I was just playing. I'm sorry."

Maddie has tremendous guilt and shame over her reaction, perhaps the same way a parent feels about giving a child a smack on the bottom or a tap on the nose to a dog that is putting his face into the trash. It is not something any of us ever want to face. We vow we will never do it again, and chances are we won't. Knowing that hitting is an indication of something else might have made Maddie react differently. Perhaps Maddie wasn't paying enough attention to her mother at the moment while they were in a place that might be scary (the doctor's office) for her mother.

Negative behaviors may be related to:

❖ Physical pain or discomfort
❖ Overstimulation

---

[2] Alzheimer's Association free brochure called *Behaviors*

- ❖ Unfamiliar surroundings
- ❖ Complicated tasks
- ❖ Frustrating interactions because of inability to communicate

To change the behavior:

Step One: Examine the behavior

Once you rule out pain (constipation, gas, an infection, an injury), a UTI or medication reaction as the cause of a new or negative behavior, your goal is to try not to take it all personally, don't get upset. If the new behavior turns to striking or biting, or leads to self-harming activities, call the doctor right away to determine the cause.

Step Two: Explore potential solutions

Work on calmly distracting or diverting your parent away from the situation that triggered the behavior. Speak slowly, make eye contact, use a gentle touch to connect (but don't startle by coming from the sides or behind), provide reassurance, and focus on something new.

Try inviting your parent to help you with something they are physically able to do without difficulty, like folding laundry or setting the table, drying dishes, etc. Something uncomplicated and familiar will usually work. Or begin a song or dance. Start playing a game, pull out a jigsaw puzzle, or read a simple book aloud. Do something creative like painting or flower arranging, go to the garden, start sketching or coloring. Bring in an animal to embrace and talk to.

Ask your parent a question about something from when he or she was younger to prompt a story: "Where did you meet Mom? Who was your best friend when you were little? What was your favorite game?" Whatever catches your parents' interests and attention.

For example: A common frustration is when you have a doctor's appointment and your parent doesn't want to get dressed and is stubborn about it. Instead of fighting to get your parent to put on clothing, try to divert your parent to another activity (like eating or packing a purse or activity bag) and then come back to getting dressed when things calm down. Also, scheduling enough extra time for potential drama and challenges will help keep you calmer and less frustrated.

Step Three: Try various responses

- ❖ Use the KISS theory. A former boss told me this was an acronym for "Keep it simple, stupid." The idea is that things often work best if they are kept simple rather than made complicated.
- ❖ Offer only one alternative. When preparing a meal, instead of asking, "What would you like for dinner?" make it simple by asking, "Would you like a hamburger or baked chicken?"
- ❖ Break tasks into smaller steps. Just give them one or two steps at a time.
- ❖ Speak face-to-face. Conversations coming from the side or behind someone can be confusing.

❖ Use short sentences with simple words that get straight to the point. Don't talk down to your parent as a child, but try, "Let's go to the store," instead of a list of things you need to get or the menu for the week or what you're eating on which night. As your parents' ability to focus begins to waiver, continue to simplify your language.

Understanding that most of us are not doctors, therapists, or experienced professional caregivers, we admit we don't always know what we're dealing with. However, unlike professionals, you know if your parents' behaviors are out of the norm, so, especially if behavior changes come on suddenly, first take your parent to a physician or therapist to see if there's a medical or mental health issue. If all comes out clear, then examine the behavior and try various responses.

TALKING TO THE GENERAL PUBLIC ABOUT YOUR PARENTS

The hardest time of this whole journey is when your parent is still kinda with-it most of the time. However, there are moments where you're out in public and people are staring at your dad because he's shaking uncontrollably and if you shout, "Hey, my dad has Parkinson's! He's not drunk! Give us a break!" Or your mom tries to hug someone in the supermarket because she's feeling happy. "No, Mom's not coming on to you, she's got Alzheimer's and you remind her of someone she likes. ☺" Well your dad or mom is likely the one to have a meltdown listening to you trying to "explain" them to a stranger. You're embarrassed. They're embarrassed. And the public doesn't know what to do with this information.

Rachel's mother stood up in a restaurant, turned to the other diners, randomly began singing opera, and then thanked her fans for coming to see her! Rachel's mom was a professional opera singer in her younger years and she had a great voice, so at least there was that!! Rachel hurried her mother out of the restaurant as her mother continued to wave like Miss America! You just never know!

A simple, inexpensive tip to help in these situations is to carry around a business card that simply says something to the effect of "My mother/father has Alzheimer's/Dementia/Parkinson's (etc.). Please be patient."

The Alzheimer's Association has cards that say: "My companion has Alzheimer's disease. This is a brain disorder that makes communication difficult. Your patience and understanding is greatly appreciated. Thank you."

You can add information about your particular parent and whatever behaviors someone might see that could startle or scare a stranger:

- ❖ Sometimes she answers slowly.
- ❖ My companion may appear confused.
- ❖ My companion gets easily upset.
- ❖ My companion may shake uncontrollably.

Customize your message. Keep it short and to the point. Bye-bye, embarrassment!

You can purchase cards from others who have already done the work on the web. If you want to customize your own card, you can go to your local print shop, or online to get cards printed in bulk.

Only need a few? You can buy blank business cards that can be run through your home printer. You can purchase packages of blank cards from office supply stores with instructions on how to set this up on your computer and print them as you need them. It's easier to update as things change. You can probably also get blank card sheets in larger big box stores that have office supplies.

COMMUNICATING WITH DOCTORS/CLINICIANS

Tana (a former New Yorker whose mother and father lived in Florida) and I were talking about how doctors react to seniors. We've experienced the condescending doctor who talks as if the patient is a child; the officious doctor who conducts the exam at lightning speed to be able to bill as many visits as possible; the doctor who sees the patient is having trouble understanding and turns and only talks to you as though the patient isn't in the room at all. And then there's the kind of doctor who asks questions, talks to the patient, and explains things in easy-to-understand language. They are a blessing! Don't lose those professionals! I have been fortunate to have many of them working with my parents and me.

Since Tana had just moved her parents closer to her in Savannah and was now becoming a more active advocate and caregiver for them, she asked me, "What if you have a parent who doesn't truly comprehend what is going on, but believes that he or she does? You don't want to embarrass your parent by taking over the physician visit, but you know that you need to have this information, and you have questions that need to get answered. How do you manage this situation?"

I shared with Tana the conversation starter I use, and it made Tana feel really good. She suggested that I include it in my book. So here it is: I basically tell the doctors, in front of my parents, that I am there as my parents' helper and advocate and that my parents are afraid they might forget something. If my parents have a question later, I tell the doctors, if I understand everything as we're going through the visit, then I can (a) help ensure they follow through where they are supposed to and (b) answer my parents' questions when they don't remember or understand, instead of my parents calling the office again.

The doctors love this. I sit and take notes while the doctors talk to my parents.

When my parent provides wrong information or forgets to tell something to the doc, I can speak up and share, "Mom, didn't you say that you felt a little dizzy a few days ago and that you wanted to tell the doctor?" And then Mom can take over and tell the story. "Dad, you said that you are feeling depressed about your situation these days. Do you want to tell the doctor what that feels like to you so maybe she can help?" And Dad can decide if he wants to share or not, but at least the doctor has heard that there may be an issue here and can ask guiding questions during the rest of the exam.

Meanwhile, I'm writing down everything the doctor says and, after the visit, I can go through it all more slowly with my parents and we can put next appointments and medication times on the calendar and to-do list hanging in the kitchen. My parents feel relief that they don't have to remember and understand everything! I'm their backup. Their safety net.

I previously spoke with my parents, before we went to the doctors' and before health issues started getting worse, to let them know that I want to be sure they get the best care, and that as long as I know what's going on and the doctors share with me too, then I can be there for them [my parents] and they can relax knowing they can always ask me if they forget something or have more questions.

I told Tana my parents already know that they are forgetting, so this makes them feel better without embarrassing them. I'm like having a backup memory drive, if you will. And, because I shared my intention to be a helper and not my parents' "boss," they were most happy to have me there. In fact, my parents often turn to me and ask, "What did I tell you was wrong the other day? I can't remember."

Communicating pain to you and doctors or clinicians

If your parent is acting out and might be in pain, using a pain scale may give your parent a way to tell you and a doctor just how bad it is. Pointing to what hurts on the body or in a photo also helps.

This Wong-Baker FACES® Pain Rating Scale is used worldwide to help people communicate pain level. Show your parent the faces and have them pick the one that matches how they feel. [Go to http://wongbakerfaces.org to get more information about the scale and the organization.]

Wong-Baker FACES® Pain Rating Scale

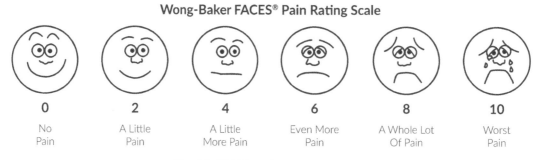

0	2	4	6	8	10
No Pain	A Little Pain	A Little More Pain	Even More Pain	A Whole Lot Of Pain	Worst Pain

Wong-Baker FACES Foundation. WWW.WongBakerFACES.org
Used with permission.

Connie Baker from the Wong-Baker Organization suggested that caregivers might find using a Pain Relief Log useful for tracking information and for doctor visits. "It is a way of keeping a record of vital information like pain meds, pain assessment, and anything else they want to track. Great for continuity of care." Connie offers a Pain Relief Log document for free by entering your contact information here: https://wongbakerfaces.org/wong-baker-faces-pain-relief-log/

Another situation that could arise when a parent is cognitively challenged or has some issue that makes speaking a challenge, is to help your parent communicate with aides and doctors (and you!) via a card system, such as Caregiver Cards—Picture-Based Communication Cue Cards for Adults with Memory, Speech, and Cognitive Challenge. Created by Caregiver Cards, this is a series of player cards in a deck that allows someone who finds speaking a challenge to pick out what is troubling them. By holding up the card, or pointing at it, they're able to let someone know where they might be having an issue. Cards cover physical as well as emotional issues. Knowing someone feels depressed or anxious or in pain can certainly help you find a resolution, as opposed to just seeing someone miserable and not knowing what is causing the unease. Bringing these cards to the doctor can help, but it's probably better for your parent to show you what's happening before you get to the doctor and then you can relay the information.

DEALING WITH A HOSPITAL STAY

When a woman is pregnant, it is expected that, as she approaches her due date, she has a packed bag that can be grabbed when she goes into labor and heads out for the birthing space or hospital. Since it's more likely than not that at some point an aging parent will need a hospital stay, when that happens, you can be prepared in advance by having everything you need packed and ready to go. This will make your life less stressful and will greatly increase the ability of the hospital staff to provide care in the most beneficial and comforting way possible for your parent. In addition to all the medical information your doctor would have—and that you should have with you anyway—here are some suggestions for extra things you might want for a hospital stay:

A. **Emergency Bag**—things you know you'll need with you to comfort your parent

B. **Tool Kit**—a bag to keep *you* comfortable and calm while caring for and waiting (shawl, sweater, socks, comfortable shoes/slippers, OTC painkillers, music, headset, writing paper and pens, coloring book and markers/pencils, deck of cards, healthy snacks, water bottle, change for vending machines, etc.)

C. **Personal Information Sheet**—Type this up in advance of your visit and ask the staff to keep it with your parents' chart. Use bullet points with short, bold headings. You might include your parents' normal routine; how to address your parent (formal or informal [Artie, Arthur, Mr. Pessin]); personal habits; likes and dislikes; any trigger behaviors that might cause a reaction and the best way to respond; nonverbal signs he or she is prone to show in case of pain or discomfort; likely reactions to touch, tickles, or pain. If your parent has hearing aids or needs glasses or any other assistance, that should be included. Let the team know your parents' level of dementia (if present) so the nurses can tell the difference between hospital delirium[3] and dementia.

D. **Hand Sanitizing**—Use hand sanitizer when entering your parents' room and before touching your parent. Expect the same of your hospital care team and all your support team members. One of the leading causes of death after hospital stays is infection passed on by hand contact.

There should be a hand sanitizer dispenser either in the hospital room or at the doorway. And there should be antibacterial soap in the bathroom dispensers.

---

[3] Mayo Clinic has information to define delirium vs. dementia: http://www.mayoclinic.org/diseases-conditions/delirium/symptoms-causes/syc-20371386

THE AWKWARD CONVERSATIONS

You want your parents to live with dignity; to age well; to live longer, stronger, and safer at home. Of course. But, things happen, bodies age, and situations change. If conversations are delayed for too long, the information you, as a caregiver, will need to have may become impossible to find and you're left to figure it out sans guidance. It doesn't have to be that way. However, to make it easier later, you have to have the awkward and difficult conversations early on.

Procrastinating on topics like death, money, driving, moving, is actually pretty common. Some of these topics feel taboo; sometimes it's just too much information you don't want to know! But you want to follow your parents' wishes, so bite-the-bullet, as they say, and try some of these gentler (No, Mom, I'm not trying to steal your money!) options for opening discussions.

Alternatively, you could engage non-family facilitators such as:

- ❖ **Mediator**—When family cannot agree, or your parents are "head-in-the-sand" types, you might try an elder care mediator. Do a web search or ask your lawyer to find licensed mediators in your area.
- ❖ **Impartial Stranger**—If your relationship with your parents is such that they won't listen to you, just like we didn't believe anything they said when we were teenagers (remember that?), consider enlisting the help of a respected advisor, trusted neighbor, or willing proxy to have these conversations with your parents for you. Sometimes the "outsider" will have better luck getting your parent on board.

Death (or Terminal Illness)

The forbidden topic. The great equalizer. Mortality. If we don't talk about it, it won't happen, right? Of course not. And yet, talking about death is forever being put on the "do tomorrow" list. So, let's get this big one out of the way first!

You're reading this book or talking to family/friends/advisors and recognize that steps need to be taken, but the thought of bringing up death seems so invasive!

Will Mom believe I want her to die?

Will Dad think I'm after the assets?

Will they think I am looking out for my inheritance or that I want it now, not later?

Will my siblings be offended if I raise this as a discussion we need to have?

End of Life

The talk has to happen. One unplanned health incident and you're in trouble. No one wakes up and says, "Hmmm. I think today I'm going to have a stroke. Let me get my affairs in order so my family will know what I want." So, pull yourself together and begin this conversation. You'll be much less stressed once everything is all processed and in your files!

How, you want to know? How do I bring this up? We feel that bringing up "death plans" or end-of-life plans will be confrontational or combative because it's so emotional. It goes to our core survival instincts. Maybe even our superstitious side: If you say it, you will bring it.

Here are some possible gentle conversation openers that are loving and should help ease your family into the dreaded death discussions—before anyone is in grieving mode:

1: I/we love you and hope you live forever, but as I'm/we're pretty sure that's not likely, I'd/we'd like to make sure that I/we understand what you'd like me/us to do for your final plans.

2: Mom/Dad, the family is getting together for us to all discuss our wishes for care in crisis, emergency, or death. We're meeting (insert day, time, location). Will you participate?

3: My friend's mother/father recently passed away and the poor guy didn't have a clue what his family wanted and what had already been taken care of. He spent $13,000 on a burial and funeral and then found a note that his mom/dad just wanted to be cremated! Can we talk about what you'd like so I don't do the wrong thing?

4: Pull out the Five Wishes document [explained in detail on page 90] and ask your parents if they will fill this out with you. Explain that you want them to know your wishes and you'd like to know theirs. Invite all of your siblings to participate and complete their Five Wishes as well. The Five Wishes will guide you through questions like:
   ❖ If you are diagnosed with a terminal illness or you are living in pain or you are unable to care for yourself, what would you like us, your family, to do?

✿   Can we talk about hospice care? How do you feel about end-of-life caregiving?

✿   Preference for palliative care at home, hospital, or residential facility?

✿   When you're not feeling well, do you want to be left to yourself or would you prefer company more often than not?

✿   How do you feel about care for a coma/vegetative state?

And so on...

Once the conversation has begun, you might want to discuss the elements that can be preplanned and prepaid for.

Can we talk about your funeral? Do you know what you would like? Have you thought about

(a)   Buried or cremated?

(b)   Where you'd like to buried?

Other questions:

✿   Do you have cremation urns selected?

✿   Have you prepaid for a funeral?

✿   Do you have funeral insurance?

✿   Did you talk to the VA about free burial in a Veterans' cemetery?

✿   What do you want on your gravestone?

✿   What kind of service would you prefer?

✿   Do you have a list of people you'd like us to notify when you pass?

✿   Do you want to donate your brain and/or body to science?

Obituaries, Headstones, and Epitaphs

While your parents are able, it might be helpful to ask them to write, or help you write, their obituary and what they want printed on their headstone and any epitaphs.

If there are specific things your parents want said about them or messages your parents want you to give to people attending a funeral, wake, or memorial service on their behalf, ask your parents to write them down so that you can include them in the services.

Completing these tasks will give your parents a sense of control and comfort.

Money

Whoa!! Another touchy topic! Ben Franklin said nothing can be certain, except death and taxes. Right? So, let's get this topic out of the way next.

First, my mother's 92-year-old friend Gloria recently told me, "Make sure you tell people that they should know about the expenses for day-to-day living. Having a spouse take care of everything is lovely except when that spouse passes, and you don't know what to even expect to pay for electricity, you are at a severe disadvantage!" So, cautionary word, make sure your parents understand their expenses and budget and perhaps they will be so kind as to share it with you so you can help if they start forgetting to pay those bills.

Most of the time, your parents probably don't feel the need for you to be all up in their personal financial business. Unless they've been getting money from you to help support them, they most likely believe their money is theirs and you should keep your hands off it.

However, what happens when one parent suddenly becomes ill and the bills need to be paid and the other parent doesn't know how to balance a checkbook or how to access and use the online accounts? What happens when the expenses for day-to-day living suddenly increase with nursing care or hospital expenses? Who will help then? What if there's a fire or flood, earthquake, tornado, or hurricane, and all the paperwork in the house is gone? Running around during an emergency or time-pressured situation to figure this all out is a sure stressor and is unnecessary if you can plan ahead.

The conversations about money don't have to be about specific amounts, but should be held to assure that when and if ever needed, you will be able to assist and get what is needed without being bogged down by having to go through legal hoops or trying to figure out even what to locate!

Avoid discussing your inheritance, or investments you want your parents to consider, or the fact that your parents could become dependent on you if things go awry, when you begin financial discussions. These are sure ways to put your parents on the defensive!

A nonthreatening conversation starter might include:

A) A friend just had to get money out of the bank to pay her mother's bills because her mom was in the rehab center after an accident. The bank wouldn't let my friend anywhere near her mom's account. My friend doesn't have a lot of her own money. Her mom could lose the condo if the Home Owners Association dues and taxes aren't paid. I don't want that to happen to you. Can we work on having me as a backup in case of emergency?

B) Maybe you can find information on one of your parents' neighbors or friends who had a difficult time with finances (your parent may have even mentioned them in a conversation with you?) and suggest that you'd like to be there to help so things never go that way for your parent. Reassure your parents that you want to make sure that your parents have the resources to get everything they need and want and retain their own money as long as possible. You'd like to help them find the right local help to be sure that happens. You're happy to be as involved as they want you to be. The more you know, the more you can help.

Katie Moore 206-343-9911
George Frank's partner

C) To demonstrate to your parent that you are not after their money, but are concerned about health service delivery, try this approach: I don't need to know the actual numbers for your assets but, if something happens to you, I will need to know where to look to settle your affairs. Could you possibly put all the information in a sealed envelope and leave it with a lawyer or friend, and let me know where and who that is, so that if something happens, I can get that envelope and handle things for you? And if you could include a Durable Power of Attorney and Health Care Advance Directive for me to handle your financial matters upon your incapacity, that would speed things along, when and if it's ever needed. (Whomever you name as executor in your Will, will take care of things after you die.)

D) Here are some articles about managing your finances into retirement. If you don't want me involved (or maybe you don't live close by your parent and shouldn't be the direct contact), I understand, but maybe you could find a reputable financial consultant to set things up for you? And perhaps you could work with a financial concierge or personal assistant who will have access to your accounts in case you need help and can't handle it personally? The financial concierge can help you pay your bills, manage invoices and charitable giving, and so on. Maybe you'll be traveling on a world cruise or you might be having a medical procedure and will need someone else to handle things! I just want to make sure someone is watching out for you.

E) I have been hearing so many stories on the news about scams targeting older adults. I don't want anything to happen to you. You've worked so hard to create a nest egg. Can we discuss your strategies? Will you agree to tell me about any new things you're looking into, so I can check to see if there's any information on whether it's a fraud?

Once you get your parent opening up a little bit, or at least get their money handled by a qualified expert with elder care experience, then you can be more at ease. In the financial section of this book, the kind of people who can help you and your parents manage this time of their lives is more fully detailed. And the documents you'll want to have on hand and have access to are specifically explained as well.

Driving

Having the conversation with your parents about the keys to the car is one of the toughest caregiving responsibilities. The first sign that they are losing independence is when the keys are taken away—and that feels good to no one!

Of course, you can avoid this conversation. On one hand, perhaps you dread having to be the person your parents call to drive them anywhere, to do anything. The longer they drive, the less of a burden they are on you. On the other hand, if they get into an accident and harm themselves, then you're possibly caring for someone with debilitating physical issues. Or, if they hurt someone else, you're now dealing with a possible lawsuit or car repair expenses, or even *jail time* for your parent. So maybe this conversation is something to prepare for?

There are multiple considerations:

1) The car itself—whose car is it? Ownership and maintenance of a vehicle.
2) Ability mentally and/or physically to drive any car at all (see assessments on page 10).

If the car is used for trips to the grocery store each week or to restaurants occasionally and that's pretty much it, you might want to bring up that the cost of car ownership may be a reason to stop driving: "Think of the money you can save!"

A lot of people can be great drivers on an empty road or in a big open parking lot. It's dealing with other distracted drivers who may be texting, putting on makeup, talking on the phone, changing music stations, dealing with children or pets, that causes the problems. The old "It's not you, it's them we're worried about!" is what we're aiming for here. Happily, this is actually true!

Other potential trouble spots: Detours and road changes and finding your way to and from where you want to be. What about construction? Snow or rain or pothole detours? It's concentrating on the road, the car in front and behind and on either side of you, while also looking out for people walking into your path, cyclists on the road, weaving cars around you, that are issues with driving.

A few days ago, a couch fell off the pickup truck in front of me on the highway—at night! Can your parent handle something like that?

Is your parent able to physically twist his or her body or head around to look out the rear windshield and both side windows before backing out of a parking space in the mall or grocery parking lot? Or are they relying on back-up and side camera technology for warnings?

Let's face it...reaction time decreases with age. Balance becomes affected. The ability to multitask decreases with age. Can you have that conversation with your parents? Or is an outside person the best one to bring this discussion to the table?

In my case, the decision about the car and whether my parents would keep a car was decided for us when my dad totaled his car on a drive from New York to Florida. The first step—taking away the car—was resolved.

The second step, the idea of taking away the keys and agreeing not to drive at all, was made by my father. He didn't want to get behind the wheel of a car again after the accident. Although, he emphasized that he certainly was ABLE to drive but he was CHOOSING not to drive anymore. He was not only scared about getting into another accident, he also recognized that he didn't know how to get home or to places anymore without someone directing him.

Helping your parent *choose* to stop driving rather than you mandating it will help your relationship in the long run. Resentment is not fun! (That should be a bumper sticker!)

In the process of talking to my mother about not driving, the conversations started easy, appeared frequently, and, over time, when I could see that her choosing to stop was not forthcoming, the worries and concerns I shared became more dramatic and scary. Eventually, my mom chose to stop driving.

1) Just because you can turn the engine on, put your foot on the pedal to make the car go, put your foot on the brake to make the car stop, and turn the car off doesn't mean that you can be attentive to all the other things happening around you while driving.

2) You may be very focused on where you're going and what's ahead of you, but a good driver also needs to be aware of someone coming between two cars to cross the road in front of you unexpectedly.

3) What happens when there's a detour and the familiar route is not available? Can you still get home or where you want to go, or will you get flustered and confused?

4) "What happens if something is falling from a truck or jumps in from the side of the road or falls from above you?" I asked my mom. Animals crossing a road, kids chasing balls, a runaway garbage can, are all common enough.

5) It might not be you who is doing something wrong, but what if someone else is on the phone or texting and does something stupid and you wind up in an accident because your reflexes have slowed down? You could be injured!

6) What if you back into someone in a parking lot and injure them? Could you live with that?

7) What if you hit someone and wind up in jail? Can you imagine the rest of your life in jail?

8) What if you injure or kill a dog, a cat, or child? Could you live with that?

9) What if you hit someone and the family sues you? Are you prepared to live without money? Bankruptcy?

10) Dad is worried about you out there driving on your own. He panics when he doesn't know that you are safe.

If the initial discussions (which will happen over time) don't work, then you might consider using a tracking device to record your parents' driving activities. Where is the car going? How often? Unusual breaking or jerky acceleration? Too slow? Too fast? Use the data either to reassure yourself that things are okay or use it to discuss what you're seeing with your driving parent. (This can also help locate your parent if they wind up lost.)

And still, are the keys gripped tightly? Ask your parent to go for a driving assessment. "How about we let a professional tell us if you still qualify to drive?" Check the internet for providers in your area for driving assessment services.

If your parent still won't give up the keys and you're sure that your parent is a danger to himself or herself and others on the road, you can ask a doctor (parents RESPECT their doctors!) to advise against driving.

Still not working? The most dramatic route: You can report your parent to the DMV or bring a note from the doctor or the report from the driving assessment. The DMV will likely call your parent in for a driving test and/or vision exam and may take away your parents' license. This one is pretty emotional. But better to be emotional now than to deal with all the possible negative consequences of an accident in the future.

My parents' driving story

The decision, after the car was destroyed and Dad didn't want to drive anymore, was that I would have a car that my mother and I would share. My parents would pay the expenses for the car and, since I lived in the same building, we would each have keys and we would use a shared calendar on our phones to let each other know when the car was being used by the other. Since I write, I don't always need to be in the car going somewhere. I spend a lot of time at a computer at home.

After a while, it became clear to me that it was not wise for my mother to be driving anymore. Her ability to concentrate was diminished greatly. She was driving the car while trying to figure out how to use the turn signal or lights, or radio. "PAY ATTENTION!" I screamed at her one day.

She would ride the white line on the right. On the highway, she was driving halfway into the service/breakdown lane. Then she would drive 10 miles below the speed limit. Slowing down so much when exiting that people behind her were slamming their brakes. First decision: No more highway driving, Mom. She agreed.

So, what was Mom doing with the car? I was taking my parents to all their medical appointments. Mom was shopping. And then returning the things she bought. That's what she did with the car.

Second step: How about going through a driving assessment at the Green Memory Center? "Okay," Mom agreed. The recommendation, after the driving test, the written exam, and the cognitive function assessment was that Mom was not to drive. If she chose to continue to drive, she should only go with someone else in the car, not go more than 10 minutes from home, stay off the highways, and not drive at night.

How did Mom take this? She said happily, "I passed!" What? I asked confused. It says here you shouldn't drive. She corrected me, "It says I am not RECOMMENDED to drive. It doesn't say I SHOULDN'T drive." And so began the struggle to try to keep Mom off the road as much as possible.

It helped that the car was residing with me because I moved to a new apartment four miles from my parents. So, if Mom was taking the car, I had to go bring her the car. Or, she would have to Uber to me to pick up the car. So, why not just let me take her where she needed to go?

I secretly added a MotoSafety gadget to the car. This allowed me to track Mom's braking patterns, how long it took her to get from one place to another, where she was stopping, any wild swerving, or unusual driving behavior.

Mom wasn't that bad. However, she was still driving under the speed limit, braking harshly sometimes, and stopping for fast food. She admitted that she nearly hit people several times when they walked behind her car when she was pulling out of a parking space. "They're so stupid! They have to watch where they're going!" she would emphasize!

Eventually, she stopped even trying to get the keys to the car. And I just took over the driving. We got her set up on Uber and she got a Palm Tran handicap permit so that she could reserve a van or car to take her where she wanted. The community center for day activities had a van to pick her up. It all worked out great. And she stopped asking for the keys.

My big clincher in the discussions came when Dad admitted he was not happy about Mom being out with the car at 10:00 p.m. coming home from a photo competition. "Why does she have to drive at night?" he worried. He was a wreck whenever Mom was out on her own with the car. So, when I suggested she stop driving, he was thrilled and told Mom he thought she shouldn't drive anymore either.

Months later, my mother told a group of people that she is still upset about not having a car to drive whenever she wants. However, the next day, she didn't even know an ambulance was coming and asked me why I was waiting when the light was green. I said, "Can't you hear the siren?" She couldn't. That reassured me that I had made the right call.

Leaving Home

Conversations around leaving a home to move to a child's community, or moving to independent or assisted living, or investing in a continuing care community are never one-day discussions. It can take months or even years to find the right fit and get your parents to agree to make this kind of move. For them, it means giving up the familiar and safe to head to new and foreign. As we age, familiar = good.

Scott Solkoff, a certified specialist in Elder Law, said the biggest lies people tell themselves are (a) I'll never need a nursing home and (b) When I get sick, I'm going to live with/near my child.

The natural instinct of most people is, "I want to die at home. Leave me alone." Then, they defensively ask, "Why are you trying to take my home away from me?"

You become the enemy if you force your parent to move before the decision is agreed upon. At some point, the physical condition of your parent may influence a move. Making the decision of where to go before that happens is optimal…if not always possible.

Having agreement among all the siblings is best. If one child wants the parents to stay in their own home and the other siblings want the parents to move, it becomes a tug of war, an "us-against-them" battle. Before you talk with your parents, I would do everything to gain full agreement among all of your siblings. "We all think this is best for you at this time," is a much better position to be in than one child wanting parents to move to her own home, another wanting parents to move to a facility, and another wanting parents to stay put. It's confusing for your parents. It can be a who-do-you-love-most emotional battlefield—whichever idea your parent chooses, is seen to make a statement.

Scott suggests that having a doctor or elder law attorney be the "bad guy" can sometimes keep family harmony while presenting facts and opinions from professionals who deal with this issue frequently (if not daily). This allows the family to point to professional advice to evidence their concern.

My mother's 90-year-old friend Sarah's three boys took her to a senior residence for lunch a few months after her handicapped husband had passed away. Sarah told my mother that her boys said, " 'This is where you're living now. Here are the keys to your new apartment.' And then they just left me there!" I can pretty much guarantee that it wasn't like that, but that's how Sarah is telling everyone her children treated her after the death of her husband. It would have been a different story recounted to my mother if Sarah had been in agreement with her boys about moving.

The debate rages on for whether waiting until the last possible moment or moving while you're still well and able is best. There are pros and cons for each. If you wait and live at home as long as possible, you'll save money. The environment is familiar and friendly. The schedule is already set and known. Close to doctors, friends, service people, etc.

If you stay at home, however, you could fall or get injured and no one will know. People have been left lying on the floor for hours or even days with no one checking in. The physical environment at home may not be safe: Climbing over a bathtub to get into a shower, old and possibly dangerous appliances, roofs or doors or windows needing repair, the home being safe during a storm or emergency and needing backup power, etc.

When both parents are together, moving as a couple is much easier than waiting for one parent to pass and then moving a newly single person into completely strange surroundings. Adding the stress of packing up a home, moving, making new friends, eating new food, and generally being surrounded by everything unfamiliar after losing a spouse is a quick ride down a spiral staircase.

In fact, one of the points I made to my parents was a key factor in their decision-making. "What happens to Mom if Dad passes first? Mom will be left without the ability to drive herself around, in a lovely condo complex and a familiar apartment, but with very few friends still alive, no activities on-site, and no one to take care of or talk to. She will be lonely and get depressed and I fear she would be miserable." Dad did not want that. Even though Dad loved his view and liked to be alone in the apartment, he knew Mom was a social person with a need for contact and new people to talk to all the time. Physically, Mom really needed daily exercise classes. A new residence that had everything social for her and a view for him was the challenge proffered. Dad's response was, "It's not going to be easy to convince me, but if you find a place I think I can tolerate, for your mother, I will agree to look." He gave me a list of standards, pretty confident that I wouldn't be able to find what he wanted.

Oh boy—when I found *everything* he asked for, he admitted that it was pretty spectacular. And if he was going to move, this would be the right place. Of course, I took him to some runner-up facilities where he told me he would throw up every time he walked in the door if I made him move there! So, this was a big surprise that he found a place he liked. They moved. And later, when he was depressed about not being in his familiar home, he said, "I'm not mad at you. I know I made this decision for your mother's happiness. I will make it work, for your mother." (FYI: My mother was SO happy there that she said if Dad wanted to move out, she wasn't going anywhere!)

Here are some discussion points to consider sharing. Maybe not all at once, but over time, drop these hints. And there will be more points that are relevant to your specific situation, I am sure.

Physical:

❖ You can't walk that well anymore, what if you fall? Will someone be around to lift you up if you're here at home?

❖ Wouldn't it be nice to be in a place where everyone is trained to help and there are doctors, nurses, physical therapists, etc. around to help you and answer your questions?

❖ There's a pull cord in this new apartment that can bring you emergency help if you need it.

❖ Everything in the new apartment is set up to prevent falls and tripping. It's built to accommodate a wheelchair or walker if you ever need that. There are grab bars, special easy-to-turn handles, protection for the temperature of the water, no-slip floors, cushioned flooring in case you do fall, etc. We all feel much calmer knowing that you are in a safer residence.

❖ If you don't move, then we are going to have to make some pretty big safety renovations to this home. That could get costly and will be most inconvenient for you with construction dust, drilling, hammering, jackhammering, etc. It could last for [a few weeks, a month, a few months, etc.] and you'll be miserable.

Security:

- ❖ If you don't come down to eat at a communal living place, someone will come looking for you. Don't you want to know that someone is watching out? Someone cares? I know that I (and my siblings) would like to know we can call and send someone to find you if we can't reach you.
- ❖ I/We don't like you driving around all the time. What if you get lost or have something happen to you? Isn't it easier to just have someone drive you? At this new place, they have a driver on call to take you places and they have bus trips to shop and such so you can go with a group of people and maybe make some new friends!
- ❖ We get nervous when you're out on your own/home on your own. What if you get attacked? Who is there to watch over you while we are out of town or busy with work? If you don't want to move out, we should put in a security camera. One on the outside and one inside the house. We just want to know you're safe!

Financial:

- ❖ Owning your own home is expensive. Things break down. You won't have to worry about that anymore. You pay all these different expenses every month now and you are going to need [insert...new appliances, water heater fixed, a/c replaced, dying tree removed, etc.] and that is going to cost big bucks. Wouldn't you rather use your money for things you enjoy?
- ❖ You'll have an in-house handyman for anything that goes wrong!
- ❖ It's getting more difficult for you to manage all your bills. Wouldn't it be nice to know you have one bill to pay each month and everything is handled?
- ❖ I understand that you would rather be in your own home with an aide. Right now, you don't need one full-time, but you might someday. A full-time aide costs $25 an hour, which totals about $80,000 a year. A live-in aide will cost $40,000 to $80,000 a year, and you have to find a substitute if they get sick or need vacation or have a family crisis and have to leave. Plus, you still have to pay for the ongoing household expenses.

[FYI: (a) An investment in a continuing care community (CCC) guarantees that residential and medical needs will all be taken care of for life at basically a low monthly rent from when you move in. (b) Long-term care insurance will cover you at home for medical expenses but not household expenses, and there's a limit to how much they'll cover—based on the policy purchased.]

Emotional/Spiritual:

- ❖ I know your friends are passing away or moving. It's hard to deal with that alone. We'd like for you to be somewhere that has activities and new people for you to meet. You haven't made any new friends in a while here at home. Aren't you feeling lonely?

❖ If you moved in with us [the response they offer as to why they won't be lonely!] we're at work/school and out all the time. You'll be bored and have no one to talk to.

❖ The place we are recommending for you has religious services on-site. You can go every day/week if you like. Or the driver/van will take you to services where you like to go. And you might even have friends go with you!

❖ You must be getting bored doing the same thing all the time. Wouldn't it be nice to have someone else plan great activities and trips for you? You would get to do all these cool things that someone else plans and handles all the details! Alternatively, if your parent is an organizer, "Think of all the great activities you can plan for all your new friends and neighbors!" or "Imagine how your new neighbors and friends would love learning all about [insert favorite activity or skill]."

❖ You can share your talent for [fill in] with the other residents at the new place. I'm sure they would be so happy to have someone with your skill/talent.

❖ Wouldn't you like to get to know the staff and a new home while you have time to acclimate while you're aware of what's going on? Do you want to wake up one day in a strange place when you're really sick and not know anyone? Not know how to get around? Not know the schedule? I don't want you to be a nervous wreck in addition to being overwhelmed.

Guilt: (It's not like your parents never pulled the guilt card on you!??)

❖ I am so worried about you and your safety that it is impacting my life.

❖ My relationship with [my spouse, my partner, my ability to date] is challenging. We can't take a vacation because I'm always here with you.

❖ My job is being affected. [I can't travel, missing meetings, can't put in the hours I need, too distracted to get work done correctly, etc.]

❖ The stress of worrying about your health and safety is causing me to have health problems. Now I worry if I get sick, who's going to be here to help look after you?

❖ It would be easier for me to just be your child and come visit you and enjoy time together instead of me trying to manage your home and health and life to keep you safe/well every time we talk and get together.

Once your parent is thinking that he/she/they are open to exploring...

❖ I/We want YOU to make the decision of where you'd like to be. You should never feel that I/we are pushing you into a place you don't like just because we *have* to make a decision because of your health.

❖ While you're still able to decide, why don't I take you to a few places I've already screened and then you can choose the one you like? And we can discuss when would be best to move in after you make a selection. Maybe it will be soon, maybe it will be when we reach certain criteria with your health/finances, etc.

PART III

WHAT TO DO AT EACH PHASE OF CARE

NOTES

SOMETHING'S CHANGING WITH MY PARENTS: WHAT DO I DO?

Every situation is different (as if you didn't know that). Providing a specific timeline of when to do what would be too complex. If you live in town with your parents, your timeline will be different than that of someone living far away. If you are coping with illness of the mind vs. mobility challenges vs. heart disease or cancer or diabetes or, most awful, more than one of these, your timeline will also be different. If you have long-term care insurance, a family fortune, no money at all, or anywhere in between, your solutions and the order in which you do things will require adjusting. So, in general terms, what follows are my recommendations for your consideration. You will get a sense of what needs to be done now and what can wait.

First of all, as you delve in, don't panic! Realize that you will most likely not need to do *all* of the things on the following lists! I am providing a wide variety of suggestions that may or may not be pertinent to your situation and/or your budget.

At the end of this book, you will find resources that may help direct you to find what you seek at little or no cost. And many of the larger items might be covered by insurance or long-term care policies. So, again, DON'T PANIC!! You can do this!

PREPARING FOR AGING CHANGES

It's torturous and frustrating, depressing, and anxiety-producing to watch your parents start to change. "It's not supposed to be like this!" you think. You're the child; they're the adults. They probably taught you how to walk, talk, eat, and use a toilet. And now, you're faced with the likelihood that you're going to be managing these functions for them as they move further and further away from independence.

On the bell curve of life, the first things we instinctively do as an infant (eat, poop, cry, feel pain, feel love) are the same things we do at the end of our life. The older we get, the pieces of the brain that stored the information we learned so many years ago start to disintegrate, almost like Swiss cheese (a solid broken up with holes). And some of the things we take for granted, we start to forget. We regress back toward our infant status. We forget how to read, we have difficulty with hearing and finding words to speak, we lose our teeth and ability to eat and taste, we might lose control of bladder function, and so on. So, in reality, as caregivers, we are indeed parenting our parents as they age.

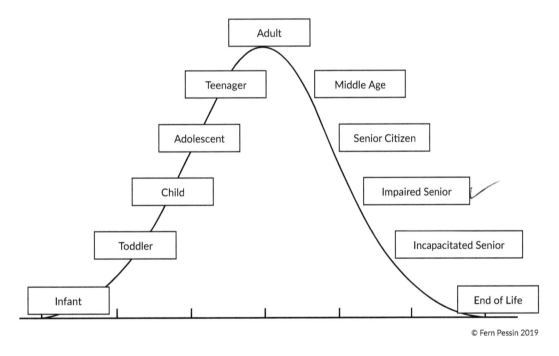

© Fern Pessin 2019

A little preparation on your part can help make the aging process less agonizing and can improve your parents' quality of life and keep them independent as long as possible, while giving you peace of mind for their safety.

To help you prepare, I've organized the Phase sections in this book as follows:

Seniors (Independent Living)
Minor Impairments (Independent to Assistance Needed)
Major Impairments (Assistance to Full Nursing/Memory)
End of Life

The charts on the next few pages are designed to provide some basics for getting your parents and the home ready at each level of decline. The first chart is for cognitive/mental decline. The second chart is for physical decline. These, naturally, can overlap—parents often have both mental and physical issues to varying degrees. The Phase sections and chapters that follow the charts provide much more detail.

Preparing for Mental/Cognitive Decline

Based on my experience with my parents, I've devised my own Phase Scale Identifiers for people with cognitive decline:

1. *Senior*, for my purposes, applies to the beginning of their decline. This is the time when signs of aging are starting to show up and you find yourself asking if your parents may need some help. Your parents are probably misplacing things and repeating stories at this point. These are the typical signs associated with aging.

2. *MCI* is **Mild** Cognitive Impairment and refers to more frequent memory lapses, issues with thinking skills, starting to exhibit physical issues related to aging, trouble with managing finances, and perhaps loss of concentration.

3. *MCI2* is **Moderate** Cognitive Impairment, which would refer to parents needing a bit more help in daily living activities. Memory loss is to the point where they might not remember their address or phone number, when birthdays are, or how old they or you and your siblings are. They might not be able to pick out their clothing, probably can't do math exercises, may have trouble concentrating on reading for any length of time. They might fall asleep just sitting in a chair.

4. *ACD* is **Advanced** Cognitive Decline and refers to parents needing help with daily living. They probably need help to get dressed and with toileting or eating. They may wander if not supervised, probably don't sleep well, and they may start behaving differently. You have probably determined at this point that it's best for your parent to have an aide or live in an assisted living center.

5. *SCD* is **Severe** Cognitive Decline—the most severe level on my scale. At this point, your parent would be best served in a nursing or memory care environment, as he or she would need almost continual care. Your parent probably needs help to eat, may not understand or be able to speak language, does not necessarily know where he or she is, is most likely wearing a diaper, and probably needs help with mobility. Mood changes and new personality traits may be exhibited.

WAYS YOU CAN HELP A MENTALLY DECLINING PARENT

Phase	Activity
Senior	Start going on doctor visits, take notes, ensure compliance
Senior	Monitor medicines (photograph pill bottle instructions and pill schedulers/containers and make charts)
Senior	Create spreadsheet with current medication to bring to doctor appointments
Senior	Screen caregiver provider organizations before hiring paid caregivers becomes necessary
Senior	Visit Independent, Assisted, Rehabilitation, and Nursing care facilities before needed
Senior	Enter all contacts and important numbers and access codes into a database. You will need this to update address (if moving parents to a residential facility) or, upon death, to cancel accounts.
Senior	Start scanning photos, cards, letters, and memorabilia so you can discard originals but keep digital copies
Senior	Get driving tracking device—for parents who are still driving
MCI	Sort, label, and pack up family memorabilia in stackable bins or boxes to bring to residential facility with your parents, distribute to various family members, or donate to nonprofits (if possible).
MCI	Label contact names in phone contact list with **ICE** (**In Case** of **E**mergency) and put those names in Favorites list. (Ex.: ICE, Jane, daughter)
MCI	Separate similar-looking products (e.g., toothpaste looks like anti-pain cream or moisturizer, suntan lotion, etc.)
MCI	Set up parents' phone with a "Find my phone" function
MCI	Tracking device attached to frequently misplaced items (wallet, hearing aid or eyeglasses, keys, TV remote, etc.)
MCI	Reduce noise (loud music or TV); get headsets
MCI	Reduce clutter (too many objects and knick-knacks create clutter in the brain and lead to confusion, plus a safety hazard)
MCI2	Disconnect food disposal systems
MCI2	Oven/stove safety device
MCI2	Hot water control—avoid burning
MCI2	Safety razors
MCI2	Put nightlights along footpaths on way to bathroom, kitchen, and around outside of home
MCI2	Add moisture-proof bed liner (under sheets)
MCI2	Provide bladder-release panties or pads
MCI2	Velcro™-closing sneakers and clothing (no ties or zippers)

Phase	Activity
MCI2	Schedule manicures and pedicures (to avoid overgrowth, infection, and fungus)
MCI2	Learn CPR (if you're in-house)
MCI2	Locate AED (or buy one for house, if possible)
MCI2	Put important phone numbers on household phone base and receivers
MCI2	Put labels on wall above sink and on bathroom mirrors with routines for grooming (washing, brushing hair, and brushing teeth)
MCI2	Write out instructions for use of television remote, computer, printer, microwave, etc.
MCI2	Label shelves and cabinets (to help aides and a parent with memory loss put things back where they belong)
MCI2	Spy Cam—for security and to watch for parent falling (and/or to check-in on home health workers)
MCI2	Create a binder of daily/weekly routines and medication for reference use by your parent, yourself, and rotating caregivers, siblings, first responders, doctors, etc.
ACD	Put name labels over buttons on phone for speed dial ("Sue" instead of "1," "Joe" instead of "2," for example)
ACD	Remove razor blades, scissors, pointy tools, and sharp knives from view and store in locked or child-proof drawers, containers or cabinets.
ACD	Cover a door to an unsafe room with a picture of a book case, to make your parent think it is a wall rather than a door.
ACD	Substitute china, breakable items and utensils with unbreakable and easy to hold items (e.g., mugs should have handles, soup bowls should be mugs with handles, plates should have rims, utensils with rubber grip handles, etc.)
ACD	Add gates to stairwells
ACD	Get rid of throw rugs and extension cords (tripping hazards)
ACD	Hide coats, keys, shoes, wallets, and items that could inspire someone to walk out of the house (for wander risk)
ACD	Walker, canes, grabbers (to get objects without standing on ladders or bending), possibly scooter, or wheelchair
SCD	Tracking device/procedure for wandering family members
SCD	Locks on cabinets (babyproof house)
SCD	Put caps on power outlets.
SCD	Inside door locks with hidden keys (wandering parent)

Preparing for Physical Decline

This chart for preparing for the challenges that accompany the aging process focuses on Seniors still living independently, then Older Seniors where they may be independent or in group situations or need an aide. I've then broken out different physical challenges that may arise and what you can do to help.

WAYS YOU CAN HELP A PHYSICALLY DECLINING PARENT

Phase	Activity
Able Senior	Start going on doctor visits, take notes, ensure compliance
Able Senior	Monitor medicines (photograph pill bottle instructions and pill scheduler containers and make charts)
Able Senior	Create spreadsheet with current medications to bring to doctor appointments
Able Senior	Screen caregiver provider organizations before having paid caregivers becomes necessary
Able Senior	Visit Independent, Assisted, Rehabilitation, and Nursing care facilities before needed
Able Senior	Enter all contacts and important numbers and access codes into a database. You will need this to update address (if moving parents to a different residence or facility) or, upon death, to cancel accounts.
Able Senior	Work together to scan photos, cards, letters, and memorabilia to discard originals but keep digital copies
Able Senior	Get driving tracking device—for still-driving family members to determine if physical skills are impacting driving
Older Senior— Physically unable to help	Sort, label, and pack up family memorabilia in stackable bins or boxes to bring to residential facility with your parents, distribute to various family members or donate to nonprofits (if possible).
Older Senior	Label contact names in phone contact list with **ICE** (**I**n **C**ase of **E**mergency) and put those names in Favorites list. (Ex.: ICE, Jane, daughter) and on push buttons for speed dial.
Older Senior	Set up parent's phone with a "Find my phone" function in case of falls or passing out
Older Senior	Reduce clutter (tripping hazard)
Older Senior	Put nightlights along footpaths on way to bathroom, kitchen, and around outside of home
Older Senior	Get parent's house shoes with traction (no walking barefoot)
Older Senior	Put lamp close to bed, within easy reach. Cord hidden.
Older Senior	Use moisture-proof bed liner (under sheets) in case they can't make it to the bathroom
Older Senior	Provide bladder release panties or pads

Phase	Activity
Older Senior	Schedule manicures and pedicures (to avoid overgrowth, infection, and fungus)
Older Senior	Learn CPR (if in residence)
Older Senior	Locate AED (or buy one for house if possible)
Older Senior	Take parent for vision test annually, then biannually when issues appear
Older Senior	Spy Cam—for security and to watch for falling (and/or to check on home health workers)
Older Senior	Create a binder of daily/weekly routines and medication for reference use by parent, yourself, and rotating caregivers, siblings, first responders, doctors, etc.
Older Senior	Hook up virtual or digital assistants that work on voice command ("Call daughter," "Turn off bedroom light," "Order pizza at Sal's," "Play Frank Sinatra music," "Tell me a joke," etc.)
Older Senior	Teach parent to use speaker phone and/or install wireless intercoms for inter-room communication
Older Seniors (coupled)	If one partner is hearing impaired, use headsets for television, hang flashlights in locations for easy access to get partner's attention, set up TDD/TTY phone system
Older Senior	Set up delivery services for groceries and essentials (via internet or call local businesses)
Out of breath or hard to walk or mobility challenged	Install handrails and grab bars around the house, put a seat in the middle of long hallways, carry cane with built-in seat
Stiff joints, hard to bend over, vision challenged	Velcro™-closing sneakers and clothing (no ties or zippers)
Stiff or painful fingers	Clothing that doesn't require zipping, buttoning, or tying. Pants with pull-string waist; shirts or pants with elastic, Velcro™ or magnet closings
Stiff or painful fingers	Devices and extenders that don't require fingers to bend for daily use of toothbrushes, hairbrush, dishwashers, soap dispensers, etc.
Trouble grasping and holding items	Substitute china and breakable items and utensils with unbreakable and easy to hold items (e.g., mugs should have handles, soup bowls should be mugs with handles, plates should have rims, utensils with rubber grip handles, etc.)
Shoulder or upper body restrictions	Clothing that can be put on without raising arms (open in front and loose-fitting)
Hearing Challenged	Get TDD/TTY phone and put captions on television
Vision Challenged	Put enlarged important phone numbers on household phone base and receivers
Vision Challenged	Get books on tape (library offers free downloads) so parent can continue to "read." Subscribe to auditory newspapers/magazines.

Phase	Activity
Vision Challenged	Put magnifying glasses around the home. Update subscriptions to large print versions; sign up for online large print books and periodicals.
Vision or Mobility Challenged	Put a phone near the floor so parent can crawl to it if parent doesn't have digital assistant, cell phone, or fall detector.
Vision or Mobility Challenged	Paint contrasting color on edge of stairs, ramp areas, curbs, etc.
Mobility Challenged	Move frequently used items to lower shelves if physical challenges make reaching up more difficult. Add sliding doors if access is difficult. Remove doors if chair needs to roll up to sink or counter.
Mobility Challenged	Build wooden ramps outside or use rubber sectional ramps for getting from room to room in homes with small steps
Mobility Challenged	Get rid of throw rugs and extension cords (tripping hazards)
Mobility Challenged	Move coats, keys, shoes, and wallets to eye level for unobstructed easy access
Stiff joints, vision challenged, mobility challenged	Walker, canes, grabbers (to get objects without standing on ladders or bending), possibly scooter or wheelchair
Stiff joints, mobility challenged, low strength	Remove locks on cabinets and add easy pull handles

For more ideas, I recommend books by Shelley Peterman Schwarz. She writes about home accessibility for people with all kinds of general issues, plus specifics for Parkinson's disease, Multiple Sclerosis, and more.

How To Use the Phase Sections

I've defined the Phase sections that follow by exhibited behaviors rather than any chronological age. Western society defines a senior as someone over age 65 (senior discounts!) or the age you take Social Security benefits in the U.S. In fact, *you* may qualify as a "senior" and yet still be taking care of your aging parents!

A trauma to the brain or injury to the body can bring on sudden physical changes. Previous medical conditions, pharmaceuticals, or emotional trauma might have kicked cognitive decline into action at a young age. Only your observation of your parents will let you know which Phase to focus on.

Each life phase herein builds on the previous phase. To avoid being repetitive, what you'll find in the senior/independent phase is not included in the later phases. Each phase has additional and new information, but older material is only in the original phase where it appears. Therefore, it is advisable that someone new to this book review all of the phases from Senior through End of Life.

As you go through the phases:

1) Identify what has been accomplished on your list already.
2) Make new lists of what needs to be done now, when you've identified your parents' current phase.
3) Set up a planner for things you want to think about for the future as you start recognizing further signs or progression.

PHASE I

SENIOR PARENTS (65+)

NOTES

WHAT YOU'RE CURRENTLY SEEING
WITH YOUR SENIOR PARENT

- Living Independently (with or without spouse/partner/roommate)
- Active and engaging with friends, family, community
- Fully functioning daily living skills (grooming, dressing, eating, toileting, exercise, etc.)
- Able to get around independently to appointments, engagements, and completing errands
- Able to clearly communicate

Now is the ideal time to get these tasks into your to do list/calendar/budget and get them DONE!

- Get the legal work done. (Pages 83–96)
- Get your name on all financial accounts.
- Create a long-term care plan. Know if you're going to make use of public or private funding.
- Complete the Five Wishes document (or something similar)
- Are your parents open to organ donation? If so, do they have any restrictions?
- Do your parents have resuscitation wishes? File a Do Not Resuscitate (DNR) with all their physicians if they will accept them in advance.
- Locate important papers and key numbers.
- Gather contact info for specialists and experts.
- Collect key contacts in the local area.
- Start taking classes and/or reading to educate yourself.
- Set parents up for video chat (if you're not local) and call on a regular basis to talk with them and see the home behind them in the camera. OR install a video camera (with their permission, of course) so you can check in. Discuss whether volume should be on or off.
- Work with your parents to begin clearing the house of unnecessary items. (Clearing clutter will reduce the amount of things that will need to be taken care of later on. Donating, distributing, or gifting special items to family will be easiest on your parents vs. throwing everything away.)
- Consider a family discussion to have parents inform the entire clan of what they want (before illness sets in) during and after their lives.
- Create lists of medicines with dosage and frequency and put copies of the lists in the wallet for each parent.
- Create an emergency contact card with medical conditions, medicines, primary care physician, preferred hospital, blood type, allergies, and any other critical info to hand to emergency response team and to keep in car(s) in case of an accident.

CREATING AN EXPERT TEAM

Let's face it—you don't know everything. There are experts and professionals for just about everything you will ever need, so it's time to collect their information and have them on call for when you might eventually require their services.

Working with professionals who specialize in your situation can save you time, money, and, most importantly, headaches and mistakes. Whether you are right next door or around the world from your parents, keeping a list of qualified professionals with familiarity of your parents' specific situation will be a huge relief during the process of caring for your loved one. When I wake up at 5 a.m. with a question, being aware that during business the next day I know exactly who to call to get the answer can help me fall back asleep.

Perhaps you have a varied family with members who are lawyers, accountants, financial planners, doctors, etc. I, regrettably, do not. If I need someone to fix a computer or bind a book or set up a teleprompter, I'm covered. I'm a writer, event planner, occasional pet sitter, nonprofit fundraiser, and former teacher. I recognize the skills I have and what I need to learn or turn over to someone more qualified.

I have not required the services of all the professionals I've included in this section, and you may never need all of them. But I collected a list of specialists potentially pertinent to your parents' care. Maybe reading the list will trigger holes in your support network that you can fill. When I get stuck and need another opinion before making a decision on parent care, I just open my phone and give one of my talented support team members (that's what I call them) a call.

A word of caution: Always check references and look for reviews before signing any agreements or paying any fees. As more people age and retire and search for answers to new challenges, the repertoire of shams and con men targeting the aged grows. Buyer beware! Find someone you can trust, with a solid business and a good reputation. And listen to your instincts.

[Note: There are separate chapters with BOLO (be on the look-out) on pages 241–243 and 263 that go into more detail on protecting your parents from abuse, scams, and fraud.]

A word of advice: Once you have all your professionals selected, you might consider (especially if you're managing all this from out of town) hosting regular Care Plan meetings.

Having your parents' lawyer, accountant, and financial planner meet together at least once when you begin and then perhaps biannually (or more frequently if you have a lot going on) to have an understanding of how each of the things they are recommending impacts your situation as a whole is going to be very helpful. One plan, all providers move forward in agreement.

Having your nurse, home health aide, nutritionist/dietician, and any other staff that interact with your parents meet all together with you on a regular basis (weekly or monthly as necessary, based on level of care) will help them each understand what the other is doing, and you will be clear that all duties are properly assigned and being administered. And this will help reduce harmful drug interactions.

Bring in the doctors as needed. They are not likely to join your weekly meeting, but they should be contributing information on the care of your parent.

If you are managing from a remote location, these meetings can be via video chat (FaceTime or Zoom or Skype, for example) or phone conference calls. Take notes and send a summary to each person included. If you are not staying informed and if the people involved in your parents' care don't have anyone taking an interest, then everyone will do what they do in a silo and things could fall through the cracks.

CHECKLIST OF EXPERTS/ PROFESSIONALS

I suggest that you enter the relevant information in the following section to keep it all in one convenient location, but whatever form your collection takes doesn't matter as long as you have it!

Checklists (provided for a quick overview and for reference) are followed by more detailed information about what each skilled professional can offer to support you and why you would want to collect the documents and information I have listed here.

Legal

Lawyer(s)—business, estate, elder care, Medicaid

Elder care consultant (for benefits from Medicare, Medicaid, Social Security, Veteran's benefits, pensions, etc.)

Legal Documents You'll Need

- ❖ Deeds/Ownership Documents For Property
- ❖ Last Will & Testament
- ❖ Power of Attorney
- ❖ Durable Power of Attorney and/or Healthcare Power of Attorney/Proxy
- ❖ Beneficiaries List
- ❖ Living Will/Advanced Healthcare Directive
- ❖ Five Wishes Document
- ❖ Funeral Service Paperwork (Policy/Prepaid Info), Cremation Or Burial Wishes, Cemetery Location And Plot, Contacts

Financial

Accountant

Certified Financial Planner/Investment Advisor

Financial Concierge, Certified Money Manager, Business Manager

Notary

Estate Executor

Financial Documents and Information You'll Need

- ❖ Revocable Or Irrevocable Trust
- ❖ Back Tax Returns (5 to 7 Years)
- ❖ IRA/401(K)/503B Account Details
- ❖ All Bank Accounts
- ❖ ATM Cards
- ❖ Credit Cards
- ❖ Monthly Auto-Pay Accounts
- ❖ Real Estate Taxes
- ❖ Community Common Charges
- ❖ Monthly Bills

Health

Physicians (for each specialist as well as primary care)

Preferred Hospital

Preferred Medical Office

Preferred Imaging Center

Preferred Laboratory

Pharmacy/Pharmacies of choice

Psychiatrist/Psychologist/Counselor

Physical Therapist

Personal Trainer

Medical Supply Store

Medical Rental Store

Health Documents And Information You'll Need

- ❖ Medication List
- ❖ Medical History
- ❖ Insurance Cards and Plan information
- ❖ Donor Information
- ❖ DNR or Healthcare Directives

ACCESS

I have taken to putting all my parents' important numbers into my phone contacts. I also created for my mother a Word document for passwords and account information that she keeps in a binder, like an old-fashioned phone book. I am frustrated that Mom never seems to find any electronic files I set up for her as Judy Heft advises that "Passwords should never be listed on paper." For highly sensitive confidential information, I use an app which keeps all my passwords, membership numbers, policy details in one place. If you can get your parents away from keeping passwords on paper, things will be a lot more secure! But I understand how difficult it is with a certain generation to get them acclimated to trusting technology. If this is the only way to collect the data, do what you've got to do and then lock up the info so people passing through your parents' residence wouldn't have easy access to the contents.

On one hand, you might need this information while your parent is around to make certain arrangements and redeem the benefits of various policies. On the other...the information will be needed when they pass so you can cancel all policies and agreements or contracts. This is especially important if payments are on auto pay and a bill might not even show up.

You'll need:

* Contracts
* Identification Numbers For All Accounts
* Passport Information
* Driver's License Information
* Login Information For All Accounts
* Important Facts, Figures, Items
* Computer Access (logins and passwords)
* Social Media Accounts (user name, login, passwords)
* Telephone Message Retrieval Passwords
* Keys To House And All Doors (for home and all other property)
* Combination Or Keys To Safes In Home and/or Office Or Other Location
* Account Information, Box Number, And Keys To Safety Deposit Box(es) Along With Location, Contact At Bank, And Size Of Box
* Keys To Padlocks *Storage*
* Passwords And Account Numbers For All Utilities (cable, Wi-Fi, phone plans, water, electric, sewage, trash, etc.) Plus Billing Addresses
* Time Share Account: Keys, Schedule, Costs, Partners, Management Company Contact Information

❖ Storage Facilities (boat, cars, papers, household or business items, etc.) Facility Address, Account Numbers, Passwords or Keys for Locks, Billing Address, and any Auto-Pay Functions. Itemized List of Contents Would Be Ideal. Insurance Information.

Primary home key location: _____

Seasonal home key location: _____

Car key location: _____

Boat key location: _____

Other: _____ Location: _____

Combination or key to safes in-home and/or office or other location

Home safe location: _____ Combination/key location: _____

Business safe location: _____ Combination/key location: _____

Account information, box number, and keys to safety deposit box(es) along with location, contact at bank, and size of box

Safe deposit box location: _____ Key location: _____ Contact: _____

Safe deposit box location: _____ Key location: _____ Contact: _____

Mailbox location: _____ Key location: _____

Keys to padlocks: _____ Location: _____

Passwords and Account Numbers For All Utilities Plus Billing Addresses

Internet access company: _____ Account: _____

Online password: _____ Pin: _____ Phone: _____

Cable account: _____ Account: _____

Online password: _____ Pin: _____ Phone: _____

Telephone company: _____ Account: _____

Online password: _____ Pin: _____ Phone: _____

Water company: _____ Account: _____

Online password: _____ Pin: _____ Phone: _____

Electric company: _____ Account: _____

Online password: _____ Pin: _____ Phone: _____

Sewage: _____ Account: _____

Online password: _____ Pin: _____ Phone: _____

Gas/oil company: _____ Account: _____

Online password: _____ Pin: _____ Phone: _____

Trash collection company: _____ Account: _____

Online password: _____ Pin: _____ Phone: _____

Time Share

TS company name: _____ Account: _____ Phone: _____

Keys located: _____ Management company contact: _____

Storage Facilities (boat, cars, papers, household or business items, etc.)

Facility name: _____ Stored item(s): _____

Physical address: _____

Phone: _____ Email: _____ URL: _____

Slot: _____ Monthly fee: ☐ Auto ☐ Month by Month

Key location: _____

Online password: _____ PIN: _____

Facility name: _____ Stored item(s): _____

Physical address: _____

Phone: _____ Email: _____ URL: _____

Slot: _____ Monthly fee: ☐ Auto ☐ Month by Month

Key location: _____

Online password: _____ PIN: _____

Household & Wellness

Housekeepers _____

Household help _____

Professional organizer _____

Driver(s)/transportation _____

Companion care _____

Home Health Aide _____

Hospice resources _____

Pets

Veterinarian _____

Dog walker/feeder _____

Pet daycare _____

Kennel/Pet hotel _____

Pet sitter _____

Affiliations & Memberships

Military History

Discharge papers _____

Rank _____

Medals _____

Clubs/Memberships

AAA _____

AARP _____

Country Club _____

Golf or Tennis Clubs _____

Travel Groups _____

Social Groups _____

Fitness Center(s) _____

Other: _____

Seattle Yacht Club
Lake Washington Garden Club

BUILDING A LEGAL TEAM

Attorney

An attorney is one of the first professionals you should find when you begin your role as caregiver. The term that is used in the elder care world is "elder law attorney" and that is the term used by United States bar associations to denote lawyers who focus on the needs of the elderly. A competent lawyer is a worthwhile investment and a must-have for anyone who owns any property or has any money to protect. This book offers you an overview of some ways elder law practices can help your family.

Elder law attorneys are trained and knowledgeable in the practice areas described in this section and those described in the Medicaid paragraphs below. An elder law attorney will be able to explain everything and how all the pieces relate to your specific situation. Your local lawyer will know of new laws that may help your parents in ways we cannot yet understand.

Yes, any competent lawyer can work through the legal system to handle the documents you should have on hand, but an elder law attorney executes a multidisciplinary strategy where he or she will walk you through the complicated maze of local laws on estate planning and protection of assets—with an emphasis on your aging parents' needs.

An elder law attorney will be able to explain to all parties involved (you and your parents and possibly siblings or other involved parties) how to:

❖ Protect assets
❖ Assign gifts
❖ Prepare for Medicaid transition
❖ Access veteran's benefits
❖ Transition estate to family or a charitable foundation or nonprofits

Make sure the attorney you select has experience in the areas of concern for your family.

When looking at advertising or attending lectures, please note that the term "specialist" has a certain meaning in the law. For example, no lawyer is allowed to call themselves a specialist unless they have been certified as a specialist by their state Bar association. Any lawyer can join national, state, or local Elder Law committees, sections, or organizations but those who become certified have been professionally vetted for proven knowledge and ethics. Becoming certified in Florida, for example, requires testing, peer review, a clean Bar record and other requisites. Be aware of these differences when you interview attorneys in your local area.

An elder law attorney can connect your family with an entire network of local professionals, direct you to social service agencies, and create a plan in cooperation with your other professional team members to encompass everything through the rest of your parents' lives so you only have to do this once! Don't wait for a diagnosis or health event to occur before finding your lawyer.

When your loved one passes or becomes incapacitated, you are typically not in a mental state to manage complicated legal matters. It is reassuring to know that all the details have been worked out as your loved one wanted, and you just have to make one phone call to the lawyer to activate everything when needed.

Legal Documents

The list of legal documents you want to have in your fireproof/waterproof safe is not long, but is essential for easing your way through most situations that arise in the care of an aging individual, and ultimately managing the estate of someone who has passed away.

Basically, an elder law attorney will create a document to divide and assign assets upon death, a directive to clarify who will manage and how to handle medical issues while your parent is still alive but not able to make informed consent, and a Trust to protect assets and enable assets to be transferred easily without going to probate and without extra fees upon death. A Durable Power of Attorney will provide authority to a designated person for making financial and/or medical decisions when your parent is incapacitated. All powers of attorney for your parent will expire upon the death of your parent.

Some states have special rules that allow someone to create a power of attorney that only becomes valid once your parent has been declared incompetent. If this interests you or your well parent, ask your chosen attorney about this option in your community.

There are other documents that you might need if there are properties, businesses, or assets of a large nature that need to be managed in specific ways.

Note: Some states require certain documents to be updated on a regular basis (e.g., every two years) to make sure that the information is still current and applicable. Things like a Living Will or DNR might change or be added or deleted, and updates need to be filed with doctors and hospitals you use.

All documents legally valid in one state must be honored by every other state. However, being honored does not mean that they are effective for your parent's goals. Many states require that legal documents be created for that particular state. For example, I learned from my attorney that a Will created for my parents in New York needed to be redrafted in Florida when my parents' legal residence changed.

Differences in terms, language, and titles used by each state could make enforcing a document from another state difficult or impossible and/or make the terms in the document unnecessarily expensive to administer. While a lawyer may know how to reconcile these different terms, a well-intentioned healthcare provider may not. It is most likely well worth the cost to have a new, locally drafted document created.

MEDICAID

If your family has long-term care insurance and/or financial assets to cover expenses for the foreseeable future, you may not need Medicaid preplanning. And, if the government changes how it works and Medicaid is eliminated or Medicare for All is enacted, you definitely won't need Medicaid planning!

However, if your parents' assets are not limitless and you or they would be hard-pressed to come up with funds if a critical situation requires expensive ongoing care ($10,000+ a month per person), I recommend that you talk to your elder law attorney to be sure you've structured all you have so you can qualify for help, should it ever be necessary. Working with a specialist in this area also means that someone else who knows the system can get your paperwork processed much more quickly than a novice could. I learned that I could have made better decisions on structuring the household and our assets early on that would have prevented restructuring later in the game.

Ask your local lawyer to explain spousal refusal laws in your area if money might become an issue for parents to cover caregiving costs. My understanding is that this is a kind of "financial divorce" that allows Medicaid to pay the hospital and care bills for the sick spouse without leaving the healthier spouse devoid of funds for daily living.

I went through the legal paperwork with an elder law attorney when I first began the process with my parents. My parents were living in two states, in two homes, and both parents were healthy. A few years passed and one property was sold, my parents had relocated permanently, revenue from selling a home was added to their assets, and their health was beginning to decline. At this point, I found a practice with experience in the Medicaid world to ensure that my parents' revised situation would be taken into account.

Lawyer—Elder Law Attorney:

Contact: _____

Address: _____

Phone(s): _____

Email: _____

Website: _____

Other: _____

Elder Care Consultant

If you have any concerns about having the knowledge to manage the benefits that might be available to your parent or the time to go through the complications of applying for those benefits or programs, an elder care consultant could help.

The consultant will meet with you and/or your parents privately and set up a list of benefits and services to handle geriatric care management and/or fiduciary services. In fact, an elder care consultant can also provide you with lists of all the other reputable professionals you need to have on your contact list if you're not local and referrals could speed things along.

Elder care consultants often have specific skills for particular needs. For example, my elder care consultant works with veterans. My father is a veteran of the Korean War. He is entitled to VA benefits including things like free burial, medical care, prescriptions, and hearing services (tests, hearing aids, and cleanings). I did not know that until I met with Kathy. I did not know there was an Aide and Assistance program to help my dad, the veteran, and benefits possibly, for my mother, the wife of a veteran.

The VA (at the time of this writing) offers respite care services a few times a month so that my mother can get a break from caregiving and know that a free, qualified home health aide, companion, or nurse will come to my parents' home to keep an eye on my father so Mom can do something to care for herself.

Most elder care consultants will be able to give you general advice on how you might structure your finances in order to qualify for government programs that can make aging easier, way before you actually need them. Make sure you doublecheck with an attorney and/or financial advisor before making any big moves (someone who specializes in your parents' home state laws) to be sure the advice works within the parameters of your specific situation.

A word of caution: An elder care consultant is not legally permitted to dispense legal advice or act in the same capacity as a certified financial planner.

When it comes time to applying for various programs, an elder care consultant can handle most of that for you or guide you through the process.

There is a fee for this service. I paid a retainer fee and received a fixed cost for future services, to which the retainer is applied. The remaining amount is due if and when I use the services.

Note: If you have already hired an elder law attorney, you won't need to duplicate efforts by hiring an elder care consultant.

If you do like the idea of the extra support, if your parents would take advice from a stranger before listening to you, you can find good specialists by attending free (or low-cost) presentations at senior centers, libraries, or houses of worship, and at special events (like conferences and trade shows) that focus on resources for aging. Articles in local magazines and newspapers, website blogs from people/organizations in your area, and/or programs offered through elder care agencies or Alzheimer's agencies in your area are also good sources. If nothing else, you will get tons of free valuable information by attending these presentations.

To handle things on your own and save the fee, consider taking a class or attending a paid workshop led by an elder care consultant. Do your research online. Ask for advice from friends and family and your professional team. As always, apply due diligence before signing papers or giving information that can be used to take assets from you or your parents.

Elder Care Consultant:

Address: _____

Phone(s): _____

Email: _____

Website: _____

Other: _____

LEGAL DOCUMENT PORTFOLIO

As I said in the beginning, I am simply a daughter, in service to my parents, and I am sharing what I've learned with those who are likely being placed in a similar role. Because each person's case is different, because laws and rules change rapidly, because different states can have different laws, and because this book was not written as legal or financial advice, you should not rely upon this book or any other resources herein as legal advice. Use information provided here to create your list of questions to ask your attorney and advisors.

Legal documents are a part of life. "If I have nothing, I don't need legal documents…right?" Sorry, not so much. You need them. You don't have to spend a lot of money to get these documents written, filed, and processed legally, but some of these are to protect you as a caregiver, some are to protect your parents, and some are to ensure that you don't lose everything as you or your parents go through the process of aging, possible illness, and then dying.

There are comprehensive books and online resources on how to write the following documents, how to get them processed, what is legal in your own state, and where to find the right attorney or free resources and alternatives, so I won't go into a ton of detail here.

My parents didn't know much about what they needed to have done legally, but their friends were all talking about visits to lawyers to get their ducks in a row. My mother attended Estate Planning seminars at her senior center and through the library. She came away with lists and lists and a lot of printed material. Then she got overwhelmed, handed everything to me and said, "What do we need to get done?" Oh my. And so, began my quest for that elder care consultant I mentioned in the last section. She gave me the low-down on the most critical documents and recommended some local lawyers.

At this point, my goal here is just to give you a list of important documents that most people will need and why you need them. If you have this full list in advance, you can save some time, energy, and money by getting things done as a package, well in advance of needing them. And please note that the titles of these documents may vary by state. Your attorney will tell you what the documents are called.

In fact, as I was learning about all these documents, I realized that as long as I was doing this for my parents, I might as well get mine done too. It feels good to know things are settled should anything happen. There are those buses that go out of control that everyone talks about—you know the "Well, I could get hit by a bus tomorrow" rationale.

Last Will & Testament

Commonly referred to simply as a Will, a Last Will & Testament is meant to communicate a person's wishes with regard to their possessions and property upon death. Every state has its own requirements and there are variations of a Will. In Florida, for example, there's something called a Pour Over Will. Check with your local lawyers and advisors.

Within the Will, someone might include instructions for how specific items and property should be dispersed among dependents or donated to organizations, or it might be more general instructions, such as, "Distribute all my worldly possessions equally among my children." A combination of the two might look like, "Distribute all my worldly possession equally among my children, but I designate my jazz record collection to my nephew Andrew and my mother's pearl necklace to my granddaughter Molly." Some lawyers, to keep things less complicated when changes may need to be made, would recommend that a letter or specific instructions on bequests be attached to a Will instead of including minute details in the Will itself.

Additionally, a Will may also specify how all debts left by the deceased should be settled. A Will names someone to handle the settlement of the estate (which includes paying off all the debts) and identifies any final wishes of the deceased. Again, each state has different titles for the person who handles this responsibility. I have heard both executor and administrator used. For this book, I will stick with executor, but you should know that it could be called something else near you.

On a basic level, with not much to distribute, only one person gets everything, or if it's an equal division by all, you can download a generic Will on the internet or pick up a template that you can copy from a book at the library. Office supply stores may have template fill-in-the-blank versions as well.

I'm not positive that this would stand up legally everywhere, but if chances are good that no one is going to argue over your parents' "stuff" in court, writing last wishes in their own handwriting and having it witnessed by multiple nonfamily people (have the witnesses sign it) and/or notarized (much more legally accepted) can suffice in a pinch.

According to findlaw.com, if you die without a Will, it means you have died "intestate." When this happens, the intestacy laws of the state where you reside will determine how your property is distributed upon your death. This includes any bank accounts, securities, real estate, and other assets you own at the time of death. So, check the laws of the state where your parents reside if you don't know if there is a Will already or if your parents don't want to have one written.

In most states, all Wills must go through some type of court process. In most instances, this is known as "probate." A court process is necessary regardless of how much money the person has. If there is one dollar and someone wants that dollar, a court process is usually required in order for the financial institution to release the funds. Probate can be very expensive, usually costing thousands of dollars. An attorney can typically set things up so that probate can be avoided. This done by titling assets in certain ways and sometimes by using trust agreements.

Durable Power of Attorney

Before your parents are unable to make decisions and process thoughts; before your parents can't express how they want things to go after they pass, you'll want to have legal documents created that communicate and legalize your parents' intentions. This is not just for the court system, but should also be distributed to the rest of the family and all caregivers, physicians, and financial institutions. Naming an agent with a Durable Power of Attorney lets all others know who has been selected as the designated representative. This person may or may not be a family member and there are state laws dictating who can serve.

By the way, attending every doctor's visit does not automatically grant you the power to make medical decisions or sign medical documents on behalf of your parent. HIPAA[4] laws could also keep you from retrieving information about your parent's health unless the doctor/hospital has a document confirming that your parents are okay with them sharing information with you.

If your parents trust you to manage their health and finances, you can be named as their agent under a Durable Power of Attorney. If you have siblings and your parent wants to divide responsibilities so that you all work together to make decisions, these powers may be granted separately. Often, one person is named as primary and a second and/or third are also named in case the primary is unable or unwilling to assume the responsibilities. Some people name more than one agent to serve at the same time. A properly drafted Durable Power of Attorney can direct how the signatures are to be made when there is more than one agent and can include language to protect your parent's wishes and to protect you from unnecessary liability.

Essentially, a Power of Attorney gives your parent a legal way to assign you the power to act in their place. It recognizes that they believe you will act in their best interest. If, however, your parent becomes mentally incapacitated, you'll need what are known as Durable Powers of Attorney for making decisions on medical care and finances. Scott Solkoff recommends that Durable Power of Attorney is the only document you require. When you have Durable Power of Attorney, it is valid even when your parent becomes incapacitated and unable to make decisions. Without the "durable" designation, your Power of Attorney authority ends when your parent becomes incapacitated.

Another important thing to know is that Powers of Attorney do NOT survive death. After your parent dies, the executor of the estate handles closing out the estate and managing all legal and financial matters according to the provisions of the Will. You may name the same person to do both jobs, but they are wearing different legal hats.

Summarized from uslegalwills.com: The executor of a Will is imbued with responsibilities of settling debts, paying expenses and taxes, and handling any claims before turning over what remains to the beneficiaries. The executor has certain powers to manage the estate, including selling, keeping or investing the property, cash and assets of the deceased.

Your parent can designate Power of Attorney status to an attorney, any family member, or even to a friend and also name that same person as executor of the estate, or name the executor as someone different from the Power of Attorney. You might want to discuss this with your parents. For example, you can choose not to be the executor but remain as Durable Power of Attorney or vice versa.

---

[4] HIPAA = Health Insurance Portability and Accountability Act (ensures privacy of your health information)

Unless a general Power of Attorney has a specific expiration date (not allowed in most states) or your parent revokes it in writing or some event occurs that terminates it according to local law, the Power of Attorney should remain in effect until the death of your parent. Note that there are special rules, different from state to state, about how a Power of Attorney must be revoked and to whom notice of revocation must be given.

There are websites that offer simple forms with instructions to help you create a Will, Living Will, or Power of Attorney. Generally, the document must be signed, witnessed, and notarized by an adult. If you will have to deal with your parents' real estate assets, some states require your parents to put the document on file in the local land records office. This might be handled for you by the lawyer who is drawing up the real estate documents.

Making Healthcare Decisions for Your Parents

The Healthcare Power of Attorney—a.k.a. Medical POA, Healthcare Proxy, Healthcare Agent; (titles and responsibilities/rights vary by state)—will give you the authority to make decisions about your parents' health when they are unable physically or mentally to do so. A Health Care Power of Attorney is typically done in addition to the primary document of Designation of Health Care Surrogate (or Proxy in some states). It also can specify in great detail or general terms exactly what kind of medical treatment your parents want. With this authority, you might be further directed and guided via the Living Will (end-of-life type decisions) or Five Wishes (any medical or life situation) documents your parents have completed.

After having discussions with my parents, I know that my father would choose to be treated at home as much as possible, whereas my mother prefers a hospital or professional healthcare setting. My dad wants to be unplugged if he's diminished (which Alzheimer's has brought on), whereas my mother wants us to keep trying no matter how "out of it" she is. But neither want to carry on if they're brain dead.

The Durable Power of Attorney gives you the authority to manage the medical decisions, but it also allows you to act on financial decisions that need to be made when your parent is incapacitated for medical reasons.

Making decisions on the spot is easier once I know the parameters of my parents' desires and, by giving me these official powers, my parents are comforted knowing their wishes will be met, even if they can't speak up for themselves.

Signing as Power of Attorney

Have your Durable Power of Attorney document with you when you sign anything on your parent's behalf. I was warned to be cautious about instructions on websites. Ask your attorney in your state how to go about signing for your parent. The law does not designate exactly how to sign, but the more clarity the better, lest the signer be deemed individually liable.

- ❖ Write your parent's (principal's) name
- ❖ Sign your own name after the principal's name, after including the word "by"
- ❖ End the signature by indicating that you're acting as "attorney-in-fact" or "through Power of Attorney."

It would look something like this:

Arthur Pessin by *Fern Pessin*, Attorney-in-Fact

Hedda Pessin by *Fern Pessin*, Through Power of Attorney

Living Will/Advanced Healthcare Directive

While a Last Will and Testament outlines how your parent expects his or her estate to be handled upon passing and a Durable Power of Attorney gives someone the right to act on behalf of a living person who has lost the ability to make decisions for himself or herself, a Living Will is a document that outlines specific medical instructions to be applied when your parent is alive but unable to communicate with doctors or family. A Living Will or Advanced Healthcare Directive (or whatever name it's called in your state) gives a person the opportunity to spell out his or her own wishes for medical treatment when unable to communicate them directly.

Imagine being unable to speak but aware of what is happening around you or being under anesthesia only to wake and find out that you are paralyzed and will never be able to move again because you were resuscitated with a spinal injury or anything else happens that you didn't want…it's a horrible thought. One person might want to live and work through it, as God's will perhaps, and another might have wished to pass to eternity rather than have to live dependent on others. So, work out what your parents' wishes are and then put that in writing so you and your family and the physicians can follow it.

As someone's designated healthcare agent, you can carry out your parents' wishes outlined in the Living Will. What a blessing it will be for your parent to know that everything is taken care of and someone they trust will ensure that all their wishes are followed. And, for you, it'll be such a relief to not have to make these decisions in the dark, guessing what your parent may have preferred. You have a document that spells out what is wanted. Boom. Done. No guessing.

The lawyer who helped me by providing and reviewing much of this information wanted me to let you know that anyone over 18 years old should have an Advance Directive created and filed with family. So, figure out what services you and your parents require and be done with them at the same time! :-)

Here is a summary of 10 TIPS AND TREASURES ON LIVING WILLS, an article from Solkoff Legal. Your attorney can give you more detail and clarify local rules on these:

1. Examine your own wishes. Your signing the form requires others to comply with your wishes.
2. Pain medications may be deemed "artificial procedures" and could be withheld if you don't specify meds are okay.
3. Consider a liability shield for doctors and facilities to be sure they will honor your wishes instead of worrying about a lawsuit.
4. Allow one signature for authorization instead of requiring several, which could hold up action if all people who have to sign are not available immediately.
5. Make sure the surrogate you assign meets all the requirements of local laws.
6. Make it clear if you are pro or against experimental procedures.
7. Have your lawyer explicitly state in your documents that "my surrogate(s) shall not be liable or responsible for any costs or expenses of my medical treatment or care."

8. Make the directives "Self-Proving" so witnesses do not have to come to court to prove the person actually signed a Will.

9. Remember to include and be clear about your organ donation wishes. Are you okay with this or not?

10. Provide copies of your advance directives/living will to all surrogates, your doctors, hospital, etc.

This brings me to the next document that you will find incredibly helpful...

Five Wishes

Broaching sensitive topics is never easy, but this document, the Five Wishes, is an easy way to segue into a lot of difficult discussions. Five Wishes was created by the nonprofit organization Aging with Dignity. It has been described as the "Living Will with a heart and soul." You can get a copy on the AgingwithDignity.org website. It's used by over 40,000 organizations to help people communicate and understand wishes for well-being and treatment of care when not well. Everyone, at any adult age (in my opinion), should have one completed to express their own wishes for care in varying situations when decision-making may not be easy. I recommend that you use the Five Wishes framework to help you figure out what your parents want to include in their legal documents. Five Wishes should be done in addition to the legal documents you create with your attorney.

I found it totally enlightening to complete the Five Wishes with each of my parents. I completed the questions for myself, as well. When we all sat down to discuss them together, my mother said, "Oooh, put that on mine too! I like that," when I mentioned that, if possible, I would prefer to be in a hospital room with a window and again, if possible, with a view of a tree or water or something alive.

Once we finished going through all the answers (I had them all entered on my computer), I emailed the entire document for each of my parents and for myself to my siblings. If something happens, we all have the same information. If something happens to me, my siblings know what my wishes are.

Questions in the Five Wishes focus on how you want to be treated. It's not about medical treatments per se, but more about comfort and personal likes and dislikes. Questions vary and range, traversing many areas. Some things I had to think about when I filled mine out:

- ❖ Do you want to be alone if you're dying or would you rather have people there? If people, then who would you like there? Strangers so you won't be alone, or do you only want companionship if family or friends can fill the seat?

- ❖ Would you rather end your days in a hospital, hospice care, or at home if you're diagnosed as terminal? (My dad wanted to be at home, my mom wanted to be in a hospital. They looked at each other with eyebrows raised when they realized they wanted different things!)

- ❖ What kind of grooming care do you want if you're incapacitated? Some people like to have their hair brushed, nails polished, lipstick on if people are visiting, toenails clipped, nose or ear hair trimmed, etc.

- ❖ What kind of music do you like, if any at all? Do you have a favorite book or poem you'd like read to you if you're confined to bed?

- ❖ How do you want to be buried? For example: Do you want cremation or a casket? Where do you want to be buried? Who do you want to know you've passed? What would you like to be said about you at your funeral? How would you like to be remembered?

Some approach the Five Wishes as a homework assignment that they need to complete in one sitting. Others use this as a way to open discussions about many things, discussing one question at a time at family gatherings. This can help bring a family closer together. Others take the questions and spend some time evaluating what they want and return it when completed—however long that takes.

I promise you it's eye-opening no matter how you approach it. And, like having a Living Will, knowing that your wishes are clear to your family makes the aging process less stressful and much more peaceful.

Naming Beneficiaries

You've no doubt had to name beneficiaries when you've signed up for health insurance, auto insurance, life insurance, bank accounts, etc. Even joining the Automobile Club of America asked me for a beneficiary! Often, when you start a job you're asked to name emergency contacts and beneficiaries.

Your parents will name beneficiaries in their Will and other legal documents, but beneficiaries might appear on older documents, like property deeds, retirement accounts, annuities, pensions, etc. Some Power of Attorney documents may grant the ability to change beneficiary designations on any or all of those other documents. Holding Power of Attorney means that you have a fiduciary duty to act in good faith as your parents intend. Talk to your parents to make sure you know who they want as beneficiaries on all their documents and policies.

It is also important to note that the executor of the Will has the responsibility of contacting and paying out all of those beneficiary designations. **Beneficiary designations outrank the Will**. If you think that you only need to write a new Will and everything that came before disappears—NOPE. Your parents' Will does not override what is named in the beneficiary designation on any of the other policies and plans that may have been purchased.

You might want to check with the local laws to see what happens when the executor has to transfer property after death and there are beneficiaries already listed on the deed and other policies (property or homeowners' insurance, for example).

How assets are titled is of critical importance in your parents' planning. Knowledge and advance planning can save people tens or hundreds of thousands of dollars and thus impact their quality of life. Asset titling is informed by whether and how wills or trusts are used. In some cases, with very small amounts of assets, it is best not to use a will or a trust. If there are joint owners on accounts, the creditors of every person can get to the assets. If there is an untimely death or disability of a joint owner or a beneficiary designation on an account, there can be significant problems. Broken record here...this is where your local attorney can help make sense of what is best for your individual situation!

Funeral

Eventually, we all die. It's the circle of life. When going through the family papers to scan them as we packed up the New York apartment, I found the contract for my parents' cemetery plots. Apparently, my mother's family has a group plot and my parents bought their grave sites when they got married!! That's over 60 years ago. But, here was the interesting thing…they didn't have two plots, one for each, like I was expecting. They had three plots. WHAT? I wondered how they knew that I would be single again and might need that????

When I asked my mother, she said that they did it just in case something happened to one of the children growing up. Ick. I didn't love hearing that, but I guess that might help you understand how practical my family is and why I quickly learned and absorbed all these forms, documents, and legal stuff that had to be done as I started to care for my parents. I didn't get any flack when I said, "We need to make an appointment at the lawyer's and here's what we need done."

So, nice to know I have a plot, should I need it. However, that plot is in New York and I now live in Florida. My parents' plots are also in New York and they live in Florida. So, our discussions are burial or cremation? New burial plots in Florida or ship my parents to New York? Donate body parts to science or follow religious law and leave bodies undisturbed?

My sister and brother and their families live in the New York tri-state area along with most of my parents' few living relatives. So, if family is to visit the plot and Mom wants to be buried with her parents, then we should be in New York. However, Dad doesn't want to spend the money to ship the bodies back. And, if he passes first, he wants to know how will Mom visit him if he's in New York and she lives in Florida? And, if we are donating the brain or heart or body to science, how does that work? So, you can see how these discussions bring up all kinds of family issues. Having these discussions before confusion and memory gaps set in is going to make this a lot easier later.

Figuring it all out, paying for much in advance (you earn interest on the money in a prepaid account), or taking out a policy that covers payments over time might make sense. Your parents might feel great relief knowing that they are not leaving you with a big bill to pay when they pass.

And truthfully, when your parents do pass, you are not going to be in the frame of mind to start thinking about what kind of casket, which funeral home, where to bury them, etc. Knowing if your parents want open or closed casket, a wake, a memorial, a viewing, a military honor guard, or what music to play, or even what food to serve will reduce your decision-making anxiety.

Decisions that get made in grief, followed by the bills later, may lead to regrets. Better to be planned and managed ahead of time when level heads prevail. Better to agree on what is wanted so you don't wonder, "Is this what they would have preferred?" Once everything is planned, let the whole family in on the arrangements. And keep the papers where you can find them easily. Share them with siblings (and/or your religious leader) so if you're too distraught, someone can pick up the slack and get done what needs to be handled. One phone call to the prepaid funeral home and you're done if it's all been worked out in advance.

In our family, my sister wants our plans for our parents' burial to include the memorial chapel in New York. My dad didn't think we needed it. My sister said that *she* had a lot of friends who would want to come show their respects, so it was important to her. Hmmm. Glad we got that cleared up now instead of arguing about it later. "Sometimes it's not all about what you want, Dad!" my sister smiled with a pointed eyebrow raised at him!

Paying for the Funeral

Prepaying for funeral plans at the funeral home may not work if there's a chance (a) the funeral home might go out of business or (b) the person for whom you paid might move to a new location before passing away or (c) you want to invest your money somewhere or (d) you don't want to lay out all the money up front.

Some funeral homes have escrow accounts to hold your prepaid funds where the funds earn interest each year. Putting money away for someone else's funeral may have tax benefits for you. Check with your accountant. Funeral expenses are currently tax deductible when they are paid by an estate. Check to see if your situation qualifies.

Burial insurance, funeral insurance, and life insurance with funeral pay-off plans exist. Some are sold by funeral homes and others are sold by individual brokers. Do your research to make sure the plan you buy is from a stable company with a secure history and solid funding. Scams exist for people around these emotional purchases.

Other Options

* ❖ Purchase an FDIC-insured CD with enough funds for the funeral and name the beneficiary as the person who will handle the funeral arrangements.
* ❖ If your parents' funds are in a brokerage account, The Motley Fool website recommends that you look into changing the account type to a Totten Trust, which will "transfer on death" or "payable on death" to a beneficiary to handle the funeral.
* ❖ Set up an FDIC-insured savings account for the funeral and add money to it on a regular basis until the funds for the funeral your parent described are covered.
* ❖ Take out a small life insurance policy that covers the cost of the preselected funeral arrangements. You will pay monthly premiums until your parent passes.

When figuring out your total expenses for a funeral and how much to put aside, remember to account for inflation and rising costs over time. As you well know, costs today will not be the same five, 10, or 20 years from now.

Checklist: Legal

When all of this legal paperwork is done, make sure you have copies. Make sure you know where your parent keeps his or her copies. If it's been done at a lawyer's office, they will retain copies on file. And as long as you have permission while your parents are alive or so long as you're the executor or beneficiary of the Will, you will receive access to these files.

Living in a hurricane zone where evacuation is not unusual and/or sudden storms can rip a building to shreds, I don't want to take a chance that I might lose all the legal documents and not have records. I took photos and scanned all copies of my parents' important signed papers and I keep those on my phone in case I need them or need to refer to them. For example, sometimes a doctor might need to see my Healthcare or Durable/Medical Power of Attorney for my parents and I can just pull it up and email it to the office right then.

The lawyer we used for our second round of revisions (once my parents moved to independent living) actually gave each parent and me a business card-size USB flash stick with all these necessary documents to keep in our wallets. We can just hand the card/stick to whatever doctor or hospital needed them. The lawyer's info is printed right on the "card" so, if we have a question or someone in the medical office has one, they can just call to get what they need. Handy dandy technology. Love it.

This chart will help you identify where each of these documents and arrangements is located.

DOCUMENT	COPIES LOCATED...
Last Will & Testament	
Durable Power of Attorney	
Healthcare Power of Attorney	
Name Beneficiaries	
Living Will	
Five Wishes	
Burial and Funeral Agreements	
Deed to Property (properties)	
Contracts (car lease, maintenance leases, a/c, boiler, pool, etc.)	
IDENTIFICATION NUMBERS:	
Passport	
Birth Certificate	
Driver's License	
Health Insurance	

DOCUMENT	COPIES LOCATED...
Life Insurance	
(Eventually) Death Certificate(s)	
OTHER LEGAL DOCUMENTS:	
Adoption Papers	
Marriage Certificate	
Prenuptial Agreement	
Post Nuptial Agreement	
Child Support Agreements	
Citizenship Papers	
Any name-changing documents	
Divorce Papers	
Birth Certificate	
Domestic Partner Agreements	
Charitable Trust Agreements	
Life Insurance Trust	
Military Discharge Paperwork	
Other:	

BUILDING A FINANCIAL TEAM

Time for you to look at the family finances? No one really wants to talk about finances. It's uncomfortable; maybe either you or your parents (or all of you) feel like it's intrusive. Don't get me wrong, you can avoid it like many people do. But then a nursing facility will ask how you're going to pay for services or an assisted living facility wants to see back tax returns to admit your parent. You try to collect benefits from Medicaid and you can't find any of the paperwork to prove that your parents aren't zillionaires. Bills start coming in and your parent has slipped into a state of confusion after a health crisis, an accident, or dementia onset and you don't know what bank they use or how much they have in an account or if someone is already on payroll to manage these things. Your parent is unable to communicate, and suddenly you're getting notices that the house/condo is in foreclosure or huge fines for nonpayment of community common charges are being assessed or your parent is being evicted because rent hasn't been paid. Yikes. Maybe a conversation isn't such a bad idea after all? (Remember, easy starters for this talk are in Part II on Communication.)

No one (except probably me) goes through life thinking that tomorrow may bring an accident or incident that sends you into a coma or causes the brain to shut off, but it does happen. My 48-year-old friend got a headache, got into bed early, and had a stroke. Her husband administered CPR until EMS arrived and then she was kept alive in the ambulance. When she came out of the medically induced coma, she didn't know who anyone was. Her husband, brother, and friends were all strangers. Six very difficult months of residential rehab followed before she even remembered that she owned a business. Her husband and brother stepped in and learned the business from scratch through employee anecdotes and reviewing previous paperwork. It was more than a year before my friend could even go back to working part-time in her own business. Two years later, she is back in charge.

When the person is someone older, it is so much more difficult to recover from any kind of incident. The point is, you never know. "Plan for tomorrow but live for today," is my personal motto.

Since knowing financial information can make a huge difference in how decisions are made, the discussions must be held. My recommendation (from personal experience) is to take a sip or drink of whatever takes the edge off (wine, vodka/tequila, or chamomile tea all work for me) and begin.

At the very least, find out where all the information you might need is being kept. You don't have to see it all right now, but know where it is. That's an easy first step. Not so threatening. Not so intrusive.

On a more comprehensive level, you'll want to understand your parents' portfolio. Your parent may have much more or less than what I'm outlining in this chapter. I'm providing a general collection of important information as a starting point, so you can amend this list based on your conversation with your parents and your understanding of the home/estate in question.

On the most all-encompassing level, to make your life a thousand times easier (which in turn helps your parent), see if your parent will agree to put your name on all or most of their accounts. If you are a cosignatory and/or co-owner of an account, you can skip a ton of legal stuff if/when incapacitation comes along and you need immediate access. Sometimes your parent will agree to this only if your siblings are also on the accounts. All equal.

From listening to legal advice and the experiences of people in my caregiving groups, having too many signatures and authorizations required can cause a delay in getting things done. It makes things more "equal" in the eyes of your parents and siblings, that's true, but let's say you are the child who moves close to your parents to be there for them and your siblings are busy living their own lives somewhere else. Something happens and an account needs to be moved or shut, or you have to make a medical decision on the spot, or the bank has a question and needs authorization to remove a fee...it gets tiresome to wait for all parties to be on board to get everything notarized, faxed, etc. You can all agree to communicate regularly and include each other in decisions, but when it comes to processing the paperwork, it's up to your family to decide the best way to manage all that.

Accountant

In addition to filing annual tax returns, an accountant will know the local and national laws pertinent to elder issues and finances. Your parents may have someone already or you may want to search for someone with elder clientele experience.

A Certified Public Accountant (CPA) is the title of qualified accountants in numerous countries in the English-speaking world. In the United States, the CPA is a license to provide accounting services to the public.

To simply file annual tax returns, if your parents don't have properties, businesses, or complicated investment accounts, you don't need a CPA. You can use a tax advisor service. You may know them as tax consultants. Some well-known national tax consultants are Jackson Hewitt or H&R Block.

You can also use a software program. Most years (when we don't have a real estate sale, a move, sale of assets, or extraordinary medical expenses), I find Turbo Tax software covers my parents' needs (and my own) quite well. Then again, my father was a tax consultant and I worked for him for eight years, so I kinda know what I'm doing. Lol.

However, when you eventually start taking over your parents' financials, especially if you have a hectic life or don't live in the area, you might want some assistance in paying their bills, paying staff, reminding you about estimated tax payments, etc. There are many services beyond doing taxes that might be fulfilled by your accountant's office. If not by the accountant, then ask for a referral for a bookkeeping service or a financial concierge, a Daily Money Manager.

An accountant can guide you through caregiving compensation questions/issues that you might not have considered before:

❖ Perhaps you are giving up your career or a job to care for your parent and would like to be compensated?
❖ Should you create a service contract with your parents? How does that impact your own income/ tax situation?
❖ When should you pay an occasional independent care provider as a service contractor?
❖ How do you handle independent contractors vs. paying an agency?
❖ How do you file a 1099 for independent contractors?
❖ Who pays and how do you pay taxes for employees?
❖ What about setting up benefit programs for care workers?
❖ And what are the financial and legal implications of each decision?

An accountant will be able to show you how each decision you make for your parents' care will impact all family finances, including your own. And, equally important to you, are the potential deductions you can take on your own return for expenses you incur in caring for your parents and/or how to claim gifts or transfers of money and assets into your name.

Accountant:

Company Name: _____

Contact: _____

Address: _____

Phone(s): _____

Email: _____

Website: _____

Other: _____

Certified Financial Planner/Investment Advisor

In addition to a tax consultant or a CPA, especially when you first start reviewing your parents' assets, you might want to consult with a Certified Financial Planner (CFP) or investment advisor. You can find CFPs doing public speaking engagements, authoring articles in local papers or financial advice columns, or on the radio. I've found the best way to find a CFP is to ask people in your network for references and to then check out their online reviews.

There are advisors at some banks who have Investment Divisions (under the umbrella of Merrill Lynch, Morgan Stanley, Goldman Sachs, Credit Suisse, and others), which may come in handy.

Steve Brill, CFP, Benjamin F. Edwards & Co, advises people to look for someone with experience working with elderly clients. "Usually an advisor with 20 or more years of experience has taken early-stage retirees into later stages of retirement and is familiar with potential financial pitfalls that come from a family that doesn't properly plan for aging and living a long time." The investment strategies for a young family, an individual business owner, and a retired couple with physical challenges are completely different.

To date, the most important concern my siblings and I have discussed is how long will Mom and Dad's money last? And the answer is almost impossible to determine unless you know what all the costs are for options you might be considering. Some concerns for our parents were to:

- ❖ Stay in their own home
- ❖ Stay home with part-time care
- ❖ Stay home with full-time care
- ❖ Move to an independent living community
- ❖ Stay home but go to a daycare facility (one or both parents)
- ❖ Need nursing home (one or both)
- ❖ Need assisted living (one or both)
- ❖ Need memory care (one or both)

A CFP can run profiles for you, and then recommend how to make any money and assets last longer. Based on your (and your parents') risk profile and where your parents are in the process (are they in their seventies, eighties, or nineties, and how is their health?) a proposal will be drafted for your consideration. Should you sell some assets? Convert savings accounts to CDs and Money Markets? Stay in stock funds or move to more secure funds? How much should they withdraw from pensions to put into other investments? And so on. Options and questions are based on your situation and thus are too numerous to include here.

Fees for CFP services can be nothing if you have a lot of investments for them to manage, or a flat fee to run a report and make recommendations that you can then manage on your own. Or the fees may fall somewhere in between. Depending on where you live and the work required for your proposal, you could expect the fees to range from hundreds to a few thousand dollars.

Initially, I visited a CFP to find out how to manage my potential inheritance, money for my service contract with my parents, and what to advise my parents' about their money (while they are able to comprehend consequences and make decisions for themselves) to help it last longer. Steve gained my parent's confidence and was then able to help me safeguard my parents' assets.

Unless you're really good at this stuff, having outside perspective and someone who knows the latest options, regulations, and long-term consequences is very helpful. My recommendation is to ask people you trust for recommendations for someone they use and respect (not just someone they got a card from somewhere) and then ask for references from the CFP you are considering. You should be able to interview the CFP and gain some insight into how he or she works without paying any fee.

It's not unusual for a CFP to visit you at your home for an initial visit. I, personally, like to see the office of anyone I'm working with. I can tell a lot from the staff, the space, and the energy. But that's my process. I want to know if someone is just starting out or has too many clients to manage me personally. Are they connected to a larger company or independent? Are commissions and fees needed to pay a lot of staff? Does the office feature technology to keep up on the latest info and resources?

Certified Financial Planner/Investment Advisor:

Company Name: _____

Contact: _____

Address: _____

Phone(s): _____

Email: _____

Website: _____

Account Number(s): _____

Other: _____

Day-to-Day Household and Finance Management

If you are leading a very hectic and complicated life yourself, running a business or have family responsibilities, or if you are living far away from your parents, you might find the services of someone to help with your parents' paperwork extremely beneficial. It's draining and stressful to add managing a second household into your current responsibilities. Splitting the duties among siblings is a possibility, but you would never want to get into the, "I thought you said you took care of that!" disagreements.

Your parents might be making errors and forgetting to pay bills or sending the wrong check to the wrong company or are being bamboozled by people claiming to be from charities and taking money from your kind and generous parents...which means that you might need some help. These household managers go by a variety of names and each person offers different kinds of services. Once you determine what you're looking for, you can find the right person for the job.

What do you want help with for your parental household? Some thoughts...

- ❖ Paying bills
- ❖ Charitable giving management and tracking
- ❖ Supervising household staff and vendors
- ❖ Managing the house
- ❖ Managing sale of a home
- ❖ Groceries, food delivery, and other shopping tasks
- ❖ Balancing the checkbook and banking
- ❖ Ongoing bookkeeping
- ❖ Managing mail and emails
- ❖ Communication with family
- ❖ Managing a trust or foundation activities
- ❖ Event planning for entertaining at home
- ❖ Managing pet professionals (groomer, walker, vet, trainer, etc.)
- ❖ Organizing and managing paperwork

Consider:

Do you want the person to do this in your parents' home? Or at the service professional's office?

Do you want/need access to the files online to supervise this professional's duties or would you like a monthly status report? Or are ongoing meetings needed?

All of these specialists can help. Each offer something slightly different and each provider likely has a unique set of skills and personality for your consideration:

- ❖ Financial Concierge
- ❖ Daily Money Manager
- ❖ Business Manager

- ❖ Bookkeeper
- ❖ Personal Assistant
- ❖ Estate or House Manager
- ❖ Virtual Assistant

You can find someone through word of mouth, recommendations by the Area Agency on Aging, your parents' doctors, or the support groups you or your parents attend. Ask the financial planner, accountant, or lawyer for referrals. You can find household support people online, you can post a job opening, or you can check local bulletin boards in senior centers or at the library.

Judy Heft is a Certified Money Coach, a financial concierge. With over 20 years' experience, clients nationwide have asked for Judy's help with their parents who live in the Fairfield County, Connecticut, area. Her clients praise her for helping get tax return information ready come tax time, taking the burden of household bill paying management off the long list of things to do, and ensuring their parents don't give repeatedly to the same charities. Judy recommends finding someone like her in your parents' area by looking for members of the Association of Daily Money Managers.

Make sure, Judy cautions, if you're letting someone handle your parents' money (or your own for that matter), that whomever you hire is bonded and insured. Vet the person or firm thoroughly by speaking to clients and reading unedited reviews online. Look for any lawsuits or negative news articles.

One of Judy's elderly clients had her teenage grandchild living in the house purportedly to help make things easier. Judy was overseeing finances and took notice of checks written in large amounts that weren't related to direct bill paying. She shared this with her client, the elderly woman's son, and upon further investigation, it seemed that the grandchild was forging his grandmother's signature! It took a $10,000 check for action to be taken by the family. Thus, Judy says, a family member should always be supervising and double-checking things because you never know who might have persuaded grandma to give away her money or to share information that makes it easy for someone to commit fraud.

From mischievous grandchildren to staff (i.e., the new "best friend" health aide) to con artists, we all need to be vigilant about where our money is going.

Before hiring someone to take on this responsibility, Judy recommends that it is best if the parent has shared what accounts and assets, debts, and responsibilities he or she has with you and hopefully, designated you with financial Power of Attorney.

Take a look at the blogs on Judy's webpage [judithheft.com] for great tips on how you can be sure your parents' (and your own) monthly financial responsibilities are handled safely, effectively, and efficiently.

Rosemarie has experience as an estate manager and helps seniors with bookkeeping tasks. They may be unable to write checks due to shaky hands or foggy memory, unable to balance accounts or remember who to pay and when. Rosemarie visits her senior clients a few times a month to help track, process, and manage the basic duties of household finance management. Her fees are hourly with a minimum per session.

Daily Money Manager:

Company Name: _____

Contact: _____

Address: _____

Phone(s): _____

Email: _____

Website: _____

Services Offered: _____

Other: _____

Notary

On the chance you don't know what a notary is, in most basic terms, it's someone who will sign as a witness that the person whose signature is affixed to a page is actually that person. Notaries can also attest that a person giving testimony is the person they say they are.

To attest that you are who you say you are, the notary needs several forms of ID (photo ID, usually with a signature), proof of citizenship in some cases, and verification that you live where you say you live. The required proof documents you need to provide will change based on the documents the notary is being asked to authorize/notarize.

The fee for this service is usually regulated by the state and thus varies based on where you live. Some states allow notaries to charge a travel convenience fee if the notary comes to you. Fees could be a few dollars, or it might be $20 to $40 per document. Mostly I've paid in the $10 range for a simple signature notarization. Notary fees for real estate closings and documents seem to be higher rates.

For your on-call professional list, you want to know where to find a notary when you need one. When you begin managing paperwork for your parents, there are a lot of situations where things need to be signed and your parents' signature needs to be notarized if they are not coming with you for the meeting. Having knowledge of where to find a notary, costs, and hours can save you last-minute stress and hassle.

If you're lucky, you or your parents already know of one. Often, as in the case of my parents, if you live in a community complex or development where there's a management office, one of the staff there is probably a notary and can help out when you need something urgent. That's certainly geographically desirable.

Alternatively, most banks have a notary on staff. Since you probably have an account somewhere, it should be no problem to get the notary to notarize your documents. Some banks don't charge clients for this service. Other banks only offer the service for their clients. And others offer the service for a fee to anyone who walks in.

Another option is your lawyer. Most law offices have a notary on the premises. And your accountant, financial concierge, or tax advisor is also likely to have a notary in the office. Your local UPS stores and Kinko/FedEx-type places may have a notary on staff during certain hours. Occasionally, I've found public libraries with a notary service. Your library card helps here.

If none of those are available to you, or you need something off hours, you can always do an internet search or look in the phone book (virtual or otherwise) under "notary."

Notary:

Company Name: _____

Contact: _____

Address: _____

Phone(s): _____

Email: _____

Website: _____

ID: _____

Hours: _____

Other: _____

Estate Executor

When you begin working on your parents' legal documents, the lawyer will ask your parents to designate an executor (or whatever it's called in your state) for the estate. Your parents may already have someone in mind, or they may have previously selected someone.

An executor is responsible, upon death of the person for whom he or she is the designated executor, for making sure that any debts and creditors are paid off and that any remaining money or property is distributed according to the deceased person's wishes. An executor is not entitled to proceeds from the sale of property of the estate. Typically, the executor is paid a percentage of the estate as a fee.

Beneficiaries of the Will and/or estate and people with Power of Attorney (Durable or otherwise) are not automatically named as executor for the estate. However, very often the main beneficiary is chosen as one of the executors. A family member is often selected when trust is not an issue. The person (probably YOU!) who has taken on the mantle of caregiving for a parent is usually asked if he or she wants to be named as the executor.

When a Last Will & Testament is constructed by a lawyer—perhaps done long ago, before you took on the caregiver the role—someone may have already been designated as the executor. Please note, a person does not have to agree to be named beforehand and may decline to act if they want to. So, if the Will is given to you after a parent's death and you find you are named, you can opt out and assign someone else or ask a professional to handle these matters.

FYI: A lawyer may function as executor for a fee.

Estate Executor:

Executor Name: _____

Address: _____

Phone(s): _____

Email: _____

Relationship: _____

Financial Considerations

As our parents and loved ones age (us too, by the way), consideration for evolving financial changes should be discussed. Plans put in place far in advance of need are obviously best but, barring that, from today forward, where do you stand on the following? Ask your parents (or investigate on their behalf):

- ❖ Can you buy long-term care insurance?
- ❖ Do you qualify for Medicaid help?
- ❖ Are you a veteran who can find assistance from the VA?
- ❖ Do you have money in retirement accounts that can be accessed? And how does that impact your taxable income status?
- ❖ Are there pensions or payouts other than Social Security to use to pay for monthly expenses?
- ❖ Is hospice or full-time care likely to be needed?

Advisors and consultants for all of these are available in your area to help with decision-making and proper steps to move forward. See the Resources section for where to find help.

FINANCIAL DOCUMENT PORTFOLIO

Revocable or Irrevocable Trust

On one hand, my elder care advisor said that I should have all my parents' assets moved into an Irrevocable Trust, which would then basically mean that my parents didn't have any of these assets and thus, if they needed to go on Medicaid, they would have no assets to speak of. There were some tax benefits too. Irrevocable Trust moved control of their assets to their assigned representative (beneficiary). That sounded logical to me.

However, it also meant that my father could not change his mind about how he wanted his assets distributed or what to do with them. The beneficiary (that would have been me) would have the right to manage the trust and everything in it. This was not kosher with my dad, who wanted to control his assets while he still felt quite capable. I agreed.

My parents were as healthy as two people in the eightyish range could be and were able to live independently. Taking away their ability to manage their own lives and finances was not something we wanted at the time I had this advice. Medicaid seemed a forever-away proposition. So, what are our other options? I asked. Next stop, elder law attorney. On his counsel, we moved all the assets into a Revocable Trust.

"Why bother with a Trust if you already have a Will?" I asked. Because you can avoid probate costs and moving assets after death becomes immediate instead of months of paperwork. Okay—this sold me. So, I put copies of the Trust Agreement in that impenetrable box in the apartment that should survive an apocalypse!

Living Trust

According to Craig Donoff, PA, a Living Trust and Estate Planning Attorney for over 40 years, the benefits of a Living Trust are:

- ❖ Allows you to control your assets while alive
- ❖ Provides for you, spouse, and children without court supervision if you become sick, injured, or disabled
- ❖ Provides for your loved ones in exactly the way you want after your death, avoiding probate
- ❖ Makes sure your assets aren't made public where strangers can know what's going on with your estate
- ❖ Saves on estate taxes

I know what assets my parents have and what they want done with them when they pass. We also have a Will.

Back Tax Returns

In the US, all people are advised to hold onto five years of tax returns and support documents in case of audit. But for your senior parents, you need to know where these returns are located. Medicaid currently looks back at five years of income to determine eligibility, so it's handy to have five to seven years of back tax returns available. Access to Social Security statements will also help.

If your parents have assets and either they feel ready to move or you've determined with your siblings and the doctors that it would be most beneficial for them to move to a community with support, the back tax returns may be requested to complete the admissions review.

IRA/401(k)/503B

Without a statement of incapacity from several doctors, you will not be able to touch your parents' IRA accounts while they are alive. But, knowing the passwords, account numbers, who to contact by phone and/or email, and setting up access to account viewing on a computer will help you guide your parent to make decisions.

Bank Accounts

You might have all the accounts on one statement at one bank. How wonderful that would be! However, many people disburse their finances across different banks and have multiple accounts. You'll want to ask your parent for account numbers and statements for each: checking, savings, CDs, money markets, etc., along with access passwords and contacts with any personal representatives at the financial institutions/ banks.

If you are able to work with a financial planner to determine various options for your parents (regarding affordability of living space and care services needed), the CFP will need to see the account information for these assets (tax returns, retirement accounts, bank accounts) to help you determine how long your parent can live in each situation based on current financial situation. A CFP with an elder clientele/practice should be able to provide you a comparison chart for your options (e.g., stay at home with aides vs. assisted living vs. continuing care community).

Other info you should know how to locate:

❖ ATM cards and PIN codes/passwords
❖ Credit cards and online passwords and, possibly, security question answers
❖ Monthly auto-pay accounts

What accounts are on auto pay at the bank or auto pay through the provider? Your parent may have a power bill that is amortized to an equal amount over the course of the year and is on auto pay. Or the lease on the car got a discount for signing up for auto pay through the finance company. A charitable organization may be receiving a monthly donation. The Home Shopping Network may be charging in monthly installments. Maybe the cable bill or cell phone or internet service are on auto pay. That money is going to be deducted from bank accounts or charged to a credit card (whoo hoo frequent flyer points!) and will obviously impact the amount in the account, but someone needs to make sure those accounts are funded to pay those bills. And, at some point, when the parent moves, those utility accounts need to be discontinued.

If accounts are not currently on auto pay and your parent is having trouble managing finances but doesn't want you to pay the bills for him or her, you can suggest setting up auto pay so it can be paid from one account at one bank automatically. That way it's definitely done each month. One less headache for your parent that it's done correctly, and more reassurance for you to know your parent won't have the power or water turned off; prescriptions not delivered; property taxes, rent, or homeowners' dues not paid.

Auto pay is especially helpful if one parent is losing capacity and the other has never learned how to write a check or balance a checkbook, or has never had to pay bills, or is a procrastinator and will never get it done on time. (Ahem—one of my parents may recognize themselves in this list!)

Property

Deed and Title to ALL Property

If your parent is not renting or staying in someone else's home, there should be legal documents that pertain to ownership of their property—not just where they reside at the moment, but any seasonal properties or vacation locations, as well. In the case of incapacity or death, the documents proving ownership will be essential to enable you to conclude all business related to those properties and retain any value or sell it/them. Without paperwork, the local laws will dictate to whom and where the properties will revert.

If you haven't already been added to the deed for your parents' property (they may have a Homestead tax agreement that makes it a foolish financial move), you might seek expert advice and then suggest to your parents that they put the property into a Living Trust account. You could be the cosigner on the account or, at the very least, a beneficiary. Once that paperwork has been filed, you can sell your parents' property without having to go through probate in the courts. That will save you *tons* of money and months and months of time. Not to mention all the red tape you'll avoid.

If your parents have a co-op where they own shares in a property, it gets a bit more complicated, as the building needs to authorize the conversion of the shares and it might need to wait until a Board Meeting. There may be fees involved and it may necessitate recruiting a real estate agent to "sell" the shares to the building, then "sell" them back to you with your name included.

Note: I went through this with my parents. They owned a cond-op, which is like a co-op with shares, but condo management rules (i.e., no need to check with board to rent out the apartment). It was easier to sell the property in its entirety than try to do a transfer or add a name to the share certificate.

No matter which way you go, you should have a copy of the deed(s) and/or know where the originals are kept. If no one knows where the originals are kept, this would be a good time to go through the process of getting duplicates from the court house or city hall or wherever they keep property files in your community.

If your parents have a lease instead, follow the same rules, get a copy of the lease, and know what the terms are for rolling over or rent raises, what happens if you need extended stay out of apartment (rehab perhaps?), or other situations.

Taxes

Real estate taxes can be paid annually, biannually, monthly, or a number of other configurations based on where the property is located. You'll want to know how much they are and how they are paid (to whom, when, where are they sent).

In some cases, if real estate taxes aren't paid on time, one might lose a Homestead exemption, which keeps taxes at the rate paid when the home was purchased. That could be thousands of dollars difference!

Community Common Charges

Like taxes, in a drastic case, if community common charges aren't paid, there are procedures a board can take to require the property to be sold. Don't risk losing your parents' home by not knowing how this is managed.

Loan/Lien Information

If there is a mortgage or your parent accessed a line of credit or an equity loan on the property in question, are there any death provisions? If someone has taken a lien out on the property, what happens to the property upon incapacity or death? If payments can't be made due to illness or death, you need to know the consequences and create a plan to manage that or risk losing the property.

Contracts

It seems like we can't go through living these days without acquiring and signing all kinds of contracts. Having copies of all contracts accessible will help you when you need to manage the household. Examples of possible contracts to procure include:

- ❖ Car lease or ownership documents
- ❖ Maintenance leases (a/c, boiler, pool, exterminator, gardeners)
- ❖ Items on auto delivery (household oil, water, pet food, wine-of-the-month club)
- ❖ Extended warranties (for household appliances, computers, tires)

Safe

Do your parents have a safe? My parents don't really need a safe anymore because the value of their items is not that great and everything is insured, of course. In their New York condo, they had a large safe in the closet (black, iron, about 200 lbs., and hard-to-move kind of safe). Dad used to keep cash from his business until he could drop it at the bank in the morning, my mother's small collection of jewelry, Dad's emotionally important necklace and watch from his father, a coin collection, some collectible items and the purchase receipts and provenance for artwork and knickknacks they collected over the years. They also kept all these papers I've outlined in previous chapters of this book.

When I moved my parents full-time to the southern apartment, they didn't get a new safe. (We left the old safe for the new owner of the New York apartment.) They found hiding places. LOL

Now, we've got a portable safe file box for all the important papers. The box is waterproof and fireproof and heavy enough to make it difficult to walk out with without being seen, but light enough that I can put it on a hand cart and take it with us if we evacuate for a hurricane.

You'll want the combination or keys to the safe. Again, Mom or Dad can put a copy in a sealed envelope and leave it with a lawyer, bank safe deposit box, or anywhere else they trust, for you to access when necessary. [Note: Safe deposit boxes at the bank are not open 24/7.]

Checklist: Finances

Review this checklist of financial documents and arrangements to make sure you know where they are, if they exist, or if they should go on your to-do list to research.

Documents:	Copies Located:
IRA/401(k)/503B	
Back Tax Returns (5–7 years)	
Trust: Revocable Trust or Irrevocable Trust	
Real Estate Taxes	
Community Common Charges	
Monthly Bills	
Insurance Policies	
Other:	
Credit Card Numbers and Passwords	
ATM Cards, the Numbers and Passwords	
Monthly Auto-Pay Accounts	

Social Security Information

You will need this information often if you're trying to help your parent by coordinating with a vendor on the phone or online. The last four digits of someone's Social Security number and date of birth are the most common verification methods used to be sure the person on the phone is permitted to have access to account information.

Investment Account Information:

Account	Company	# Shares	Contact Name	Address/Phone	Type
IRA					
Mutual Funds					

Bonds

BONDS:				
Type				
Yield				
Maturity Date				
Certificate Number				
Issuer				
Owner Name				
Rep Name				
URL/Email				

Pensions

PENSIONS:				
Type				
Employer				
Account Balance/Date				
Beneficiary				
Contact at Company				
Distribution (Annual, Monthly, Other)				
URL/Email				

Other

Benefit	Company	Representative	Contact Info	Contract/Account Number
Stock Options:				
Annuity Plans:				
Death Benefit:				

Bank Accounts

Bank/Address	Account #	Balance	Date	Contact

Bank	Line of Credit	Contact	Balance Due	Date

Loan/Lien/Mortgage/Lease	Lender's Name	Contact Info	Amount Due	Date Logged

ATM Card #	Bank	PIN	CVV	Exp	Password	URL/Phone

Credit Card #	Bank	PIN	CVV	Exp	Password	URL/Phone

Monthly Auto-Pay Accounts

Company	Service/For...	Account #	Amount Due	Date Due

Property

Property Name	Address	Annual Taxes	HOA/Monthly Maintenance	Contact Name	Phone/Email

Utilities

Company Name	Service/For...	Account #	Amount Due	Paid From

Insurance Policies

Type/Company	Policy	Value	Contact Name	Phone/Email	Beneficiary
Auto/					
Auto/					
Business/					
Disability/					
Flood/					
Homeowners/					
Hurricane/					

Type/Company	Policy	Value	Contact Name	Phone/Email	Beneficiary
Kidnap/Ransom/					
Liability/Umbrella/					
Life Insurance/					
Life Insurance/					
Long-Term Care/					
Malpractice/					
Pet/					
Property/					
Property/Mortgage/					

BUILDING A MEDICAL, HEALTH & WELLNESS TEAM

Physicians

A list of physicians responsible for your parents' care is essential. This list should be something you put into your smartphone (perhaps in the Notes section or as a contact called "Parent Physician List" together with all the names/numbers of the specialists who care for your parents), plus carry a printed copy in your car, and post it in a visible place in your parents' home.

It's better to have this information ready when needed rather than trying to collect the info in an emergency situation when you feel anxious and rushed. Completing this work in advance also ensures you'll know the doctors' affiliations and preferred facilities. This is critical to know as your parents' insurance may only be accepted in limited places. Remain up to date on insurance policies and changes your parents may have made.

As you complete this list for each physician, be sure to include:

❖ Physician's Name, Practice Name, Specialty
❖ Address
❖ Phone & Fax
❖ Website/Patient Portal:
❖ Email (if they offer you one—many doctor's offices won't)

Primary Care Physician is first on the list. You may find your parents have selected a GP (General Practitioner), IN (Internist), or a specific specialty—like cardiology—as their go-to doctor for everything.

Cardiologist, gastroenterologist, gynecologist, pulmonologist, oncologist, neurologist (all the "ologists") should also be on the list. Whatever doctors your parents visit frequently should be included.

After you finish with the doctors, you'll want to also include the most frequently visited clinical sites.

❖ Blood Lab
❖ Radiology Centers (for mammograms, MRI, CT, etc.)
❖ Rehabilitation Centers (for physical, emotional, or addiction recovery issues)

Your parents may pay cash at a concierge physician service perhaps, use Medicare, have private health insurance, and/or a supplemental insurance plan like AARP. Knowing how payments will be/are made will reduce surprises while checking out or after a medical visit.

Facilities

In addition to your parents' physician list, research and maintain a list of the facilities and offices that your parents may visit or may need at some point. This is critical if you are not living in the area where your parents will need treatment.

- ❖ Clinics for various specialties (e.g., cardiology, podiatry, psychiatry, gynecology, neurology, rehabilitation)
- ❖ Specialty centers for various conditions (e.g., cancer center, women's cancer, Multiple Sclerosis, Alzheimer's, Lupus, Parkinson's)

Try searching your area for a Memory and/or Wellness Center. In Boca Raton, Florida, the Louis and Anne Green Memory & Wellness Center is on the campus of Florida Atlantic University (FAU). You may find a center that doesn't have "Memory" in the title. The Green Center offers the following services to the Southern Florida residents and campus students and staff, so while doing your online search, you may want to look for an office that has specifically what you seek:

- ❖ Memory and Wellness Evaluation
- ❖ Geriatric Assessment at Home
- ❖ Driving Evaluation
- ❖ Adult Day Center
- ❖ Physical Therapy
- ❖ Research

They also offer programs to sustain caregivers including:

- ❖ Support Groups
- ❖ MINDSET—a series of classes to exercise your brain
- ❖ Self-Preservation Activities for Caregivers (SPA days)
- ❖ Care Consultations
- ❖ Counseling/Psychotherapy
- ❖ Caregiver Library

Mobile Physician Services

If getting your parent to a doctor is near impossible on your own, there are mobile physician services that will come to you. They are usually covered by Medicare and health insurance plans, like any other physician. This kind of service is especially helpful if you, as a caregiver, can't get to take care of yourself because you can't leave your parent alone. The mobile services can work with you too.

Mobile medical units are practical when a parent is too large to move or be moved; if there's a physical disability; if too many gadgets, tubes, and machines are hooked up to your parent; or if both you and your parent have mobility obstacles.

Barry is taking care of his father who is confined to a hospital bed in the house. But Barry himself is in a wheelchair because of various illnesses and obesity that make it impossible for him to walk any distance, plus, he has to carry oxygen with him. Mobile medical care is especially helpful for his family.

Alternatively, a medical transit van can also work in these situations to bring you and your parent to medical care if some mobility is possible but challenging.

Psychiatrist/Psychologist

It is very rare to find someone in their senior years who isn't taking a collection of drugs and supplements. It is very common to find older people (especially if it's someone living alone, or someone caring for a loved one) exhibiting signs of depression, anxiety, or stress. A monthly visit to a geriatric psychiatrist for drug management will ensure that all the various doctors' remedies for each symptom are not contraindicated and causing more problems collectively.

My mother was seeing a psychiatric nurse practitioner every few months. They billed Medicare for a 1.5-hour meeting each time. My mother shared everything going on in her life. When Mom said she couldn't focus on cleaning up the den, the practitioner prescribed a drug to give Mom focus and energy. Then Mom said she couldn't sleep—so another drug was added to bring Mom into relaxation mode at the end of the day. Anxiety over caring for Dad with Alzheimer's? Let's add some Zoloft to combat anxiety— take the edge off, enable Mom to cope. Blood tests showed that Mom doesn't assimilate folate well, so we'll add a pill for that. But it's bio-identical Mom said—so it's not really medicine. Getting older? Okay—let's add CoQ10, some calcium supplements, some vitamin C to ward off colds and flu, a women's multivitamin. Throw in some B12 and some vitamin D.

Mom was diagnosed with a rare form of bone cancer in 2006 and underwent chemotherapy (which didn't work) and then got into an experimental program using proton radiation. Every day for seven weeks, the spot with cancer was radiated. Miraculously, 12 years later and counting, the cancer is still in her bones but hasn't grown at all. It is dormant. But the chemo and radiation took a toll on her and Mom has neuropathy in her foot. Okay—so let's throw in a drug for that, even though she is experiencing no pain at all.

And finally, the cardiologist said her cholesterol was too high, so we'll add in Lipitor to manage that.

When I totaled how many drugs and supplements my mother was taking every day, it was more than 11 in the morning and more at night. My mother was walking around like a zombie. She would stay up until 2 a.m. and then sleep until 9. She still couldn't focus on clearing any clutter and would stack papers, baskets, gadgets, tools, clothing, and more on my father's side of the bed (where was he supposed to sleep?), on the floor of her closet, all over the bathroom sink, the dining room table, the coffee table, in baskets, and all over the floor and countertops and closets in the den.

When my father expressed that he was upset with her for any reason, my mother would appear to listen, nod, and say, "You're right. I don't know why I do that." But her behavior never changed. When I tried to talk to her about things we needed to do, she would look at me with a blank expression and then smile and walk away. When I said I did not want her to drive anymore because she was incapable of focusing or concentrating or completing a task, she thought I was trying to take away her independence.

When we went back to the psychiatric nurse practitioner (I went, my sister went, my father went— three different visits) and kept saying that my mother was a walking zombie, the practitioner said that she was following protocol. Eventually this practitioner said Mom should maybe take Ritalin to help her focus and be more responsive. WHAT???? Add another drug?

I suggested an alternative, "Why don't we cut down on the drug that is making her sleepy and keeping her numb?" "Oh," she said. "I guess we could try that." Frustrating is not an adequate word to describe what I felt, but it was part of it. I was also furious!

When I finally found a qualified geriatric psychiatrist, he agreed with me. He said the drugs were interacting in a way that was numbing my mother. We started reducing the dosage of her pills and weaned her off a few of them. And voilà, Mom was back! Her ability to carry on a conversation resumed. And, while she is still listening to Dad, nodding and agreeing but changing nothing, at least she seems to comprehend what is going on around her and is able to have a conversation again!

A weekly session with a therapist (psychologist, social worker, whatever) can be hugely helpful. Either in addition to or instead of a one-on-one session, a regular support group can provide a network of people who your parent can talk to outside of family to feel understood and able to vent. Sometimes a parent doesn't want to trouble you with their own issues. Or, in my parents' case, I am the person they want to talk about to others!!! And I'm okay with that. Having a child take on responsibilities you are "supposed" to be able to do is a difficult transition. Feeling yourself slip out of control, forgetting things, finding yourself unable to write a check, or not understanding why you do certain things is terrifying. Feeling you're not alone and being around people who don't judge can make a world of difference in self-esteem and ability to cope, can offer a reason to leave the house and venture outside, and can be a source of additional friendships and people that care. Find a situation for your parents to have support outside of family.

Caregivers are 63 percent more likely to pass away before the person they are caring for. If one parent is taking care of the other, emotional support resources are imperative.[5] If you are taking care of a parent, this kind of support for you is going to sustain you through this challenging process.

---

[5] Study by University of Pittsburgh researchers Richard Schulz and Scott Beach reported in the *Journal of the American Medical Association* in December 1999.

Personal Trainer

Eventually, bones and muscles start to erode. No matter the condition you're in for most of your life and the kind of diet you eat, aging does stuff to a living body! The degree to which your body manifests common aging ailments is related to the aforementioned lifestyle, but also to genetics and the environment.

Working with a personal trainer to increase bone mass and density will stave off osteoporosis, release endorphins (the "happy" chemical inside of us) to ward off depression, reduce stress effects on a body, and provide your parent with human contact that is all about him or her. Plus, it's nice to be the center of someone's attention—even for only an hour!

If your parent is independent and able to follow directions, a few weeks of three times a week with a personal trainer to teach your parent a routine and to get your parent into a habit will be a great start. If things go well, and if you can afford it, you can transition to once a week on an ongoing basis for a refresher, to check progress and add variety.

If you have the resources for your parent to belong to a fitness facility or there's one in the building, the trainer can work there. Otherwise, a trainer can come to the home.

If finances are an issue, a trainer can come to the home and recommend using household items as weights. For example, lifting milk cartons filled with different levels of water (depending on strength ability—the stronger, the more water) works great. Using stretchy rubber fitness bands are easy to carry and inexpensive. Try the fitness programs on your television cable system under Sports, Fitness, or Recreation. They may have chair-based exercises. Or take classes at the local Y or a senior center where prices can often be negotiated on a sliding scale—possibly with free transportation! Is Mom or Dad internet savvy? Tons of free information and classes are available for watching on the computer! And, never forget, there's always a DVD collection to buy (try thrift stores) or borrow from the library.

Personal trainers usually offer packages; the more you purchase in advance, the lower the cost per session. If you have two people in one session, the cost is less per person. So, if Mom or Dad has a friend who could also benefit from training, then you're setting up a regular workout buddy along with reducing costs.

Trainers in big cities, at the time of this writing, range from $45 to $95 per hour for single sessions. In smaller communities, $25 to $55 per hour. Savings of 10 to 25 percent for multi-session and/or group packages are common.

Trainers should be certified (be sure to ask about that). A Personal Training certification usually ensures that the trainer knows CPR, has studied muscle groups, knows how to adjust the program for different ages, and can work in multiple settings. Someone with AED training is helpful as well. There are several well-respected national certifications to look for, including NASM (National Academy of Sports Medicine) or ACSM (American College of Sports Medicine), which are heavily science-based and very intensive; NCSA (National Strength and Conditioning Association) or ACE (American Council on Exercise) and some chain fitness facilities offer their own training programs. Trainers with certification need to take continuing education classes to keep certification current. If you go to the websites of any organization you can learn more about what the graduates have learned, plus you can find lists of trainers in your area with those accreditations.

The trainer you are interviewing may have a college degree in Kinesiology, Sports Medicine, or Physical Fitness. You might find someone with training provided by the military.

Not all trainers are perfect for your needs. Some trainers prefer to work with athletes or sculpt people's bodies to bulk up or lose weight. Other trainers enjoy working with the elderly or people with challenges. There are trainers who have a background working with cancer patients or people with mental cognition issues. Make sure you find someone who has worked with someone similar to your parent. Ask for references. If you live locally, ask your parents' friends for recommendations.

The personality match is important, so arrange for one visit before committing to a long-term package. A trainer's gender may also be a factor in comfort for your parent. Trainers have different motivation styles. Some are coaxing and gentle and ease someone into the process, some believe you have to push a client through to help you reach your full potential and find your limits. The kind of trainer that will work best for your parent depends on your parent's personality. You don't want your parent to give up because he or she either is unmotivated or feels bullied. The old "No Pain, No Gain" mantra is *not* appropriate for seniors!

Consider how far someone has to travel for the session. Get references. Don't worry if someone is just out of school or newly certified. Info is fresh in their mind and they might have the latest techniques and a lot of enthusiasm and a wider schedule of availability. A new trainer will also be less expensive than one with a large following and client base. If your parent has special needs (e.g., has had cancer, has foot issues from diabetes, mobility issues, arthritis, memory issues, is obese and inactive...), finding a trainer with experience in those issues is worth the extra research and possible supplemental cost.

A word of caution: Sending your parents off to do exercise on their own without supervision and without learning proper form could potentially lead to injury. That's why a qualified personal trainer is needed to demonstrate and watch your parents and then to keep working with them until it's a safely practiced routine. ALWAYS check with the physician to get permission for the type of exercise you're promoting to your parent!!

This is kind of cute...my mother believes that if you pay for Weight Watchers, you'll lose weight. If you have exercise videos (yes, she still has VHS VIDEO tapes!) or you pay for a fitness membership, have a gym in your building or dumbbells in your home, you will build bone mass. Never mind actually doing what's required!! Never mind that the plastic wrap is still on the video tapes and the weights are used as door stoppers! Or that the treadmill is a great place to hang laundry or dry cleaning. Doing the work matters.

Physical Therapist

If, despite your most convincing smile and persuasive talents or medical recommendations, your parent doesn't take the preventive measures suggested above, you may eventually find yourself in need of a physical therapist. A physician may give a referral for physical therapy, which looks an awful lot like personal training, but the physical therapist is going to focus on a specific skill or risk area or recovery needed vs. full body training. So, it's not a substitute for personal training as prevention and full-body fitness.

You don't want to wait until someone has had a bad fall or a stroke and has to be in a physical therapy residential center situation before working with a physical therapist. However, having information on hand for a center near you, covered by insurance, that works with your physicians, is helpful. These facilities can range from $6,000 to $10,000+ a month, depending on where you live.

If you are working with a long-term care policy, make sure you meet the criteria for payment. If you are working with Medicare or Medicaid or a health insurance plan (like AARP Supplemental for example), make sure the facility you have on your list takes those forms of payment. Insurance benefits and requirements vary widely by provider and by state.

Be proactive, before there are any issues, and have a physical therapy home assessment early on. My dad might have been able to self-correct if someone bumped him from the sides, but he would have gone down if he bumped his shoulder on a corner or a door, or if something hit him from behind. The physical therapist my dad worked with recommended a series of exercises to strengthen Dad's tibialis anterior muscles ("His what?" I asked!).

Recently, we did a follow-up assessment for my father and the therapist said that my father's proprioceptor reaction ability (his ability to know where he was in time and space, a brain function—not his muscle) was way down and, if he hadn't been doing all his exercises, he would have most certainly have had a critical fall episode. Not something any caregiving daughter wants to hear! Prevention and precautions are the keys to sustaining health!

Confidence is something people don't think about when caring for an aging person. Giving an older person the tools to help themselves, to feel independent, to feel secure in knowing how to take care of scary situations will go a long way to reduce anxiety and depression. And, not to mention, it will give you a sense of security knowing your parent has those tools. Less worry for you!

My father has always been an athlete. He doesn't think he would *ever* fall because he has great reflexes. He used to walk up to six miles a day around his community. Then he walked the parking lot every day; two to three miles a day in front of his building so he wouldn't get lost and so that someone could always see him. Now he walks the hallway in his independent living community. It's wide, well-lit, carpeted in case he falls, and has walls to lean against if he feels lightheaded. And, most recently, he now uses a cane. He can run to the bathroom if he needs it because he's only just up the hall.

Unfortunately, his muscle memory and strength are no compensation for a Swiss cheese brain from Alzheimer's. Dad recently fell two days in a row. First, trying to bring in the newspaper from his doorway. He went backward trying to stand up and fractured his back. He couldn't remember how to stand up. My mother had to bring him something to hold on to so he could get himself up again.

Then, the next day, his foot missed the plastic stool in the shower. The stool flipped and cut a seven-inch gash in his leg. He fell back against the wall in the shower and wound up looking like an embryo folded on the floor against the white tile wall, with red gushing down his leg, creating rivers to the drain. Thank heavens he wasn't still in his original Florida condo, where a porcelain tub and having to lift his leg over a bathtub to get in and out would have led to many dangerous falls!

Physical therapy helped Dad avoid falls for as long as possible, but when the mind starts to decay, it simply forgets how to operate the body. Creating muscle memory is critical, and physical therapy can help with that. It's been keeping my father from having much worse situations.

Medical Supply Store

You can get many medical and healthcare supplies (especially in communities where seniors tend to retire—like Southern Florida, Arizona, Southern California, South Carolina, etc.) at the local drugstores, big-box stores (Target/Walmart/Kmart), and even supermarkets. However, there are certain things that you will need from a medical supply store. On your list of key phone numbers and contacts should be a medical supply store that is relatively near your parents.

For one thing, they have supplies you don't find all over. For example, they may carry supplies for diabetes care, like specialty shoes and socks or insulin kits, ointments, and creams that doctors recommend for wounds; urine test kits for PH balance or UTI-testing at home; unique bandages that cover large wounds or wrap a cast or boot; a variety of canes and walking devices; and specialty toilet seats that can be used bedside.

The people who work in these stores are experts. They can find you the right item, get you something you need but don't see, and help you try the items or custom fit to the person. If you can go there vs. ordering on the internet, you'll have a much better understanding of the best choices for your parents' situation and how to use what you purchase!

When my mother had trouble getting to the bathroom fast enough in the morning, I went to a specialty shop and got a bedside toilet with handles. My mother was appalled and didn't want it. She was fine having a moisture mat under the sheet on her bed. However, in searching for this item, I found out that they come in various configurations for people of different sizes and weights with adjustments for travel (if it has to be moved between several locations, like for snowbirds, for example). And I was able to set up several in the store and look at what would work in the space between the bed and the window with the furniture in the room. My mother didn't want it, but I kept it anyway. I will need it someday. Paying a fee for these items in a rehab facility can be as much per week or month as just buying it!

Months later, when talking to my parents about moving to a one- or two-bedroom assisted living residence (there's quite a difference in pricing), my father said he was fine with a one bedroom if we had the extra toilet available for an urgent situation. It wouldn't be often that both parents need the toilet at the same time, but what if one is already on the toilet and the other has to go immediately? The portable would be handy in this situation!

I've even thought that it would be practical for camping if you don't like squatting over grass or fear bugs and snakes and such. (But that's a whole other topic and may not be relevant to this book!) Or for long road trips with a person that may have to go suddenly. When transporting an elderly person from one location to another for a long ride, this is a handy amenity to have in the car with you. And it fully folds down to the same size as a folding walker.

In the store, there were also toilet seats to help raise the height of the toilet so that someone wouldn't need to sink down and then need a lift to get back up. Well, that turned out to be helpful for me because the apartment complex I rent from had toilet seats made for a child's height—and I am a tall lady! My knees cracked and creaked every time I had to stand up! Using the lifted seat was a savior for my knees!

The most valuable part of having a medical supply store on your contact list is that they usually deliver. You come home from a visit to a doctor, or maybe an emergency room visit, and you need something urgently, so you make a quick call. If you are living on the other side of the country, you can call and know that your parent will get what they need, right to the door. And, if the item doesn't work out, the store rep will come pick it up and exchange it. And, when you're all done with a nonconsumable product, they might take it back and sell it on consignment for you. Or take care of donating the items to someone else in need.

I tend to like supporting small local businesses. I like the extra customer care and the familiarity they have with resources in the community—beyond what's in the store. Check out the bulletin boards and business card section of the store. Handouts and pamphlets are always full of helpful info you didn't know you needed!

Medical Rental Store

Different from a medical supply store, although you can often find these two functions combined in one location, you want to have the info for a medical rental place on your contact list. These places will provide you with any nonconsumable items you need to keep a parent comfortable in his or her own home.

When your insurance says you need to leave the hospital after three days, but there's obviously a need for further recovery and you need a bed that can lift the head or feet or has bars that enable a leg elevation lift, or you need to hang an IV bag or hook up oxygen, etc., you can rent all of this from a medical rental store. What if you find yourself in need of a wheelchair (with or without motor controls)? While you can perhaps get one from the VA (Veterans Affairs), you might have a gap between request and appearance. A rental store can rent you what you need for any size person with any ability level and deliver it and set it up, often within hours.

What if you need an oxygen tank for COPD until you can find a system you like? Want to get a lift for your car to carry a scooter while you're in town? Need stuff delivered before you can catch a flight or drive to get to your parent? A medical rental supplier is the answer.

When you're in this situation, you do not want to have to start calling different locations and figuring out which one can help you. Keep this number on your handy-dandy list!

Medical Document Portfolio

Do you have the following information regarding your parents' health resources? If you haven't collected the information yet, here's a place to be sure you have the most important documents that need to be carried when visiting doctors.

Document	Account	URL	Login	Password	Contact
Medicare Card					
Medicaid Card					
Health Insurance(s) policy numbers					
Healthcare Proxy					
DNR					
Living Will					
Medication list					
POLST[a] form					
List of doctors and preferred hospital/clinics					

[a] POLST = Physician Order for Life Sustaining Treatment (This is the Florida Form. There are different names in different places.)

Medical Support & Facilities

If something were to happen, do you know where to bring your parent that would be covered by insurance?

What types of health insurance(s) does your parent use?

Medicaid	Work/Employer	Gap Insurance (Medigap)
Medicare	Self-Insured	Disability
Supplemental	Affordable Care Act	Long-Term Care
Veteran's	Dental Insurance	Vision Insurance

Company	Policy Type	Policy #/ Group #	Exp Date	Contact Name	URL/ phone	Beneficiary

Labs, Testing & Other Facilities

How often does a parent need to go for visits or testing? Regular testing for INR[6] levels for people on Coumadin, diabetes/insulin regulation, kidney dialysis, annual mammograms or PET scans, ultrasounds, and so on will require labs, clinics, and testing centers.

What local labs are approved by parents' insurance?

Lab Name	Address	City/St/Zip	Phone	Hours

---

[6] INR = International Normalized Ratio—calculated from a blood test; used to detect how well blood thinning medications are working.

Imaging (Radiology) Centers approved by insurance:

Lab Name	Address	City/St/Zip	Phone	Hours

Local Rehab or Physical Therapy Centers covered by insurance:

Facility Name	Address	City/St/Zip	Phone	Hours

Local clinics you might need:

Clinic Name	Address	City/St/Zip	Phone	Hours

Counseling (counselors, psychiatric care, social workers, etc.)

Center Name	Address	City/St/Zip	Phone	Physician

PHASE II

MINOR IMPAIRMENTS

NOTES

HEALTH/MEDICAL PREPARATIONS

I started noticing little things that were getting me worried more often than not. My father forgot that he was boiling eggs on the stove and walked out of the room. A microwave was turned on instead of the stove. Getting in and out of chairs was requiring concentration and effort. Balance issues were showing up more often, leading to "almost" falls. When there was a fall, the ability to get back up was not automatic. Everything took more attention and thought. Conversations were more repetitive but also cyclical with no end until Dad was distracted. Because my parents have each other, they fill in the blanks and can support each other and remain independent. But things were changing and my own level of anxiety was rising because I felt I needed to be there more, just to check in. When I visited, I felt like "normal" things now seemed like obstacles and challenges.

What you might be seeing:

- ❖ Living independently and might have an aide, or go to a day program
- ❖ Living with spouse/partner/roommate
- ❖ Active and engaging with friends, family, community but might have gaps in memory or inability to function physically in certain situations
- ❖ Skills for daily living are fully functional (grooming, dressing, eating, toileting, exercise, etc.)
- ❖ May start to require assistance for cooking or driving, etc.
- ❖ Ability to communicate is stable

Doctor Visits & Records

Important! If you live near your parent, start going with them to their doctor visits. While there, take notes and capture what needs to be done going forward to ensure compliance. These notes will track the health progress of your parent and will provide information for other caregivers who may be around to help you at some point.

If you don't live locally, and it's possible, speak with doctors on a regular basis or after visits to find out what is going on and if there is anything you need to know to help your parent comply with instructions. Or, if the doctor resists phone meetings, see if the doctor has a patient portal. Then you can sign your parent up for the service and just log in and see reports and test results, as well as prescriptions and other recommendations. If a portal isn't available, ask the doctor's office to send you a copy of the report from the latest visit. You'll have to do this after each visit. That report should have any further testing or prescriptions that were assigned. (Due to HIPAA laws, (a) your parent will need to have preauthorized the doctor's office to do this and (b) medical offices, for privacy, often do not email information regarding patients to anyone. They can fax or mail information. Check with your doctor and local state laws where your parent resides.)

Suggestion: Create a binder with all of the reports you collect. Section the binder chronologically (by month/year) or by doctor. This is a handy resource to have if medical history is needed in an emergency, or eventually for transitioning staff, or for the files of a new care-oriented residence.

If you're computer savvy, set up a spreadsheet or use a log book to record each visit. Stats you can collect and monitor include blood pressure, heart rate, weight, test results, next steps, doctor orders, and any prescriptions ordered. When changes happen, the log will help you notice more quickly, and you can bring that up with the doctor.

Having your parent wear one of the latest fitness trackers (e.g., watches, bracelets, necklace, on iPhone) can help with tracking statistics of general health (mentioned above).

Questions to Ask the Doctor

Do you know the questions to ask when you accompany your parents to a doctor or call afterward for the follow-up?

Here's a suggested starter list of questions. See the Agency for Healthcare Research and Quality (ahrq.gov) for more guidance.

❖ What is the test for?
❖ When will I get the results?
❖ Why does my parent need this procedure/test/surgery/medication?
❖ Is there a natural alternative to this test/procedure?
❖ Can we try something at home first?
❖ Are there any alternatives to surgery/medication?
❖ What are the possible complications?

❖ Which hospital is best for my parents' needs?

❖ How long is the recovery process?

❖ How can I make recovery easier for my parent?

Additional Rx questions you might consider:

❖ How do you spell the name of that drug?

❖ Are there any side effects?

❖ Will this medicine interact with medicines/supplements my parent is already taking?

❖ Are there natural alternatives to this drug?

❖ Is the generic version okay to take?

❖ Can we start with a lower dosage?

Ask for natural alternatives where possible. Nonchemical, nontoxic, behavioral options may exist before adding another drug treatment or surgery. The more your parent is putting in or on his or her body (toxic or non-toxic, natural or man-made), the more chances of negative interactions, which can cause a whole host of other issues!

Testing When There's Nothing That Can Be Done

Sometimes, a doctor will offer to do tests to diagnose cause. But, if there's no safe remedy or action to take once the cause is identified, then having an invasive procedure or test that won't change the outcome could cause health or stress issues on its own. All tests and procedures need to be thoughtfully considered before giving the okay.

Keep in mind that a doctor may simply offer a test option just to be sure that he or she is covering all bases in order to avoid a potential lawsuit in the future.

What To Expect At Every Doctor's Visit

At every doctor visit you should expect:

❖ Weight and height measurements to be taken

❖ Blood pressure, pulse, and oxygen levels checked

❖ A review of current medications, frequency, dosages (every time you go!)

At the end of the visit:

❖ Check out at desk and make an appointment for a follow-up visit.

❖ Receive prescriptions for any medications and orders for any tests required

❖ Get referrals for any other specialists your parent may need

Information You'll Need to Bring:
Pharmacy:

Pharmacy Name: _____

Address: _____

City/St, Zip: _____

Phone: _____

Fax: _____

Account: _____

Preferred Pharmacist: _____

MEDICAL HISTORY:

Condition	Date	Doctor	Status

MEDICATION LIST:

Medication Name	Dosage	Frequency	Time of Day	Doctor	Location in Home	How Taken?

Medication Name	Dosage	Frequency	Time of Day	Doctor	Location in Home	How Taken?

MONITOR MEDICATIONS

Forgetting a dose of a pill or taking a double dose of a pill are all possible as a person ages, often by having put the wrong pills in the day-by-day pill organizer. A missed dose could cause toileting issues (e.g., urinary tract infection, diarrhea, constipation, incontinence, cramps, stomach pain, nausea), dizziness, headaches, allergies (hives, rash, breathing issues), light-headedness, unsteady gait, etc. Even the most diligent and organized people can mess up.

My solution has been to take photographs of my parents' properly filled medicine organizer and then every week I check to make sure the pills in the boxes match the pills in my photographs. I look to see if anything is left over or missing as the week goes on. If I see suspicious symptoms in either parent's behavior, I check the medicine organizers first.

I have a chart with what pills are taken, in what dosages, each day, for each parent. That chart is posted on the inside of the kitchen cabinet door where all the pills and pill organizers are. Consider day-of-the-week plastic pill organizers for a.m. and p.m., and/or midday pill-taking times. I keep a photo of this list on my phone.

Create a spreadsheet with current pills to bring to doctor appointments to update if/when prescription or dosage is changed or supplemented after each doctor visit. Doctors will ask for updated information each visit. Having a copy easily accessible (in a wallet perhaps) will help speed things along during your visit and ensure nothing is forgotten.

Wound Care

Many seniors are more susceptible to infections because of weaker immune systems. Infections are associated with death related to pneumonia, flu, or viruses. Tuberculosis, shingles, and gastric issues all become life-threatening as a senior. If your parent has an open wound and visits a doctor or has a hospital visit, chances of a major health-threatening infection increase dramatically. Make sure wounds are cleaned, then covered. Use antibacterial creams if approved by your parents' physician.

Find out if wounds can be washed or need to stay dry. Using plastic wrap on top of bandages is effective at keeping a wound dry during light bathing.

Julie shared that she used the plastic umbrella covers (offered in the local supermarket entrance lobby) to cover her dad's arm and leg wounds during showers. Slip it on and tape down the edges with shipping or painting tape or bandage tape meant for skin. Safely use whatever you have available to keep healing wounds dry.

Vaccinations

The Centers for Disease Control and Prevention (CDC) recommends that adults should get a seasonal influenza (flu) vaccine every year, TD or Tdap (tetanus, diphtheria, and pertussis) vaccine booster every 10 years, shingles vaccine for adults over 50 years old, and pneumococcal vaccine for adults over 65 years old. Check with your healthcare provider for recommendations specific to you or your parents' situation. You can also visit cdc.gov/vaccines/adults/index.html for current and comprehensive information on adult vaccines.

When my father sliced his leg open, the doctor immediately gave him a tetanus shot. Two months later at the VA, when Dad was getting his annual physical and cognitive exam, the doctor said we should have gotten the Tdap with pertussis protection. Knowing what to ask for in advance can help avoid having to have multiple vaccinations. Logging or tracking the vaccinations received and putting them on the medication list is something I've now added to my routine.

HELPING PARENTS LIVE AT HOME

From a cost and comfort perspective, staying in one's own home is the optimal choice. However, as signs of aging (physical and mental) appear, your assistance, or that of another designated support person, becomes advisable. A home that was just fine for most of your parents' life may suddenly be filled with dangers and ongoing home maintenance may be delayed, with procrastination easier than recognizing that things are becoming more problematic.

In addition to the tips from the Phase I section, here are some additional things you can do to help your parents remain independent and at home for as long as possible:

- ❖ Research care agencies or private service aides/nurses to help you when needed. Get pricing and set up accounts to be activated as needed.
- ❖ Connect with resources that provide benefits and services if finances are an issue (Veterans Administration, charity groups, foundations, unions).
- ❖ Research driving services to shuttle parents to/from doctor appointments and testing facilities.
- ❖ Have bills sent to you (e.g., medical, aides, housekeepers).
- ❖ Find a financial concierge to (or you can) take over bill-paying processes for ongoing monthly expenses.
- ❖ Set up auto pay from your parents' bank account wherever possible for fixed expenses. (Use a bank check paying system so all the information is in one place online and on one statement, vs. setting up auto pay at each utility or provider.)
- ❖ Set up a visiting nurse to manage pills (usually every two weeks to set up daily pill containers for morning, midday, and evening).
- ❖ Ask parents to wear slip/trip/fall detection technology. This will notify you and others, automatically dial 911, and alert a dispatch center that will call your parent and assist as needed.
- ❖ Provide parents with cell phones they carry all the time. Consider large touchpad or phones with volume adjustment for hearing and vision issues. If dialing is an issue, make sure the phone has an autodial function by the push of a button and put your name on that button via label maker. Or a phone with Siri-type service where your parent can tell the phone what to do. Add a label on the back of the phone with your emergency contact information, name, and relationship.
- ❖ Provide emergency contact cards and place them in your parents' wallet and car and hang them on the refrigerator or kitchen cabinet and medicine cabinets in case emergency personnel are called and enter without you there.

nurse manage pills + drugs ea week
slip, trip / fall technology
Check feet + toenails.

- ❖ Find neighbors and friends to do regularly scheduled, frequent, or random check-ins on parents and report back. Optimally, it would be ideal if siblings and/or immediate family rotate this responsibility.

- ❖ Set up account for food delivery from a local market. You (or your parent) calls or goes online and it gets delivered. Or, if budget is an issue and nutrition is being compromised, see if you can sign your parent up for a Meals-on-Wheels-type program in your community. Hot, nutritious meals delivered by volunteers will come on a regular basis to supplement whatever other foodstuffs are in the home. The bonus is that the volunteers offer a friendly face, possible companion time, and may alert you if your parent isn't answering the door.

- ❖ Set up auto delivery for frequently used supplies (e.g., toilet paper, paper towels, adult diapers, bandages, medicines, etc.).

- ❖ Set up accounts with several restaurants for takeout if cooking isn't possible anymore.

- ❖ Arrange for a housekeeper to come to organize and clean every week (if financially possible), to ensure your parents won't fall over loose items left scattered about and that the home remains hygienic to avoid infections. Cleaning bathrooms, kitchen, changing bedding, and doing laundry are essential needs when people are dealing with illness, mobility challenges, or disorientation.

HOUSEHOLD AND WELLNESS MATTERS

One of the largest frustrations of aging is the diminishing ability to remain independent. No one likes this! Dylan Thomas' poem expresses it so eloquently:

Rage, rage against the dying of the light....
Do not go gentle into that good night....
Their frail deeds might have danced in a green bay,
Rage, rage against the dying of the light.

If you are becoming a caregiver for your parent, chances are it's because your parent is less able to take care of certain basic functions. Unless you are living in the home with your parents, you'll want to add some more names to your resource list. Your parents are going to be kicking and screaming and digging those heels into the ground, swearing they can still do this on their own—until they can't. Until something happens that makes it clear to you and/or to them that outside help is needed.

Even if you are living with your parents (temporarily or permanently, as required), the people I've described in this chapter can be huge lifesavers to your peace of mind and/or ability to take respite from caregiving.

Housekeepers

I don't have a lot of money but, for me, an essential treat to myself that is worth giving up other luxuries, is having a housekeeper every third week. It's not *that* expensive in the long run and I'm probably saving future money on therapy or a funny farm, but having someone make my home fresh and clean, neat and tidy, so I can walk in and relax, is worth every penny. I am valuing myself in this little gift. It's true, I have a bad back and scrubbing toilets and cleaning the refrigerator can put me into a day of bedrest and recovery. But, even if I didn't have those issues, with all the stress I face in being my parents' caregiver and keeping my siblings informed of everything, I need this extravagance.

Your parents may need this too. Coming into a clean home; having linens changed on a regular basis; keeping the bathrooms free from scum buildup or hard water spots; vacuuming the rugs and washing the floors to keep them free from harboring germs, bugs, or becoming tripping hazards; or clearing countertops and washing out the fridge, oven, microwave, coffee maker, or toaster oven brings such relief when you're so stressed out. It's one less thing to worry about! And it's a gift of feeling civilized and special.

But even more critical is keeping the home safe. My parents have a weekly housekeeper now. The housekeeper for my parents helps keep hoarding and cluttering at bay. Newspapers are put into organized baskets instead of falling off chairs onto floors, where my unsteady dad might slip and slide. Bugs and ants won't set up residence and invite their families in the kitchen and bathrooms if things are sanitary. And sanitized surfaces, fresh linens and towels prevent colds and infections (including UTIs), which is critical when dealing with weakening bodies and immune systems.

Aging also brings on vision and hearing issues, which may make the proper cleaning of the home by your normally fastidious parent less likely. Strength or flexibility to reach high places or scrub with vigor becomes more difficult. Arthritis, dizziness/vertigo, or back issues may make it hard to bend over. When you notice your parents have food stains on clothing or have crumbs in the corners of the countertops, you can bet that vision issues are preventing them from doing a thorough job.

Paid home health aides may be able to help clean (usually light cleaning—no windows or big jobs). If your parent wants to sit and read, watch television, nap, or just prefers not to have company but you want someone there "just in case" or to handle feeding or toileting for example, the aide can help with the housekeeping chores, laundry, or tidying in between caregiving tasks. (Check with the agency or aide to be sure it's on the task list for which you've agreed to pay.)

And then you might consider having an intense cleaning service come in now and then (quarterly or biannually perhaps) to do the big cleaning—vacuuming the heating and a/c vents; dusting for cobwebs along the ceiling corners; washing patio sliders; floor polishing; steam-cleaning fabric furniture, mattresses, carpets, and rugs; polishing chandeliers; dusting fine items in a breakfront and/or cabinets, etc.

If your parents don't already have a housekeeper, you can find one through a service or through referrals from neighbors and friends. Coupons for services are often in circulars mailed to homes. If there's a security gate or doorman, ask for recommendations of people who are already doing work in the community or building. Check on college bulletin boards for students looking to earn a little cash. Look online in places like Angieslist.com or Care.com or NextDoor.com, where local people offer services and clients rate and review them. Check references. Keep your financials and valuables hidden and secure—just for peace of mind!

Fix-It Help

Like human bodies, homes age and need more attention. The longer the structure has been standing, the more that can go wrong. Again—especially if you're not living near your parents—having a list of local, licensed, experienced professionals on call will make sudden emergencies at your folk's place easier and less stressful to manage.

Two must-haves on the list: A plumber and an electrician.

Next, a handyman.

An overflowing toilet, a shower spurting water everywhere, water seeping out of the dishwasher, soap suds still appearing on clothes that were just washed, one large chunk of ice in the ice maker instead of cubes—it's all happened to my parents. Bulbs sputtering and going dark, sparks flying out of an outlet, an electric doorbell won't stop ringing, electric heat or a/c isn't going on or the temperature is all out of whack—these things happen. Unless you're good with tools and live nearby, when your parent calls in a panic, you can confidently say "Don't worry. I've got it. I'll have someone there right away." And you can make that call from the names on your list. (Right after you patiently talk your parent through turning off the fuse box or water main, of course.)

Perhaps your mom or dad loves gardening. It makes them happy. The home looked lovely—the envy of the neighbors—but now the yard is overgrown and the plants are looking tired because weeds have taken over and the plants can't get nutrients. It might be time to hire a gardener. Or, if your parent is still capable and the budget doesn't allow for a gardener, perhaps invite a local agriculture student to come and help your parent with the gardening so the tedious tasks can be done by younger hands. A neighborhood kid could use your mower to cut down that lawn. Put someone on a routine so that your parent can still take pride in the garden that was so patiently cultivated.

Names of plumber, electrician, handy man posted. Know where water, elec. shut off.

Professional Organizer

You come visit your parent and find a room full of life. Your life. Their life. Everything is too important and holds too many memories to throw away. Maybe you want to be able to pull this stuff out to look at every now and then. Maybe, if Alzheimer's/dementia is setting in, you need memorabilia to trigger memories and start conversations with your parent to help your parent hang on to their own reality.

Perhaps you're planning to create a family history video or inventory everything in the house or make a donation or hold a yard sale. In all these situations, having a professional organizer available is a huge resource. It's hard to do these things yourself when each item you touch triggers emotions. Someone disconnected from the history can get everything in order quickly and efficiently.

A professional organizer can help with a variety of tasks, aside from clearing family clutter. As memories start failing, consistency is imperative. If closets are too cluttered, anxiety will set in because too many choices are overwhelming. When you notice your parent wearing the same two or three items multiple days in a row, it's time to bring in an organizing system. When your parent is eating the same food day after day, because it has become overwhelming to find and select alternatives, then a labeled and organized system for the pantry and refrigerator might help. I hired people to redesign and install closet systems in my parents' home so that my parents would feel comfortable knowing where everything was, and the stacks and piles on the floor of the closet became a thing of the past.

Professional organizers can range from $25 an hour up to hundreds per project—more for a whole house or overstuffed garage job. Hoarding situations can be managed, but they cost a bit more. You can find qualified local professionals on the NAPO (National Association of Professional Organizers) website.

Non-professionals that can help may be found by asking neighbors, look on community bulletin boards and in the on-line local bulletin boards. Find a retired school teacher or a college student, someone caring for a parent who wants to earn a little part time income perhaps. Check your local Clutterers Anonymous chapter for referrals.

DIY Home Organization

If your own or your parents' possible hoarding or Obsessive-Compulsive Disorder (OCD) won't be triggered and you want to tackle this on your own, consider purchasing a shelf system and/or containers (possibly clear so you can see inside) that you can label and use to sort, stack, and store. Consider moving things to a storage unit so you start with a clean space and slowly bring organized items back into your space. Install a garage organization system to unclutter and give everything its own space.

Here's an idea from an old favorite TV show called *Trading Spaces*: find a friend who can do your house while you do his or hers, as an inexpensive way to go. No matter who tackles the project, being very clear on what the intention is and what kind of things stay and what can go is critical. Finishing with everything labeled and inventoried is the goal.

It might not be memories that are waiting for you. Maybe it's paperwork. There are documents from multiple homes, monthly bills that have been saved forever, travel documents from long-ago adventures, magazines that had great home décor ideas about 30 years ago, every medical test and report ever received, etc. An organizer will put things into manageable structure so that you can save, read, discard, scan, file, or shred.

Maybe you've planned to move your parents closer to you. Maybe there's a move into a senior community, an independent or assisted living facility, continuing care campus, or nursing home on the horizon. All of these moves require someone to go through everything in the existing home to figure out what moves on with your parents. If you don't have the energy or time, an organizer will handle this for you.

Being the child of a clutterer, I've learned you never know what you're going to find in the home. It is so much easier to go through the home and all the belongings with your parents if they are able to make decisions. However, like my mother, many people have difficulty letting things go. Optimally, let decisions be made by the people who care most about the items instead of delegating to an outside party. But, if that doesn't work, you can put things in storage and deal with them later or you can buckle down and figure it all out as a family. Eventually, you can hire an estate company that will come take it all away and manage the sale and/or donation process for you. Yes, those companies exist! Search the web under "Estate Sale Company."

For people with fully functioning and healthy parents, the children may never have to deal with the property until the parents pass away. But for some, when parents start showing signs of dementia or illness makes it hard to focus or fully participate in daily living, then it may be time to start organizing and prepping. Working while the parents are still able to help and contribute will ensure that things go where intended and there will be less confusion, hurt feelings, and fighting later on.

Simplifying and paring down the "things" in the home, getting organized, and selling what's not needed leaves room for necessities, allows you to bring in some cash perhaps from selling unused items, and gives family a chance to claim things before they disappear.

Eventually, when your caregiving duties are over because your parent has passed, having everything organized and sorted with inventory lists available will make the final caregiving wrap-up duties far less stressful and will allow other people to help you with estate- or property-closing tasks.

PROCESS FOR HOME ORGANIZATION

Step ONE—Do inventory

What do we have? Where is everything?

Create a list of everything in the home, categorized. If you're a savvy computer user and know how to set up a spreadsheet, then later, when you want to sell or donate or distribute, you'll have a master list that can be sorted and printed and used to track everything. You can use this list for your tax return to get donation credit, to total the amount of money brought in by sales, or to track where everything went in case someone says, "Did you take out that funny key that I taped to the bottom of the drawer? That key opens the safe deposit box with millions in cash!" and you need to track that drawer down again!

SAMPLE COLUMNS:

Item	Description	Estimated Value	Location	Status
Dinner plates	Blue and White Noritake China from 1957	Replacements.com – $1 per plate; eBay $100 for set (8)	Breakfront, lower left corner	☐ Sell ☐ Donate ☐ Consign ☐ Taken by:

Later, you can add columns for Date Sold, Charity Donated to, etc.

Step TWO—Create a plan

What are you doing with all this stuff?

Things may be fine to stay just where they are. No problem. Step away. Let it be. However, if there are things that no one is using, no one is enjoying, no one in the family wants; things that are just taking up space, then maybe it's time to do a little clearing of the house. If the items are worth any kind of money, you might consider selling them or putting them out on consignment. If the items are of small value but in good condition and usable by someone else, you might have a garage or tag sale. If the thought of opening your garage for strangers is appalling to you (what are you hiding, missy???? ;-)) then you might want to be a generous sort and make a donation to a group that will find good homes for all your "stuff" and you get a tax credit for being a giving person.

Step THREE—Implement the plan

For an estate sale, you could hire a company to come in, evaluate your property (handing them your printed-out inventory of everything will impress them!!), and give you an estimate on what they think it could be worth. If you like what they say, they take over from there. They re-inventory, appraise, polish up everything for peak sale price, arrange and display, set up a time, promote and market your sale, manage the sale, process all the payments, and hand you a check (minus their fee) at the end.

OR, they might come and collect the items they think they can sell, bring those items to a location where they may be selling the items from multiple homes simultaneously, handle the sale, bring back what they couldn't sell, and mail you a check for what they did sell.

For the garage sale, there's the DIY option that can be as simple as a few hours in your driveway and a couple of card tables of stuff, with signs printed on your computer and displayed around town. Or you can blow it up by hiring a garage sale specialist to take over and use their savvy and existing customer base to bring people to your location and handle the sale from one to multiple days. For the DIY, check the internet for tons of great ideas. The internet can also provide you with garage sale specialists. Contact people on NextDoor.com to see if anyone in your neighborhood knows of people to recommend. Or ask your neighbors if they want to have a community garage sale, where multiple homes get together to sell their extra things. Multiple-home garage sales get many more shoppers stopping by with real interest in buying.

The hardest part of all this is determining what is truly valuable, what is valuable because of your memories attached to it, and what is junk. You may have some things that would seem to be valuable, but the condition may be old and worn out or signatures of that famous guy are too faded to be seen on a display. It hurts every time someone says, "Nah—that's nothing," to something you maybe once cared about. [Note: I think if you watch too many episodes of *Antiques Roadshow* you might have a skewed interpretation of just how much your stuff is worth and that dream for the $10,000 value on a $2 item is pretty far from typical reality! Sorry Mom!]

Step FOUR—Organize

Once you've pared down items and furniture in the space, leaving healthy energy to flow more freely, it's time to organize the closets and cabinets, drawers, attic, basement, garage, etc.

Why go through this now? For one, with aging comes new needs. New people will be moving in and out of your family's space. For another, with aging comes memory loss and it's very common for someone to forget where they put their mugs, where the placemats are stored, where the keys are for the lock box. People can start looking for things in places they kept them in their childhood home or their first home. If you know where the things are, you can help locate them. If you have inventory, you know those items are still there. If you label shelves and cabinets, then someone else (an aide, a housekeeper, a grandchild) can find and return things properly without interrupting you.

And lastly, when it comes time to clean out the home entirely, it will be easy to know what to take, what to sell, what to donate, and who gets what in the family. It will be nearly mindless to pack and label the boxes or to direct someone else to help because, the truth is, maybe you really won't be up to it yourself.

Driver(s)/Transportation

If your parent does not have a car or is unable to drive, having a professional driver on call or having several driving on-demand options is going to be a lifesaver and help keep your parent independent.

My mother is savvy enough to use her iPhone to call for Uber. After my Dad's first Uber ride with my mother, he told me, smiling, "Hey, I really like that You-Ber. It was easy!" There's also Lyft and a bunch of new companies popping up as I write this. Local taxi services are getting into the game with on-call rides via computer becoming available.

GoGoGrandparent.com is an option. This is the way someone who doesn't use a smartphone or apps can take advantage of Uber and Lyft type services, plus they monitor your parents during the trip. There are 24/7 operators and the service will send text alerts to keep families in the loop. Rides can be scheduled in advance and even come on a fixed and regular basis. The drivers can take a passenger up to 100 miles from the starting location. The fee for this service is in addition to the ride cost. At this writing, it's an additional $0.27/per minute. It's like having a ride concierge who helps keep an eye on your parent for the entire duration of the travel period.

If your parent is compromised via attention span or physically, there are services in larger communities run by local government or nonprofits that offer special buses and car or van services that will pick up your parent either at an agreed upon stop or at home. These services offer transport for wheelchairs, scooters, and people with equipment. And the drivers are meant to help. You'll likely need a doctor's letter to qualify your parent for the service. Often, the passenger can bring a support person on the ride—a caregiver or aide or spouse—at no extra charge. Check your local rules.

In Palm Beach County, Florida, for example, there's a service called Palm Tran. It costs $3.50 per ride for qualified individuals who have filled out the paperwork and submitted medical support documentation of need. However, you have to call 24 hours in advance and it's a shared-ride situation. Thus, the trip that should take 20 minutes might take an hour or more and may not be on the exact schedule your parent prefers. But it's a resource that many, many people take advantage of. It may run differently in your community.

Private medical transport services are like taxis for the wheelchair and scooter crowd. They have drivers trained with medical skills who know how to move and secure equipment. These offer per-ride fees. Reservations are often necessary to secure the time and date you require. Your parents' doctors will likely have recommendations.

Nonprofit centers where seniors gather for daily activities, exercise, and socialization (or to just get out of the house) quite often offer free or low-cost pickup and drop-off service. There may be limitations for schedules or for how far the vans will go. Sometimes these are called recreation programs, sometimes it's Adult Day Care, sometimes it's a Senior Center. You have to find out what's available in your community. Check with religious leaders, look in the newspaper for promotional information on upcoming activities, and, of course, check the web.

For rides to doctors and medical-related appointments, there are other resources. You have to check in your community to see whether they're offered through your house of worship, a nonprofit, the hospital, or a government-funded agency.

A private driver might be the best option. Someone who works in the home as a paid caregiver might be able to drive your parent on errands. If that's important, when you hire a caregiver you will want to look for someone with a car, a valid license, current auto insurance, and a clean driving record.

Cal sold his business and looked for something else to do with his time. He now has a wheelchair-bound client who requires a van to get to his office and around town to meetings. Cal drives 20 minutes to his client's home in Connecticut in the morning and drives the man into Manhattan in his client's own handicap-outfitted van. The client has Cal take him from appointment to appointment, helping with on-boarding and exiting the van in each place. Cal drives off after each stop and finds a place to park (hanging with other limo drivers or running errands) until his client texts that he's ready to be picked up. It's a good job for semi-retired Cal and it's an easier process for the client. If your parent is someone active who goes from meeting to volunteering to shopping to friend visits, a private driver might be the best option. This can be booked on a regular schedule (e.g., twice a week, every Wednesday and Sunday, or weekdays from 11:00 to 3:00, etc.) or the driver can be on call.

Cal works consistently, so he earns a set salary for the week. That means he's able to focus on the one client and no one else. The client likes it and Cal feels secure. The client has a special insurance policy for the handicapped van and anyone driving it.

Lynda, facing many health challenges because of lupus and COPD, hired a young college student, the son of a friend, looking for extra money to help her with errands. She paid $10 an hour with a four-hour minimum each time she used him. Lynda carried a bulky oxygen tank around with her. Getting one day a week to visit the bank, get groceries, get a manicure/pedicure, go to the hairstylist or go the casino, gave Lynda freedom she hadn't had since her husband passed away. And then she had the young man on her speed dial for doctor's visits and other appointment-oriented obligations. However, working with people without commercial insurance or chauffeur's license can be risky.

Prices vary based on who you use. Someone who drives professionally for Lyft or Uber might be willing to be on call privately for you if you're willing to work around their paid schedule. This is a great option for a senior who is able to make a phone call but can't (or won't) use technology.

One cautionary note: Using Lyft, Uber, a city bus-type service, or a private taxi service means that the driver and car are insured. If you go with a nonprofessional who you pay, you are at risk for the person not having insurance to cover expenses in an accident. Private individual auto insurance doesn't cover paid passengers in many states.

See the chapter on Difficult Conversations to talk to your parents about no longer driving. Page 40.

Companion Care

Living with parents is complicated enough when everyone's healthy. When one or both parents are sick, living together becomes a battlefield, where the situation is like having bullet holes of destruction shot through your own brain and body. Caregivers need to get away. YOU need to have a life. You need what's known as respite care.

I've outlined experts to have on call who can help with basics for your parents. At some point (if your parents haven't moved into an independent or assisted living facility), care will be needed in the home.

When you get to this time, you, as a caregiver, need to take care of yourself as well as your parents. Find at least one, possibly several, resources to call upon to provide companion care for your parent when needed.

Remember the babysitter list you had when the kids were little? Someone to come over and keep an eye on the kids and maybe give them some food, talk to them, play with them? That's what a companion is. Someone who can come visit with your parent, keep him/her company, be there in case there's an emergency. Your babysitter list never had only one person. For your parent, you might want to have a list with a friend of your parents' or a neighbor, or a young person who you pay to call on for a last-minute situation.

You might also use an agency or a pre-screened paid aide for ongoing support and planned respite time for yourself. The VA offers free respite care time for veterans up to a certain number of hours a month if your parent is a veteran.

If you don't live with your parents or near your parents, having these contacts on your quick-call list will help when you just can't get there and you know someone needs to be on-site.

Julie's Story

Julie moved into her parents' home to help her mother manage her father, an increasingly physically ill cancer survivor. Julie had a special bond with her father. Julie's mother was accustomed to being taken care of and provided for and didn't have the ability or patience to manage caring for a very ill man, nor to take over the business side of running a household. Someone had to manage medications, trips to doctors, wound care, etc. Julie took on that role, with her mother over her shoulder, critiquing every step of the way.

Eventually, Julie's father used a walker at times and carried portable oxygen because he had trouble breathing all the time. His mood soured. He was in and out of the hospital. They hired aides and nurses to help when Julie was at work.

Julie fought with her mother constantly and came to our caregiver support group with a box of tissues, red eyes, and growing depression. "Work," she told us, "is my only sanctuary outside of these meetings."

Just when Julie had reached her limit and was looking at alternatives for care, her father passed away. Julie was left with a decision to remain in the house with her aging mother or to act in self-preservation and find a home of her own. Julie chose to find her own apartment.

Julie and her mother recognized that the big house, empty of her dad's vital energy, was too much for a woman in her late seventies to manage alone. So, at this writing, there's a companion in the house while Julie works. This woman keeps Julie's mom company and helps with household tasks.

Julie and her mother agreed to look for a continuing care independent living community for her mother to move to. Soon after they agreed to look, the idea of moving became more pressing. Her mother, who thought she was totally fine and independent, totaled her car and wound up in the hospital and then residential rehabilitation. Subsequent testing for driving ability said she should no longer drive. Moving now has a new urgency.

Adult Day Care (ADC)

"I know my parents need help, but they don't want to leave home." I have heard this over and over again in my caregiver support groups. To keep your parent at home, even with all the tools that follow in this chapter, the best option may be to invite, encourage, and then bring your parent to Adult Day Care a few days a week. ADC offers a well spouse or an adult-child caregiver some relief time to stop caregiving for a bit.

Maybe, within a couple, one person is declining more quickly than the other, or perhaps financial considerations prevent one from moving away from home altogether. Or maybe your romantic mom and dad cannot fathom *not* sleeping together, but don't need to be in each other's faces all day! For these cases, a day care option may be a good solution. Similar to a childcare center option for working parents, an ADC center is an option for adults caring for parents. With the flexibility to choose how many hours a day, how many days a week, how many months a year, ADC is a first choice for many families.

The ADC center you pick can be specific to a physical, emotional, or a combination of issues, at any level of care needed. There are centers that offer options for people with specific challenges—like an Alzheimer's center or one for the mobility challenged.

There are centers with fewer restrictions and less staff for people who don't need constant supervision but are looking for social interaction—perhaps to make new friends who want to take trips or go out to eat.

ADC offers mental and physical activities to keep a declining person active and involved and happily engaged, which can slow down disease progression.

ADC can be ramped up or down to allow for travel, scheduling, or transportation issues.

Local transportation for the handicapped offered by the ADC Center itself may help with roundtrip transportation if needed. Often this is funded based on need.

Respite Care for the Caregiver

When supervision and care for an ill person is brought in so the caregiver can take a break, this is known as respite care. A companion sitting with a parent, a trip to Adult Day Care, or having someone professional come to the home can all provide respite for you, the caregiver.

What do you do when being given respite? Anything that gets you back to being you! Respite is defined as a short period of rest or relief from something difficult or unpleasant.

Go for a hike or walk. Spar at a boxing gym. Go to a movie. Have a visit with a friend. Talk to a therapist. Learn how to surf. Attend a caregiver support group. Putt golf balls. Get errands done. Book a massage. Get your hair cut or your nails done. Go to a racetrack and drive really fast while you scream! Have a cup of tea and read a book. Take care of yourself!

Respite for you, the caregiver, can come in the form of a paid aide who comes on a regular basis. It can be a friend of the family or a sibling who comes to take over for you. It might be a group day care space provided in your community or a one-day service offered by the Alzheimer's Association or Veterans Affairs office in your community.

Take advantage of these services! When I first started this journey with my parents and was visiting several support groups to find the right fit, the advice I was consistently given was, "DON'T WAIT UNTIL YOU NEED IT DESPERATELY. GET HELP EARLY!" Over and over and over again, I heard this from the group leaders, the participants, and the clinicians at various facilities. I heard it from the teachers in the classes I took to understand dementia, aging, and being a caregiver. I now pass this important message on to you. A support group is your "family of choice." The place you can go to be accepted and listened to, so listen! Take time *for you* early in the process and consistently!

As strong as you think you are, as patient as you have been in the past, no matter how many people call you a saint, make sure to set time aside that is just for you! Take time to enjoy your passions and find stress relief as often as possible. In the beginning, maybe once a week will be enough of a break. As illness and care needs progress, the more you're needed, the more time you need to take for yourself to recover. Sounds counterintuitive, right? But the more stress you're under, the more you have to care for your body, mind, and soul.

You've heard it a hundred times before, I'm sure, but it's so true. Like the flight attendants tell you on airplane, "Put your own mask on before helping anyone else."

According to articles written in many journals in the late '90s and early 2000s, family members who care for elderly relatives and sick spouses have higher rates of chronic disease and stress and are at greater risk for depression, social isolation, and financial loss than their non-caregiving counterparts. A lot of this data was taken from a 1999 National Institutes of Health report. The situation was given a name: Caregiver Syndrome.

Numerous studies over the past decades have shown that caregiving is associated with mental anguish and poor physical health, with the impact being greater for caregivers of patients with dementia. In 2003, Dolores Gallagher-Thompson, PhD[7], wrote that 40 percent of family caregivers for Alzheimer's

---

[7] Department of psychiatry and Behavioral Sciences—Older Adult & Family Center at Stanford, home of the REACH (Resources for Enhancing Alzheimer's Caregiver Health) program

patients—whose responsibility can last 10 to 15 years—die from stress-related disorders. "We teach caregivers how to manage their time better, become more assertive in asking for help from others, channel their thoughts more positively, and prepare for the future."

AARP released a new, more optimistic study in November 2017[8], which found that, though more than half of caregivers are stressed and worried and 40 percent feel overwhelmed—over 90 percent of them say they are pleased about helping a loved one and that almost 90 percent of those loved ones are grateful for their caregivers' efforts. The survey also pointed out that caregivers who felt better prepared for their caregiving roles tended to handle them much better.[9] The fact that you are being proactive and reading a book like this bodes well for your own future health!

Family caregivers provide about $500 billion in unpaid services, the Rand Corp. estimates. And they spend on average 253 hours a month looking after the elderly. That's roughly a 60-hour-a-week job!

It is not being selfish to take time away from caregiving to be good to yourself. It is imperative that you take the time to exercise, socialize, and buy and prepare food that is nourishing and energizing rather than settling for sugary junk that satisfies a craving but ultimately depletes you.

Being a martyr and delaying time to care for yourself can potentially lead to anger and hostility directed at the person or people you care for. It could lead to overeating, drinking, or drug use to help you sleep or perk you up or turn off your worry brain. It might cause sleep disorders.

And so, (enough scaring you!) finding a respite caregiving service in the beginning and then hiring a caregiver for daytime service if you're there at night, an overnight service if you can only be there during the day, and eventually either a full-day Adult Day Care or a residential program or full-time in-home help will be necessary.

If finances are keeping you tied to your parent for innumerable hours, then look at the VA for some free respite care if your parent is a veteran. The Alzheimer's Association has programs and referrals if your parent has memory loss, dementia, or an Alzheimer's diagnosis. The Area Agency on Aging (or whatever form it takes in your community) offers free services and referrals to low-cost services. And the best thing I found was attending a conference with a "trade show" type set up so you can hear all the options in one day and attend some education sessions to hear what other people recommend.

Sometimes you just need a student—a parent-sitter—to come and sit with your parent for companion care. A few hours (four hours is good enough for a break, but not too long for your parent) of having someone sit and talk with your parent and call you if there's an issue. This kind of care doesn't require a licensed or certified person. After all, are you certified? It's just eyes-on, in case of any issues.

Included in this book is an entire section of various forms of care, where to find people, and what they should/could do when they are in your home. See pages 191–195.

A practical self-assessment tool for caregivers can be found on the Caregiving.org website: caregiving. org/wp-content/uploads/2010/11/caregiverselfassessment_english.pdf. If you're not sure how much toll caregiving is taking on you, try completing this self-assessment (also available in Spanish).

---

[8] https://www.aarp.org/content/dam/aarp/research/surveys_statistics/ltc/2017/family-caregiving-roles.pdf

[9] https://www.huffingtonpost.com/entry/the-good-news-about-the-longer-lives-of-family-caregivers_us_5a122012e4b-023121e0e9447

GENERAL HOME SAFETY

Like a child

Whether you decide to bring in companion care or an aide or bring your parent to Adult Day Care for part of the day, the home environment still needs to be safe. In particular, Alzheimer's disease and dementia cause a number of changes in the brain and body that may affect safety. These challenges can include:

- Judgment: forgetting how to use household appliances
- Sense of time and place: getting lost on one's own street, not finding the bathroom
- Behavior: becoming easily confused, suspicious, or fearful
- Physical ability: having trouble with balance
- Senses: experiencing changes in vision, hearing, sensitivity to temperature, or depth perception

Aging with physical challenges can lead to a whole set of hazards and safety issues including loss of mobility, loss of muscle tone and functionality, decreased flexibility, gradual or sudden loss of vision or hearing, shaking or spasms, dizziness or vertigo. The cautions outlined here apply to general safety ideals for all.

Kitchen Fire Prevention:

You can install oven/stove safety guards (check the childproofing websites or a retailer like Bed Bath & Beyond or your local medical supply store) that will prevent a parent with dementia from turning on, or leaving on, the stove or oven.

You can simply remove the stove/oven knobs if you have an older model appliance and turn off any pilot lights if you have a gas stove. Alternatively, you can turn off the breaker switch and teach any home health aide how to turn it back on to enable cooking, but they must remember to deactivate it again afterward. Keep a fire extinguisher in the kitchen, just in case, and put matches in childproof, waterproof boxes or containers.

Burn Control:

Adjust the hot water heater's max setting to less than 120 degrees to avoid burning skin in the shower or sink. Older skin is more fragile yet also less sensitive to temperature, so your parent might just let hot water scald them without knowing the harm it is doing.

Toxic Substances:

Separate similar looking products into different-shaped containers or lock them up only to be used with supervision. For example, a tube of toothpaste also looks like anti-pain cream, moisturizer, or sunscreen.

Put childproof cabinet locks on cabinets with household cleaners, paint supplies, or other toxic chemicals. Store cleaners in containers with childproof caps.

Label Toxic Containers:

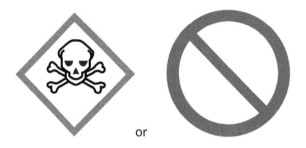

or

Make sure pills are in locked cabinets or in childproof safety containers.

Cuts & Bruises:

Look around the bathroom and kitchen, craft rooms, for anything that can pierce skin or cause an abrasion.

Use safety razors for shaving.
Hide knives, ice picks, and sharp objects in childproofed drawers. Add knife guards to countertop tools. Use rubber bands to secure scissor blades.
Put caps on tweezers, cuticle scissors, dental picks, etc.

Unsafe Area Protection:

Install a photo or image of bookcases or hang a curtain in front of doors for rooms you don't want dementia patients to enter. This hides the fact that it's an exit.

Add gates to the top and bottom of stairwells.
Put locks on doors for staircases that go down to basements or up to attics.
Put safety latches on doors leading to patio, decks, garage, laundry room, etc.
Install nightlights along footpaths on the way to the bathroom or kitchen to avoid tumbles in the dark.
Remove throw rugs, balls, weights, boxes, buckets, extension cords, and anything else that could be a tripping hazard. Anything that can move on its own with a strong wind or a slight bump or anything low enough to be tripped over if one is not looking down, should be removed.
Attach power cords and extension cords along the base of the wall and cover with firesafe protective covers.

Remove guns and weapons or put locks on cabinets. Watch for anything that can be opened with a poorly hidden key or with strong force. A determined person believing he or she needs a gun will do what needs to be done to get it.

Remove toxic plants and fake fruit displays.

Pad sharp edges of tables and cabinets with soft bumpers.

Remove fragile glass and decorative items that could shatter or splinter.

Check stability of chairs—anything that can easily tip over should be assigned to an out-of-the-way location.

Watch for rope/cords (e.g., curtain tie-backs, power cords, fringe, laundry line)

Remove baskets full of papers and books that can be tripping hazards.

Basically, look for anything you would have removed for an infant learning to walk. These items should now be removed for a senior losing agility or vision.

Security and/or Wander Risk

Secure doors that lead outside by installing inner door locks that require a key, and then hide the key in a vase, sculpture, or magnet case for quick access in emergency. (This not only prevents your parent from wandering, but also keeps your parent from opening the door for strangers.)

Another key hidden outside will help if the aide gets locked out by your parent or you need to send an emergency worker in to find your parent before you can make your way there.

Install a security camera in the most frequently used rooms. You can also install a baby monitor to listen for sound only, use a hidden nanny/pet cam in a toy with audio and video, or use a camera that you can access from your phone to visually check in.

A web-based security camera can also retain recordings for backtracking to look over the day to see when a fall may have happened if you see a bruise, or whether someone has taken medication as they promised, done his or her exercises, and stayed away from the stove (curious about those hard-boiled eggs on the ceiling?).

A camera outside the house will let you know who is at the door when you aren't there. It can track anyone prowling around the front yard. And it will give you a clue to which direction your parent went if he or she leaves on their own.

Be sure to hide coats, keys, shoes, and wallets that could inspire someone to walk out of the house.

Set up your parents' smartphone with a "Find my phone" function.

Watch out...Microchipping humans is coming. People in Europe have been chipped to use their hand instead of cards to pay for items or to use public transportation and to gain access to the gym, for example. Some corporations ask employees to get chipped so they can track productivity. When that tech is widely available, microchipping our parents will make finding a wanderer much easier!

Reduce Anxiety—Create Comfort & Calm

Reduce disturbances to the landscape or any of the five basic senses. These can bring on confusion and feelings of overwhelm for elderly and dementia patients. Such feelings might initiate a feeling of wanting to escape.

❖ Reduce noise (loud music or televisions, construction, lawn work, machines that bang; wind chimes may either soothe or irritate, so ask.)

❖ Reduce clutter. Too many objects and knickknacks all about create clutter in the brain. Clutter also collects dust and can be easily broken into pieces, which could be a swallowing or injury risk.

❖ Reduce paper piles, books, and magazines.

❖ Clear countertops full of appliances, devices, and gadgets.

❖ Organize closets so when you open the door you can identify everything inside and nothing will fall on you! Are things clearly labeled in case you need to go behind one thing to get another hidden in the back?

PERSONAL COMFORT

Incontinence

Incontinence comes upon us as a surprise. It is terrifying. It feels like the "Oh no! I really am old now!" moment the first time a bit of pee leaks out when you laugh or cough—the horror when you can't quite make it to the toilet before the evacuation begins.

This is one of those milestones that can activate all kinds of parent-child relationship conflicts and issues. After all, as a parent, when we welcome a crying baby into the world, we know we will be changing diapers and giving baths and, with a boy, we may have pee squirted up at us from that changing table! How cute. "Ha, ha, ha, did ya catch that on the video, honey?" But, as the adult child, it is a totally different thing to have to bring a parent to the toilet, wipe his or her behind after a poop, change soiled underwear, and figure out adult diaper systems.

I know, I know…you want to skip past this section. I didn't want to think about this either. But this book is about reality, so here's a reality check-in moment.

The emotional toll on your parent is significant. It's embarrassing enough to realize you're losing more control of your bodily functions, but to have to ask your child for help in this area—to expose your personal body functions and anatomy—is humiliating. A parent may react with denial ("I don't know where that wet spot came from"), anger ("Keep your nose out of my business! Who are you to be telling me what to do?!"), fear (running to the bathroom every half hour obsessively to prevent accidents), and/or possibly become depressed (you notice withdrawal and shrinking away, perhaps retreating into bed all day; possibly crying randomly).

You have options. Being prepared in advance and having a talk with your parents on a factual level can break the ice, reduce the embarrassment, and help you to understand what your parent thinks might be most helpful.

When I was 10 years old, on a steamy summer rainy day in the Catskill Mountains in New York, my mother huddled me under an umbrella with her and took me on a long walk to tell me about becoming a woman. How I was going to bleed and would need pads and panties with hooks (yeah, yeah—I am that old) every month to manage this situation. I learned all about where babies come from, received a book on what embryos look like in all kinds of creatures in the animal kingdom, and I was given a "starter kit" by Kotex filled with sanitary pads, belts, panties, instructions, and so on. It was one of the most intimate times I can remember with my mother—just the two of us—and it eliminated any embarrassment I had about that first burst of blood in my panties.

You too can help your parent feel less out of control about this situation and reduce the embarrassment. Perhaps start a discussion, "Here's what the doctors say we are likely to see at some point. Why don't we plan for them now, so we'll be prepared? I want to understand how I can help."

❖ Create an Incontinence Preparedness Kit. Purchase a stock of male or female adult waterproof underpants, diapers, whatever might be needed in the right size and shape for your parent's figure. Keep the kit someplace you'll remember for when they are needed. (Be mindful about using disposable pads. Rachel said her mother, later in the disease, caused a lot of plumbing issues because she flushed the pads down the toilet.)

❖ Put a waterproof plastic mattress liner under the sheets to protect the mattress. This will avoid awkward stains, greatly reduce the possibility of urine smell in the house, and save the mattress from mold or bugs. (Tip: Make sure you have many of these so you can switch them out when one needs to be cleaned.)

❖ Purchase wee-wee pads at the pet store if you want to save money on pads for bed and chair liners in order to cover surfaces under your parent's tush. I've been told that some newer versions of these pads have a chemical that helps attract a pet to use the pad, so if the pad is going near your parent's skin, use the kind for babies or adults. If the pad is going under the sheet or on a chair where your parent will be clothed, then you might try the pet versions. [Note, pet discount websites are a great resource to have these shipped to your home on auto-ship so you never run out; plus adds another level of privacy.]

My friend Jordana's husband has early onset Alzheimer's. At just 70 years old, he was sweet and adorable and affectionate, but losing the ability to manage his bodily functions. Out for a hamburger with them for lunch one day, Jordana took her husband into the restroom where she discovered he had waited too long before saying he had to go and had lost control of his functions. She called me on my cell phone and I ran to her car to get a bag of supplies to clean him up, put on protective undergarments, and wrap a sweatshirt around his waist to hide his accident.

As a pet sitter, I happened to have in my car a heavy-duty plastic seat liner meant for transporting pets, meant to protect car seats from scratches, spills, licks, and pee! Jordana used that to drive her husband back to the house. She soon bought her own seat liner to use for car trips with her husband from then on.

Being prepared can make even the most awkward situations more manageable. Whether your parent is still traveling around in a car by himself or herself or if your parent is using other transportation, be prepared in and out of the home.

STDs

Yeah, I know—first I'm talking about peeing and now this. And while this section is about personal comfort, this may be a little more on the personal discomfort for you, the caregiver. But I feel obligated to share this.

There's something you may not know (I certainly did not until I began my caregiving research.) The rate of sexually transmitted diseases is growing faster in the senior community (65+) while reducing in other age groups!

In February 2018, on the Very Well Health website, an article by Elizabeth Boskey, PhD and affirmed in various AARP articles, explains that in this age, when divorce rates are up and Viagra and other erectile dysfunction medications are available online, sex among the elderly may be at an all-time high. As a result, "recent statistics from the CDC have shown that the number of new HIV infections is actually growing faster in individuals over 50 than in people 40 years and under."[10] If your parent is actively dating and enjoying a vibrant social life, this is another reality check for you as a caregiver.

I won't even share the details of the story I just heard about the 90-year-old guy who has a different girlfriend in each hallway of his assisted living residence. The women fight over whose night it is for him to sleep with!

Because seniors don't fear pregnancy, they rarely use condoms. Seeking intimacy and affection from another person is a natural instinct, especially when you've spent your life in a partnership and find yourself suddenly alone. However, now we as caregivers need to make sure to have that "safe sex" talk with our parents! Buy them a box of condoms. Let them know they need to protect themselves and get screened! (I can hear you groaning all the way over here!)

One more thing...for women aged 65 or older, it is important to talk to their doctors about how often they need to be screened for cervical cancer as well. Thousands of women die from cervical cancer because once they reach 65 years old, they are not tested by their doctors for HPV. And many older women just stop going for pap smears and testing altogether.

Okay...now back to our regularly scheduled program...

Clothing

Skills like tying shoe laces, running a belt through loops, securing a watch band/bracelet/necklace, zipping a jacket or pants, and buttoning a shirt gradually fade away with cognitive decline and physical challenges in bones, joints, and muscles. Keeping your parent independent can be as simple as switching to more easily accessible options such as Velcro™ closings and elastic waists. Nothing with zippers, buttons, or anything requiring skills to make a knot should be in the closet once your parent is in the advanced stages of decline.

Grooming

As someone ages, their peripheral vision starts to diminish. A seminar I attended taught me that the ability for a senior to see what is on his or her shirt, near a sleeve, off to either side or above eye level reduces and reduces until they are basically seeing within a small square box in front of them. When you visit a place frequented by seniors, you may notice formerly impeccably groomed individuals still wearing lovely or smart clothing, but there are stains, some fading colors, or maybe a heavy hand was applied for makeup, cologne, aftershave, etc. This comes about because of what that individual can see, feel, smell, taste, and hear.

My father walks several miles a day. When his toenails get too long, frayed at the edges, the nails start to get caught in the fabric weave of his socks, which causes damage to the socks of course, but also to the

---

[10] https://www.verywellhealth.com/stds-the-elderly-3133189

nail bed, the feet, and the risk of infection goes up. Remember, he can't see his feet as well as he used to. I noticed fungus growing under the nails. I started doing a trim on his nails regularly and told him to spread ointment on his toes after his shower. Now his nails are a bit yellow from age and all kinds of thick and thinness, but at least he is free of fungus, no infection, and his nails don't get caught on his socks. He's more comfortable. No animal claws for my dad!

Not everyone bonds with their dad over toenail clipping like I do (not hardly anyone, actually!), so find a podiatrist who can clean things up to start and ask for recommendations for ongoing care. Either take your folks for regular mani-pedi treatments or set up routine visits to the podiatrist at least to clean up those toenails! Check it out near you. Many community facilities have podiatrists who make regular visits to homes. My father and mother are lucky that their podiatrist visits them in their apartment now.

Of course, haircuts, shampoos, beard and mustache trims, ear and nose hair clipping, and keeping hair clear of poking the eyes or getting in the way of sight should be on the list of regular grooming for your parent. Not just from an aesthetic perspective for socialization (even seniors have cliques and can be judgmental!), but from a health perspective as well. Your parent will feel special for this elegant grooming care, but you know that it's imperative to keep the aging body free from any chance of infection that could rapidly deteriorate into life-threatening internal bio warfare.

Moisturizing! So critical. Keeping skin from getting too dried out (when it can crack, peel, and let in bacteria to cause infection) is a must. Aside from the obvious need to drink *tons* of water every day to clear the digestive track and keep the body hydrated, keep eyes bright and clear, and keep skin plump, add using a simple skin moisturizer to Mom's or Dad's daily routine. After a shower, have them apply the lotion all over. This should keep skin looking and feeling great. Any skin issues should be reported to the dermatologist at your next regular visit.

Skin Review: Red spot. Blue spot. One spot. Two spots. Looking over someone's aging skin will reveal how much time someone may have spent in the sun when they were younger. Cracked and dry spots that change or growths or anything with hair growing out of it are best examined by professionals. Keeping an eye on your parents' skin to notice if there are big changes can help catch something that might be easily managed if caught early. Make friends with a qualified dermatologist who works with an elderly clientele in your community!

Mobility

For an aging individual, one awkward fall or bump and suddenly daily life could be dramatically altered. Maintaining one's ability to move around the home, be outside with family and friends, and take care of typical household errands are integral to a positive state of mind. The variety of tools available to ensure safety before and after an accident is expanding every day. Preventing an accident from happening should take precedence over looking cool or seeming too old.

When you visit independent living residences, you'll witness a unique "parking lot" near the dining areas where rolling and strolling tools remain until mealtime is concluded. My dad showed me that in his dining room, "Everyone looks normal sitting down!"

In addition to physical therapy, strength training, and exercise, you might consider having the following around the home (or know a place where these items could be obtained quickly when needed) for any situation that might arise.

For images and links to the following items, check out IllBeRightThere.com for current styles of products.

Walker—Walkers basically help people propel forward by allowing one to lean on a frame to keep their balance. There are models with no wheels (you probably see them with tennis balls on the legs instead), three wheels, or four wheels. Some walkers require leaning over to move them forward (which may be difficult for taller individuals or those with wrist or back injuries) and new models are available that are height adjustable and allow the person to walk upright.

Walkers are typically able to be transported to a new location easily by simply folding the sides together. Many models include a seat so that if the person gets tired, they have a seat right there, wherever they are. A back rest may also be an option.

I call some of the models pocketbooks-on-wheels, other people call them kangaroos, because the center seat area is also a basket with a lid that allows an individual to carry things from place to place without having to hold it in hand. Wallets, ID, emergency cell phone, tablet, knitting projects, deck owf cards, television remote controls, the mail or a newspaper/book can just handily move along with the individual.

Cane—From a tree limb found on a walk one day to an elaborate carved wood piece of art, canes come in many forms. They also vary in materials (wood, plastic, metal, and aluminum), which affects the weight and flexibility of the canes. Metal ones are often adjustable. Canes typically have a curved top to grasp. Some may have a wrist strap at the top. The expense ranges from a few dollars to hundreds of dollars, depending upon the material used, quality and durability, as well as workmanship and accessories.

Canes are easily found at most drug stores with a pharmacy department for last-minute needs (especially handy in 24-hour stores) but a wider variety may also be ordered online, rented at a medical supply shop, or provided on loan by a hospital or rehab facility.

Walking sticks may be foldable, can include a compass or water flask, may have a pointed tip to improve safety on slippery or icy surfaces, or have other accessories for comfort. Walking sticks can be found at retailers specializing in hiking and outdoor sports (like Eddie Bauer, REI, Outdoor Outfitters, Dicks Sporting Goods, and LL Bean.)

Scooter—A mobility scooter is traditionally designed for outdoor use, unless you have a spacious home with smooth floors, wide hallways, and plenty of room for turns. There are now lighter and smaller scooters for in-home use as well. I just saw a very stylish new scooter that folds into a trunk of a car and can do a 360 degree turn in place.

Scooters might be battery operated or electrically recharged. At some point, I suppose there will be scooters that have solar chargers. And, no doubt, hybrid options are on the way as well.

Scooters come in various weights, which will determine if you need a van to transport it by riding the scooter into the van on a ramp. Portable scooters allow you to pull the seat off, fold down the handlebars, and lift the two pieces into the back of an SUV, station wagon, or car trunk.

Wheelchair—Wheelchairs are easiest to use indoors but models with special tires work well both indoors and outdoors. Wheelchair options include no motor, battery powered, or electric charge. The wheelchair should have a manual option with the ability for a seated person to move the chair by hand by pushing a bar around the tire, using a crank, or simply pushing the wheel. Training on how to manage a wheelchair is highly recommended before leaving someone with a chair by himself or herself.

If you plan to move someone often from one venue to another, options for portability and compact size may be a big factor.

It's helpful to practice in advance to learn how to back in and out or go face-forward and handle steps or curbs, grass or stones, etc.

I traveled around Europe the summer I turned 19 with a wheelchair-bound 65-year-old German polio survivor. This was back before handicapped accessible was even a concept! I learned everything on the job, trying to get in and out of hotels, rental cars, and sightseeing venues. There was a lot to learn! One day, while on a walk in the mountains around Lucerne, Switzerland, I nearly sent Frau C into the cows grazing on the hillside below when I didn't manage the brake properly!!!

Scooter and wheelchair lifts and carriers are available for rent or purchase. They attach to the back of a heavy-duty car (don't try this on a mini-cooper or VW bug!) the way a bicycle rack, luggage rack, or motorcycle transporter with a gate and lock function works. These solutions work wonders if you always have a full trunk or if the need for a scooter is temporary.

Obviously, the strength of the people available to lift or move the scooter or wheelchair will contribute to your decision-making in model selection.

Additional considerations for your purchase or rental of a wheelchair or scooter:

- Frame type
- Weight of equipment
- Weight capacity (how much does the person in the chair weigh?)
- Seat width
- Seat depth
- Back height
- Adjustable back/seat
- Foldable
- Wheel size
- Tire-filling options (power or hand pump?)
- Brake system
- Passenger driven
- Armrest options
- Leg rests (removable, adjustable, foldable, etc.)

My mother loves the fact that the scooter we have just stops on a dime if you let go of the accelerator handle. This is a great safety feature. An adjustable speed gauge to ensure that there's no chance the scooter could bolt up to 30 mph is reassuring to those of us who have watched someone like my scruffy-faced dad in a white T-shirt and jeans zipping around the parking lot like a cross between a child on a tricycle and a Harley Davidson guy, legs extending out in front of him, ear to ear grinning, yelling, "WHEEEEEEE!"

If budget is a challenge, there are organizations in every city that collect donations of no-longer-needed wheelchairs, canes, scooters, walkers, scooter/wheelchair transport lifts, even vans and foot-free driving vehicles, etc. The VA has them for veterans. The Area Agency on Aging of your community can tell you where to find them if you are not searching on behalf of a veteran. At these places, you can find what you need at low or no cost—although the selection is limited to what is on hand when you contact them.

On a giving-back note, when you are finished with your equipment, please think about donating to a reputable organization in your area so that the next person without financial resources can be helped by your generosity.

Self-Reliance

Grabbers—Aging often is accompanied by a reduction in body height, limited reach, dizziness, aches and pains when trying to grasp something, and the inability to twist the lower or upper body. Somewhere in the home hang a handy-dandy grabber gadget that can help your parent reach for items on a higher shelf, in a corner, or something that has fallen between the furniture, off a lap and onto the floor.

Imagine the carnival game where you can operate the crank from outside the clear box in order to reach into the pit of toys and prizes to try and grab something, or the vending machine that uses a grabbing motion to retrieve your selected item. The home versions go by a variety of names: Grabber, Reach Tool, Reacher, Pick-Up tool. I admit to using a grabber every now and then. Getting that pot lid that slid behind the drawer or the pen that rolled under the couch is much easier now!

One grabber in every room is ideal. Hang it on a hook, attach it with Velcro™ to the side of a chair or a wall, add a wrist handle to keep it on a door knob…whatever makes it easy to find and grab.

In addition to the convenience and independence these tools foster, they also provide options that are safer than climbing on a step stool or ladder or bending over and crawling on the floor.

Memory Support

Since cell phones/smartphones and tech tools have become ubiquitous, remembering phone numbers and addresses (and even names) has been pushed to back burner importance. However, people with any kind of brain injury, dyslexia, or aging- or dementia-related challenges will not be able to remember phone numbers at all. You can help avoid frustration.

❖ Label Devices with Contacts: Enable your parent to feel secure in knowing he or she could reach out and call someone in an emergency by putting important phone numbers on the household phone bases and all handheld receivers.

❖ Put ICE (In Case of Emergency) phone numbers on the back of mobile phones and tablets. If the landline has a speed dial function, put labels on the keys to call directly without having to remember a number.

❖ Put lists or labels with ICE numbers over the kitchen sink and/or on bathroom mirrors.

❖ If at all possible (even the disposable phones have this), use quick dial features. Assign important ICE contacts to numbers 1 and 2 and make a label with who the number is for. So, when someone is having an issue, they can just hold down the speed dial and the call will be made.

❖ Write out instructions for use of television remote, computer, printer, etc. Include photos, if at all possible, as comprehending written words may become a challenge, whereas following images may still make sense. Remember to include the basics. What once was easy and intuitive may now be less so. Plug in, turn on, click on x, Press y, with photos of the buttons.

❖ Put the instruction sheet in sheet protector pockets or have it laminated. You can use clear packing tape or clear contact paper to handle a DIY lamination at home. Hang the sheet from the side of the object or the couch or chair near the related objects. [You can find Velcro™ tabs at home improvement or stationery supply stores.]

❖ Label shelves and cabinets. If your parent is in the same home he or she has lived in for decades, chances are finding things is pretty automatic. However, if dementia is at play, you may notice frustration when something "isn't where it's supposed to be" or "We've run out of xyz again!" This is because, as one friend of mine found out, her mother was looking for the sugar for coffee in the place where the family kept it when her mother was growing up.

If you label all the shelves and cabinets with what is meant to be where, not only might it help your parent (and you or siblings) find things, it will be handy to have if you ever have help or guests in the house and they offer to empty the dishwasher, serve a meal, find a bandage or roll of toilet paper, store the newly purchased/delivered groceries, or put away the laundry.

Adherence to Routine

Create a binder of daily and weekly routines and medication for use by your parent, yourself, and rotating caregivers, siblings, first responders, doctors, etc.

Include all critical information mentioned earlier: medications, allergies, health notes (e.g., my parent has a pacemaker, has Alzheimer's, has epilepsy or Parkinson's), blood type, ICE contact info, etc. But also include your parents' daily schedule.

My caregiver group always talks about how any deviation from a regular routine can set their loved one off-kilter for a day or even longer. A new doctor visit, lunch at an unfamiliar restaurant, or a visit to a stranger can all be a traumatic blow to the sense of security.

Here is my father's schedule as an example. He followed this retirement routine religiously, daily, for years. He used to remember it without any notes hung over the sink. But then he got to where if he forgot something, he'd panic. Posting the schedule on a kitchen cabinet—eye level—brought a nice calmness. He would feel back in control again. Years later, he's at the point where he stands in the hallway between the bathroom and bedroom and can't remember what he's supposed to do, where he wanted to go. I cry knowing this. ☹

7:00 a.m.	Wake and morning bathroom routine (brush teeth, wash face)
7:15 a.m.	Dress for morning walk
	Drink Gatorade
7:30 a.m.	Walk (2.5 to 3 miles)
	Drink water upon return
8:30 a.m.	Shower, dress
9:00 a.m.	Eat hard-boiled egg
	Take morning pills
9:15 a.m.	Read newspaper and do crossword puzzle
	Take blood pressure and record in notebook
12:00 p.m.	Eat ½ protein bar
	Play solitaire on tablet
2:00 p.m.	Nap
2:30 p.m.	Jigsaw puzzle or solitaire
3:00 p.m.	Eat ½ protein bar
3:15 p.m.	Get the mail and review/act
4:00 p.m.	Cocktail hour
5:00 p.m.	Dinner prep and eating
	Take evening pills

6:30 p.m.	*Jeopardy* and *Wheel of Fortune*
7:30 p.m.	Dessert in front of television
10:00 p.m.	Take nighttime pills
11:00 p.m.	Watch the news
11:30 p.m.	Brush teeth and wash up for bedtime

HOME PREPARATION FOR AGING PARENTS

Death caused by active intervention is called unnatural death. Accidents, falls, and mistakes happen; more and more to aging individuals. When they occur, the caregiver is likely to take on additional challenges. If they are preventable, why not try to prevent them?

People over 80 have at least one fall a year! Depending on the cause of the fall and current health of the individual, a fall could easily be the precursor to unnatural death. My mother's orthopedic oncologist told us that following a fall, people over 80 have a 20 percent risk of dying within one year! Even a small fracture followed by another fall can put someone into a wheelchair for life or residential rehab center!

Here are some tools that can be used to modify a home and thus increase the likelihood of your loved one's safety as well as feelings of personal freedom and self-reliance. For images and descriptions of the latest gadgets, visit IllBeRightThere.com.

Stability Bars—A chair rail in hallways and where people travel within a home, with a bar attached, allows someone to grasp as they walk. It's especially handy if people refuse to use a walker. Anyone with a predisposition toward light-headedness, dizziness, vertigo, or balance issues would benefit from stability bar installation. Think of a cruise ship…these bars are throughout every hallway, just in case the ship hits rocky waters.

Grab Bars—Grab bars are most often used in bathrooms and other wet and slippery areas. Someone without the strength to lift themselves up and off a toilet or in and out of a bathtub or step into the shower can grab one of these extra-thick and sturdy bars to self-assist. These bars also are there if the individual is feeling unsteady.

Note: Some stores sell grab bars that are meant for you to suction or glue to the wall. If your parent is having stability issues, I would stay away from anything that isn't securely anchored into the wall by a professional.

Anti-Slip for Rugs—When a rug moves easily, sliding across a floor, someone moving around in dim light or racing to get to a toilet before having an "accident" or running to get a ringing telephone could easily slip on a moving rug and hit the floor. The safest way is to remove rugs altogether from a space. If removing the rug is not an option, use gripping tape or pads under the rug to keep the rug from sliding. Another option is to apply silicone caulking around the back edge and a few spots in the center, flatten the silicone, let it dry, and then your rug won't slip.

Additionally, you might want to add a metal, wood, or plastic saddle lip to the rug, angled to keep someone's shoe/toes from slipping under the rug and getting caught up.

Headset for Television—We've all had a neighbor who keeps the set on too loud, plays music to obnoxious levels of annoyance…don't let your loved one be the subject of scorn from neighbors! A set of simple, easy-to-set-up wireless headphones will take care of hearing issues for television.

My father taught me to use headphones while watching television. I don't want to disturb my neighbors when I want to stay up late watching a movie. No one needs to hear what I want to watch and listen to. For your loved one, like my father, this may also help with any hearing loss issues. The headset can be adjusted so that the sound is exactly what they need and any outside and distracting noises are eliminated. Combined with closed captioning, my father is able to enjoy television.

This tool is especially helpful if someone else is watching in the same room. Excessive volume could chase friends and loved ones away!

Just remember that while wearing headphones, anything outside of the television is not likely to be heard, so the parent wearing a headset will require an in-person, in-your-face waving or tapping on the shoulder to get their attention if a question needs to be asked or if it's time to move on to another activity.

Thermostat Controls (remote and local)—With aging comes different body sensitivities. Sometimes a person feels hot, sometimes cold, even though the room temperature has not shifted. I personally use a fan remote control to change the overhead fan intensity based on how my body is feeling. Still air vs. moving air makes for a different experience. Blankets can be added and removed, but larger temperature issues should be able to be managed via remote control.

If you, as caregiver, want to warm up a home before your loved one comes in after a particularly cold day, a remote control for the heat can make that happen. Same thing with air conditioning. No need to run up higher electric bills for the time when no one is at home. Just make adjustments on your smartphone app.

There are handheld remotes for space heaters and upright or table fans. If you want master control over the temperature of the space (maybe your parent has a tendency to kick up the heat or a/c too much and it could make them ill), then you can monitor via a web-based system and you can manage the controls remotely.

Digital Assistants—Alexa, Cortana, Siri, etc.—Teaching Mom or Dad how to talk to a responsive digital assistant should be fun! If you can get through the initial rejection of a "robot," you can create a wonderful source of company and assistance for your parent. These devices can provide information and entertainment, conduct practical tasks, and more.

Most importantly, these digital assistants can call for help in an emergency. Someone falls and needs help, "Alexa, call 911!" or "Hey, Siri, call my daughter for me." If Mom or Dad is forgetting basic things and phone numbers are on that list, having a digital assistant that can dial for them with just a name or a title will be so helpful.

- ❖ Dad is bored? Say, "Alexa, play Frank Sinatra's hits." Ta dah—magic. Instant entertainment specifically to the interests of the commander! Too loud? "Alexa, lower volume."
- ❖ Trying to decide if you want to bother to go out today? "Siri, what's the weather forecast for today?"
- ❖ Cognitive ability and memory starting to fail? Doing a crossword puzzle and need an answer? "Alexa, who won the world series in 1944?"
- ❖ "Hey, Siri, who delivers pizza close to me?"
- ❖ "Siri, call Mr. Chen's Chinese Restaurant on speakerphone."

You can hook in various devices, which can then be controlled by voice command as well. Controlling lights, a self-driving vacuum, the thermostat, night lights, the radio or television, and more are all manageable by voice command. No need to clap on, clap off (although that's fun and quite practical!).

Body Monitors and Fall Notifiers—"I've fallen and I can't get up," said the famous old lady on the late-night television commercial. We all remember that ad. It seemed so funny when we were younger, when our parents were younger, and now we want to know where to get one! Mom or Dad alone at home, laying on the floor for days with no one knowing is our nightmare.

Technology has advanced to the point where you can find monitors that do just about anything you need. Ask yourself these questions and you'll know which services to look for when you start comparing models and pricing:

Do you want the monitor ☐ in-house use only or ☐ outside the home as well?

Do you want to monitor for ☐ falls, ☐ wandering, ☐ needs medical help?

Do you need GPS to track your loved one's location? ☐ Yes ☐ No

Do you want the monitor to contact ☐ family, ☐ emergency services, ☐ both EMS and then assigned contact, or ☐ a professional who can gather information, assess the situation, and contact the right person?

Does your loved one have any language restrictions/needs? ☐ Must speak [fill in language]: ☐ TDD ☐ hard of hearing ☐ doesn't understand accents

Do you want to ☐ speak into the monitor or ☐ listen to instructions?

Do you have internet access in your home? ☐ Yes ☐ No

Will your loved one wear this ☐ around his/her neck ☐ on a belt or shoe ☐ on the wrist?

[Note: If your parent has a pacemaker-type device, wearing something around the neck may be contraindicated. Check with the device providers and doctor to be sure it's okay.]

Do you prefer to pay a ☐ one-time fee to purchase the item or would you rather ☐ pay monthly for a staffed service and rental of item so you get upgraded to latest models?

Some monitoring systems work through phone carriers, some work on Wi-Fi, some are grounded and require a landline in the home.

Some of these devices detect balance and can notify you when someone may have stumbled and recovered or leaned over and got up. Others only tell you when there's a fall and no more motion. Some have the ability to detect physical signs—heart rate for example. Others require the person who fell to press a button and request assistance. And there are options for avoiding false notifications to 911—safeguards—where the attendant on the other end of the service can contact your contact list before calling for EMS to arrive. With GPS, the attendants can locate your loved one, even if you're not around.

Researching these items will take a little bit of time, and the information is constantly changing. Any list printed here would be obsolete by the time you read this. Check IllBeRightThere.com for some of the options currently available.

In fact, since I started writing this book, Apple just launched their newest Apple Watch and it now has the ability to track heart rate and to tell if someone falls and can make the emergency call. With the optional cellular and Wi-Fi connections, it can be located almost anywhere and be found, and it can make phone calls and receive calls, texts, and a thousand other things.

You can also get the watch and keep it near a connected iPhone to use the phone for services and not have to have a cellular subscription for the watch.

Video security system—My father refused to wear a fall monitor so leaving him alone in the house became a nonstop barrage of calls to ask him if he was okay. First me, then my mom, then my sister—all calling to check in. It was driving him crazy. "I'M FINE!" And he was. But what happens the one time he stumbles and doesn't find something to grab and the unforgiving floor causes him to bleed internally which, because of Coumadin that thins his blood and keeps him from clotting, he could bleed to death? What if, what if... right? The caregiver brain runs a thousand miles a minute into a tornado cycle of horrible possibilities.

The answer came in the form of a Wi-Fi connected camera. No hidden camera—just right there in the living room. Installed with Dad and Mom's permission. Connected to my mom's, my sister's, my brother's, and my iPhones. I was notified when there was movement in the room or when someone else entered.

The fish-eye view spanned from the bathroom door, past the front door, the living room, and then the dining room, and entry to kitchen. I could see when he was cooking hard-boiled eggs when he promised he wouldn't use the stove when we weren't around. I could see his John Wayne side swagger/shuffle on the way to the bathroom. When did he leave for his morning walk and did he return? Aah. What a relief. If something were to happen, I would be able to see and get someone there.

Did I watch it like a reality TV show? No. I have a life after all. I don't want to be in my parents' personal business. But, with notifications popping up when Dad was home alone, I knew he was moving around without even tuning in. When Mom was there, I didn't bother to check it at all. I didn't want to spy. I just wanted to help.

The camera is also useful when you have workers in your apartment. The handyman, paid aides, the exterminator who comes when we're not home...I can look back and see what transpired if I ever had any questions. If you want to be more surreptitious, there are hidden camera options. Check online. Go to spy stores (yes, they exist). Visit a baby supply store and ask for a nanny cam. Talk to your security company and ask for options.

Lift Seats/Recliners—There's nothing like a great chair that molds to you and becomes your haven. Your butt goes in and you relax. Wonderful. Every family television show has "Dad's chair." You don't sit in that chair—or else! The chair may be parked facing a television or it could be behind a desk. Wherever it is, it's special. And when aging makes having a comfortable chair more difficult because getting in or out of the chair becomes painful or uncomfortable, even dangerous, a solution needs to be found.

There's a wide selection, very stylish these days, of chairs with assistance built in. Some chairs lift the seat higher so "falling" into a chair is not literal, not dangerous. Some, like the snazzy blue microfiber reclining chair we got for my father at a fine furniture store, use a remote control to actually put the sitter into standing position, deposited gently onto his or her feet with no effort other than pressing a button.

When naptime is a daily thing, these chairs can recline all the way back to create a comfortable, supported space for a person to take a quick nap without falling out of the chair, or have his or her neck getting kinked up. No need to go back to bed and feel like you're frail—just sit in your favorite chair and relax, maybe meditate, for a bit.

Some of the newest chairs are like the folding beds and allow one to adjust the lumbar function and leg angles to take stress off an aching lower back or spine problem area.

Removable Knob/Lockable Stove, Microwave, etc.—On the news there are stories all the time of homes that go up in flames because someone left the stove on and forgot to check the pot. When the contents of the pot turn to cinder and sparks fly, fire is a strong possibility. My father walked away from making hard-boiled eggs for a quick run to the loo and forgot he had set the eggs to boil. A smell of something burning reminded him just in the nick of time. Now, he stands over the pot and watches it boil and waits. He will never leave that stove again. Until his brain forgets the last experience.

A friend recently told me a story of her mother who tried to turn on the microwave with the television remote. Was she looking to turn on the television or did she think she could remote control the microwave? We don't know. Like the stove, a microwave accidentally set to stay on for a long time with nothing in it is dangerous. More dangerous is putting the remote control into the microwave and trying to cook it!

So, what can you do?

Easy stuff you can do before your parent needs constant supervision: (1) you can remove the dials on a stove or oven where that is possible, (2) turn off the stove/oven or microwave at the fuse box and secure the fuse box, (3) get a stove that locks. Some stoves are programmable to prevent children from burning themselves; they have safeguards built in. Look for stoves with child safety features.

For a completely disoriented adult, you might need to secure a gate or close and lock the door to the kitchen or put some kind of bell system so that you'll hear when someone has crossed the threshold into the kitchen.

Other things to watch for around cooking areas include leaving things on a hot stove surface (melted Tupperware™ anyone? Yummy!), leaning on or reaching above the stove with clothing near a flame source, putting hands onto a hot stove top before it's cooled off. When these are concerns, you're getting to the point where supervised care is needed for your loved one.

Pet Care

Pets make a huge difference in anyone's life, but for aging adults or ill people, pets can be the lifeline that gives them purpose and keeps them motivated to wake up and function each day. Pets are a source of love, touch, and affection and may provide physical stimulation through petting. Taking a pet out for a walk is a reason to get outside in sunshine and air, a way to get some exercise. Caring and loving another living thing provides distraction, laughs, and even pain relief. In essence, a pet often gives a lonely older person a reason to live.

But when physical or mental issues compromise care of pets, it can be a source of frustration for the humans involved and detrimental to the well-being of the animal.

Helping a parent remain independent can be aided by making sure pets are cared for.

Some tools to make things easier include:

- Self-cleaning litter box
- Auto feeders
- Water drip servers
- In/out flap doors
- Wee pads
- Automatic ball shooters (for pets that like to fetch or chase)
- Balls or toys on a fishing line for animal to chase (for allowing resident to sit while engaging animal in physical play and activity)

If your parent has an animal, you'll want to have the necessary resources and contact info on hand. You never know when you and your parent will need to leave the home urgently, or if you'll be away for extended amount of time, or if someone is too ill to manage care of a pet.

If your parent's animal gets ill, you'll need a veterinarian on call. If you don't live in the area, you might need someone who does house calls, so finding the right vet is imperative. You can usually find these types of people under "Mobile Veterinary Services" with a search online.

If your parent is called away for any reason and someone needs to take care of the animal(s), you'll want a few people on your contact list. Some people can handle multiple tasks on this list:

- Dog Walker
- Feed & Water services
- Litter changing
- Grooming (long nails or knotted hair, bathing/shampoo/dry)
- Pet Day Care (perhaps your caregiver is afraid of cats or dogs and you need your animal out of the house during the day)
- Pet Sitting (can be in your home or at the sitter's home or at a facility)

NOTES

CAREGIVERS IN THE HOME

For comfort, familiarity with environment and routines of the surrounding people and community, or possibly to be near long-time friends and neighbors, staying at home is a healthy way to live. Financially, especially if the home is already paid for and no major renovations are needed, it is most cost-effective to remain in the home—IF one is able to safely manage on one's own.

If you cannot be with your parent all the time, a companion care person to sit with your parent is not available or doesn't provide enough care, and Adult Day Care is not the solution, you will want to have interviewed several agencies to find a paid caregiver (a.k.a. home health aide, HHA, or simply, aide) who fits your budget and your requirements for someone who will be in your home either part-time or full-time.

You can also research home health aide and nursing schools in your area to find individuals who just finished their program who are looking for independent work before they start with an agency.

Check around and see who other people in your neighborhood or family are using for care. Collect names and numbers, interview them, and have the information handy for when you eventually need it.

Be aware that even when you find an agency and you might find someone you really like—a perfect fit—sometimes it doesn't work out exactly like you think it will.

Rosemarie has regular aides for her mother, Marie. The full-time aide covers Marie's care 24/7 during the week. On the weekends Rosemarie stays with her mother during the day and aides take the overnight shifts.

The full-time live-in aide had a family situation and needed to take a few days off during the week. Rosemarie works and could only take the night shifts with her mother. So, she called the agency that she had used many times before to ask for some help.

A lovely woman appeared. Well dressed, well spoken, sweet, and mature—someone Rosemarie's mother could relate to. The two women met and seemed to get along wonderfully. Rosemarie was relieved.

Rosemarie came to check in on her mother at the end of the first day the temp aide was there and found her mother anxiously waiting at the door for Rosemarie to enter. Her mother was making frantic motions with her hands, circling her head (the kids symbol for "cuckoo for cocoa puffs") and pointing into the house, whispering, "She's crazy! That woman is nuts!"

As Rosemarie made her way into the house, she saw the lovely aide she had interviewed sitting on the leather couch watching television. The aide waved hello from the couch.

As Rosemarie came fully into the room and could see the front of the couch, she could see that the aide was not wearing any clothing from the waist down!

Taken aback, Rosemarie asked the aide what was happening. A confusing conversation ensued where it was apparent that the aide had no clue where she was or that she was half-naked.

Rosemarie was thinking about how she was going to clean that woman's butt off the leather couch while she packed the woman up and called the agency to come get this aide who was, she assured the woman on the other end of the phone, "in more need of care than my mother!"

Meanwhile, the half-naked aide was trying to leave the house to get into her car to drive home. She was using Rosemarie's mother's walker! Rosemarie had to play nursemaid and wait until someone from the agency could come and retrieve their employee.

So, best of intentions and all seemed fine, but you just want to stay aware, stay informed, and be involved!

Once parental caregiving is needed, one has to look at the home through new eyes. Is the space safe? Is the community safe? Are there people who can help in time of crisis or need? If the answers are all for the good, then here are some tips to navigate home caregiving:

As discussed earlier:

❖ Create systems for daily living to keep stress down. Put all the tools and devices in place to make daily living and independence possible.

❖ Create a schedule for daily living. Routine is critical to feelings of security and comfort. A daily schedule with slight variations for doctor visits and other important errands can be written up and posted or put into a calendar.

Plus…

❖ Provide schedules to paid caregivers/aides. When staff come to help with caregiving, it's best to provide them with a schedule in writing. Their adherence to the schedule is critical to the well-being of your loved one. Having the same thing happening, whether it's you there or an aide or a friend, is what makes people feel empowered and independent. Knowing what's coming next is reassuring.

Keep a caregiver shift log. Your written instructions for any changes to the schedule go in the log and your aide initials that it's been read at the beginning of each shift. Even if you have multiple paid aides each day, each of them should be reading the same thing. If there are questions, it is the aide's job to contact you to clarify.

Write instructions for aide shifts if something is new to the routine or added to the schedule:

❖ Is the aide supposed to get Mom dressed and ready at the door by a certain time for you to retrieve her?

❖ Is the aide supposed to bring Dad to the restaurant where he'll meet you?

❖ Does Mom need an adult diaper put on before bed now?

The aide in the house can also write in any incidents that occurred so the next shift will be properly informed to make decisions. You get to read this information when you next review the book.

❖ Keep a medical history log book. In addition to all the medicines, dosages, and schedules, the aides and all caregivers should record each doctor's visit and any medical procedure that was completed. It's important to include all blood tests and X-rays and the resulting reports or copies and keep any CDs with image results provided to you by the doctor in a pocket or envelope. Each shift, the aide(s) should record any symptoms or variance from routine (i.e., if your parent spits out medications, refuses to eat, is unusually thirsty or has excessive need to use the bathroom suddenly).

Compliance with keeping this log book up to date reduces the risk that you or a doctor will be missing critical information in an emergency or to diagnose new symptoms.

Compensating Caregivers/Aides

If you have hired someone through an agency, you should expect to receive an invoice on a regular basis. You will be asked to sign off on the aide's hours either daily or weekly—depending upon responsibilities, aide's schedule, and the agency.

Tipping is up to you. If the aides are coming every week, then tipping at holidays, or a birthday for example, or if there was something exceptional done (e.g., putting in unexpected extra hours, flexibility with schedule changing, a week where your loved one was very difficult) would be appropriate. Otherwise, it is up to your discretion as to whether you want to tip the aides. It is not required. In fact, it is best to check with the agency first to see if they have any policies on tipping or gifts. You don't want any misunderstandings.

If the idea of tipping with cash makes you uncomfortable but you want to say thank you, consider a personal gift that you know the aide would like (stationery, a journal book, a gift certificate to a favorite place, or gift card for coffee). We all like to be appreciated. Finding a good fit with an aide and your parent is wonderful and letting them know that their work is valued, especially with a nice note, goes a long way to keeping your loved one well cared for with a consistent staff.

Treating your aide like part of the family is another way to keep them consistently working with your parent(s).

Laura and Cheryl are both aides for Maribel. Maribel is ninety-something years old. She always has a smile on her face, wears too much lipstick, is very heavily perfumed, dresses impeccably, and loves her two aides as much as party food! Maribel's only relative is a nephew across the country in California, so her aides are her family. Laura and Cheryl arranged to do a split shift. Laura lives with Maribel from Sunday through Thursday morning. Cheryl lives with Maribel from Thursday through Sunday morning. They alternate the extra night each week. They bring Maribel to their own homes for holidays, so they can be with their own families and Maribel gets a special night out as part of a family. The two aides have been working with Maribel for over five years. Everyone involved seems delighted with the arrangement.

Finding Help

If you hire a freelance aide, you should consider doing a criminal background check. Wiki How has a description of how you can do this as an individual. wikihow.com/Do-a-Criminal-Background-Check. Consider including a drug screening.

When hiring an individual, be sure you have a back-up plan in case your aide cannot make it or resigns suddenly one day.

However, if you are hiring through an agency, then you want to screen the agency first, making sure they have enough experience and are licensed in your state. Be sure to check references, look at reviews on the web, and make sure they don't have any citations with the Better Business Bureau or other government agencies. Look into the owners of the agency and their backgrounds as well.

Examine the agreement/paperwork carefully and make sure you understand *all* of the agency's terms. Take it to a lawyer before signing if you don't think something is right or if it is unclear. Ask about how the agency trains their staff. Do their staff get trained on the specific issues your loved one has? If your loved one has dementia and the agency specializes in cancer patients or people with mobility issues, you might have a poor fit for the services needed. Knowing what to expect comes from experience and training.

How much do you want to pay? If you hire through an agency, the agency takes a percentage of the hourly billing rate. If you pay directly to the aide, the aide earns more money per hour. However, the agency may provide health insurance, liability insurance, and vacation for the aide whereas an independent aide does not have that coverage. And, when you have an independent aide, if he or she is ill or has an emergency, you are on your own to find a replacement, whereas an agency will provide someone else to fill in. And finally, if you hire an independent aide, you would be best covered by including a workman's compensation rider to your homeowner's insurance policy.

Working with Medicare or Medicaid, there are different rules as to what services are covered. There are various requirements that have to be met in order to be eligible. Long-term care insurance and Veterans Administration benefits also limit what is covered and what can be reimbursed. Knowing the services and how many hours you need will help you wade through the tremendous decisions and find the right fit and make sure that the bills get paid properly. Each state has different rules and requirements, so it's best to talk to an insurance broker within the service area.

What you need to know before looking for an aide:

* What kind of personality would your parent feel most comfortable around?
* What is your budget?
* How many hours a week would you like coverage for?
* If your aide cannot keep their shift, will you have coverage?
* What will the person be doing for your loved one?
* What ADLs are needed? (activities of daily living: grooming, dressing, bathing, toileting)
* Are mobility tasks required? (moving parent from bed to chair, bed to wheelchair or walker, in/out of a vehicle)

❖ Do you need someone who drives, has their own car, and is willing to drive your parent?

❖ Will your aide handle errands? (taking parent shopping, to doctors, other appointments)

❖ Will your aide provide companionship?

❖ Is your aide licensed to provide medication management? (giving pills, injections, applying creams, etc.)

❖ Can your aide assist your parents with exercises? (rehabilitation, mobility, stretching, general fitness)

❖ Will your aide provide cooking and/or feeding, light housekeeping, and/or simple "handyman" tasks?

Are there preferences for any specialties the aide you hire should have? For example, is the aide:

❖ Able to work with the blind

❖ Familiar with sign language

❖ Able to work with an autistic person

❖ Fluent in a required language

❖ Familiar with a potential source of trauma (combat, Holocaust, physical or sexual or emotional abuse, rape)

❖ Familiar with dietary restrictions (vegan, kosher, halal, vegetarian, diabetes, gluten free, lectin free, paleo, keto)

❖ Familiar with religious restrictions or traditions (Jewish, Christian, Muslim, etc.)

❖ Comfortable around animals

Ask the agency questions about things that are specific to your parents' needs. For example, my father wears hearing aids and has difficulty understanding anyone with an accent (except if they are from Brooklyn or the Bronx; he understands that accent just fine!). Rosemarie's mother is from Italy originally and can lapse into Italian sometimes. Barb's mother is a Holocaust survivor and has nightmares and wakes up screaming, looking for her family or fighting off an advance by a Nazi soldier. Caregivers each have some specialty or background that can either clash with or match your parents' needs.

Does the aide for your parent need to:

❖ Be female or male or is either sex okay?

❖ Work overnight shifts?

❖ Work on weekends?

❖ Work full-time or part-time?

❖ Live-in/live-out?

❖ Follow certain cleanliness policies?

❖ Do any cleaning, laundry, or cooking?

Lynda, an attractive, diminutive, spunky German woman who had just lost her husband, was fighting lupus and living with COPD when she tripped on her 50-foot oxygen cord going to the bathroom one night and fractured her elbow and shoulder. She went through aide after aide because the aides left crumbs on the kitchen counter, ate in the living room in front of the television, left food in the garbage pail in the kitchen overnight, or cooked "smelly" food. Everyone has personal preferences and letting an agency know these in advance can help the agency make a better match. And it can keep your parent from feeling uncomfortable with a "stranger" in the house.

To get pretty close to what you want/need from an agency, here are a few tips:

- Be as specific as you can. For example, offer a typical daily schedule and what you expect the aide to provide overall (e.g., Mom wakes around 6 a.m. and gets into bed around 9 p.m.; drive Mom to hairstylist weekly; make sure Mom takes her medicine at the right time; prepare meals for breakfast and lunch daily; maintain neat home free of clutter; select Mom's clothing and lay it out on bed while she's in shower; tune into Mom's favorite TV shows when requested, etc.)
- The home "rules:" We have a kosher home or we follow a vegan/Muslim/diabetic lifestyle so you may not bring x, y, z into our home. We do not permit smoking in the house. Mom is allergic to wool, etc.
- Extras: Caregiver may drive our car to take Mom on errands only. OR caregiver needs to have a car to take Mom on errands and to doctor's visits. Caregiver needs to have back-up support for her own family matters at her home so she can be at work on time every day.

Provide input and feedback to agency:

- If something happens, let the agency know.
- If you're not happy, let the agency know while it's still fixable.
- Have the agency manage conversations about service delivery with the aide. You avoid getting the aide angry at you or your parent.
- If you're not happy with the aide, ask the agency to replace the aide. It may take you a few aides until you find the magic connection.

What to expect from a home health aide:

Mostly, a paid caregiver/aide will assist your parent with effective and safe personal care and keep your parent clean, comfortable, and safe.

You can expect an aide to check vitals at the beginning of each visit. This may include:

- Temperature
- Pulse
- Respiration
- Blood pressure

Based on the diagnosis of your parents' health status, in addition to companion care, your aide may provide personal care assistance including:

- Bathing—tub or shower, sponge bath, assistance to get in and out of tub/shower
- Clothing/dressing
- Hair care: brush/comb, shampoo, and dry
- Skin care
- Foot care
- Check pressure areas
- Shaving/grooming
- Nail hygiene (but they won't typically cut nails)
- Oral care: brushing/flossing/swab/dentures
- Toileting assistance
- Catheter care
- Ostomy—empty bag
- Recording input/output from toileting
- Transferring/ambulation assistance
- Range of motion—active/passive
- Positioning—encouraging and assisting client to move/turn
- Exercise (per a care plan provided)
- Assist with feeding
- Prepare foods (based on orders/requests)
- Limit or encourage fluids (based on orders)

Your aide will be looking to follow precautions and make sure the home is safe and equipment is working properly, watching your parent for signs of distress and attention needed:

- Falls
- Seizures
- Oxygen (breathing)
- Aspiration
- Weight-bearing movements
- Bleeding

If you have a nurse, CNA (Certified Nursing Assistant), or PA (Physician Assistant) rather than a Home Health Aide, the tasks and responsibilities may be expanded to include more medical duties. While an aide can't touch medication and can only help your parent lift a hand to take medicine, a nurse can sort and deliver medicines or inject medication for a patient. A nurse can insert a new colostomy connection and bag whereas aides can keep the bag area clean. A nurse can change wound care dressings that require medication/treatment whereas an aide can put on fresh bandages.

Be aware that there are strict standards for what each type of aide can offer for a client. The agency you work with and/or your doctor will determine the best selection/skill level for your parents' care. You may wind up with a nurse for a quick visit and then an aide for ongoing care in some situations.

Keeping "THE One"

When you find an aide who your parent likes; someone who is reliable, trustworthy, consistent, and you're happy with the services delivered, you've found treasure! Especially if your parent is ornery or has difficult health issues, do all you can to hang on to this person!

Some suggestions:

Keep lines of communication open. Communicate your expectations. Share when you are happy with the aide's work. If there are issues, talk to the agency and/or calmly discuss them; set the requested behaviors in writing to be sure everything is clear. Offer regular chats to answer any questions or address any needs that arise; anything you can provide to make the job easier would be helpful toward making an aide feel valued and heard.

Give professional aides information on when, how often, and how to contact you for any decision-making needed. Provide an alternate contact person if you can't be reached.

Advise the aide of any potential schedule changes or issues far in advance. Give someone time to plan for lack of income because you are going with your parent out of town, or your parent is going into surgery and will be in the hospital for recovery and will be spending time in a rehab facility or will be taking a vacation. Anything that could impact the life of the aide, share early. Confirm in writing if possible.

If the aide is preparing meals and never gets to sit down and eat with her client, it's a disconnect. Sharing food is a bonding experience. Eating together doesn't have to be a regular thing, but it's nice to offer. However, if the agency that pays the aide has a policy against eating with the client, then your aide will appreciate the offer but may refrain. Nothing personal.

Barbara, a member of a caregiver group, kept sharing stories about how the aides for her mother were sleeping on the overnight shift, not paying attention to her wandering mother who was trying to get out the front door (one time successfully gaining exit and wandering into the street naked). Her mother was not making it to the bathroom because the aides were reading and listening to music in another room. It turns out that Barb was yelling at the aides through a camera where she watched them, directing them to do this and that. There was a constant turnover with aides in that home. And while there's no excuse for mistreating a client the way that they did, if you want your aides to treat your loved one with dignity, they have to feel that they are being treated with dignity and respect back. If dozens of aides are working only a few days before moving on to other assignments and they don't want to come back, one might want to examine the reasons why so many people are unwilling to continue working in your environment.

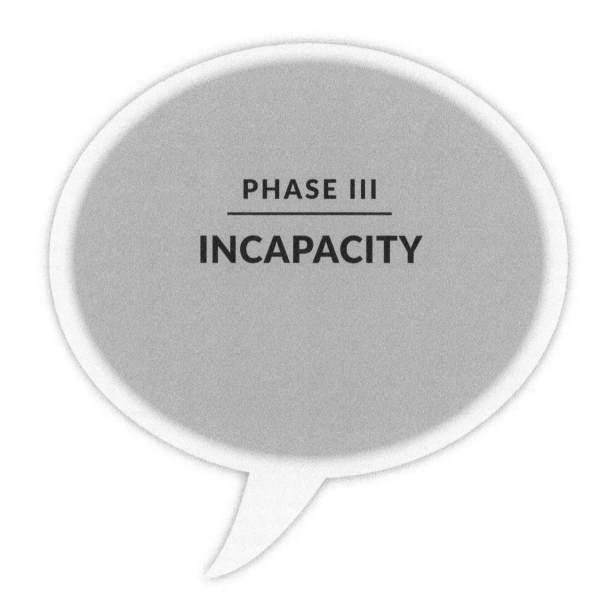

NOTES

As your parent becomes more fragile, possibly more disoriented, their care level and the need for supervision grows. This is the time when you might be feeling a bit overwhelmed and possibly find yourself sad and depressed because the parent you knew is changing and your role is evolving into more parental duties. Patience is the key word here.

This is the most difficult phase for me, I have to admit. As my parents are entering this phase and I can see the signs…there are days I wish my parents would not be aware that they have so much going wrong. My father, in particular, gets angry when he isn't walking straight, or forgets things, or can't hear people, or doesn't understand what people are asking of him. His eyes teared up when he didn't understand his standard deduction tax return—and he used to be a tax consultant. My mother doesn't realize that we just a had a very bizarre conversation about a jar of mayonnaise because half the conversation was happening somewhere else in her head and did not involve me at all. I have to tell myself, "It's the disease. Let it go," all the time.

My new mantra is PUT. I say *Put, Put, Put, Put,* like a train going up a hill…all the time. It means Patience, Understanding, and Tolerance. I am reminding myself that my parents are not the same people they were even a year ago and nothing that is happening is directed at me personally, but is more because of the disease and their emotional reaction to being less than they were.

What you might see now with your parent:

- ❖ Needs help getting dressed, handling grooming
- ❖ Requires assistance to get in or out of bed
- ❖ Motor stiffness: May not be able to hold utensils or objects in hands
- ❖ Requires assistance with eating and using toilet, bathing
- ❖ Medication needs monitoring; someone needs to supervise pill time and swallowing
- ❖ Disorientation to time, place, people's names/faces
- ❖ May not know self
- ❖ Difficulty concentrating; challenges with reading, watching television/movies, etc.
- ❖ Falling asleep in chair; wanting to sleep more often
- ❖ Speech loss, hearing loss, vision loss
- ❖ Possibly more UTIs, dehydration, sores, anxiety, stress

Once parents can't answer for themselves or care for their own daily needs, you can help by arranging for the items listed in the charts called WAYS YOU CAN HELP A MENTALLY DECLINING PARENT and WAYS YOU CAN HELP A PHYSICALLY DECLINING PARENT (pages 56–60), which were elaborated on in the previous chapters. Additional thoughts:

Specific Situations

When mobility issues or dizziness/vertigo/light-headedness appear (not in chronological order):

- ❖ Apply for handicapped parking permit, even if you or the aide is doing the driving
- ❖ Get information and register your parent for Silver Alert Program if you're worried your parent might pass out somewhere
- ❖ Remove rugs
- ❖ Add grab bars in key areas (especially bathrooms, perhaps in hallways)
- ❖ Remove items on the floor, especially near corners and doorways
- ❖ Keep cabinet doors and closets closed or remove the doors, if access is limited
- ❖ Convert tub/shower into easy walk-in access
- ❖ Add seat in shower/tub
- ❖ Install a transfer seat if your parent isn't strong enough to lift from toilet to shower on his own
- ❖ Change showerhead to handheld (in case aide needs to help with bathing)
- ❖ Adjust the toilet seat to a "comfort" level that allows your parent to sit and then stand without difficulty
- ❖ Put liquid soaps in push pump and hang sponges/wash cloths in shower
- ❖ Place heater or fans in bathrooms especially, but throughout house for customized temp control
- ❖ Add bumper guards on edges of tables and pointy furniture
- ❖ Remove glass-edged furniture (visibility could be an issue)
- ❖ Hang grab tools, canes, and supplies at seated chest level for easy access
- ❖ Consider a lift chair that gently moves your parent to a standing position from a seated one
- ❖ Install ramps where there are stairs for access to home and/or patio/deck/terrace
- ❖ Add saddles between rooms for smooth transition with walker, cane, or wheelchair; avoid tripping
- ❖ Add decals at eye level on sliding or glass doors to avoid accidentally walking into the glass
- ❖ Add slip protection mat or decals on the floor of the shower/tub

When a Wheelchair is Needed:

- ❖ Remove lower cabinet doors so your parent can pull up to sinks, desks, counters, etc.
- ❖ Consider bedside portable potty to reduce nighttime accidents
- ❖ Install a rear carry lift for car to carry power scooter or non-folding wheelchair
- ❖ Get a portable transfer wheelchair (narrower and lighter weight) to get in and out of car at various locations and have electric/power wheelchair in the home

If the parent is fully capable and aware but has only a mobility issue, consider outfitting the car with hand driving controls. Note: A special driving permit will be required. Also, check on insurance rates.

For images of these tools and updates on currently available gadgets and devices, visit our webpage at IllBeRightThere.com.

WHEN STAYING HOME IS
NO LONGER AN OPTION

You've done as much as you can to maintain the status quo for your loved one to remain in their familiar home, but now it seems that this is no longer an option. You may have tried Adult Day Care. It could be that your parent is living in your home and it's causing havoc within your family or becoming detrimental to your own health and well-being. You may be having trouble keeping aides and the rotation of new people is causing issues; or physical care requires a more monitored setting; or there are episodes of acting out, mental decline, mood changes, or physical issues that require more attention. Whatever the reason, you recognize that it's time to consider alternatives.

Making the decision to move your parents is full of possible contention and discontent. People already having memory issues can actually exhibit more symptoms and accelerated loss when thinking about leaving behind all that with which they are familiar. The earlier you make these decisions, the more agreeable the process, the better the end result.

As with my family, you might start with merging homes. This could mean moving from having seasonal homes to becoming a full-time resident in one place.

Another possibility is moving someone into your home or a sibling's home. I've heard of people who move one parent between siblings by season, or quarter, or year so that everyone is involved and taking some of the responsibility as well as getting to spend time with the aging family member. How well this works fully depends on your family dynamic and the acceleration of any disease.

The variety of options for paid housing and care to choose from is comprehensive. Each has a different purpose. Here are some of the most commonly available:

Independent Living: Ideal when you parent can live on their own but would rather be in a secure and social setting. Here, your parent will have the ability to attend programs and events without needing transportation and will enjoy the benefits of maintenance-free housing. A ready-made community of people in a similar situation can alleviate loneliness and isolation. This is valuable when friends and relatives are all passing away or have moved.

SUPPORTIVE HOUSING OPTIONS

Assisted Living: Here, your parent will be living in his or her own apartment or in a group setting. The on-site staff will help with ADLs (activities of daily living) and with household chores as well as medical support for taking prescriptions, doctor visits, nutrition, and related health services.

Nursing Home: This type of facility is best for those who require ongoing medical care with doctors, nurses, physical therapists, social workers, dietitians, etc. Care is provided around the clock in a secure facility. Typically, the resident is in a single or in a shared-room situation.

Memory Care: When someone has dementia-related signs, whether from aging or a specific disease, a memory care center is a safe space that eliminates the stress of wandering and getting lost. The specialized staff provide challenging cognitive focused activities all day long to keep your parents' abilities as sharp as possible, for as long as possible. Dining is supervised and assistance is provided. All daily living skills are guided by staff.

Rehabilitation Center: A stay in a residential rehab center may be short-term, such as after a hospital stay, to rebuild strength. Or, it may be long-term for individuals who are no longer able to get around without assistance and need persistent physical therapy and supervision.

Hospice Care: If the reason you're ready to move a parent is because of an accident or illness, hospice is designed for someone unlikely to recover from an illness or injury. When someone is told by the medical profession that he or she does not have long and that person is possibly in great pain or discomfort, hospice is a dignified way to be cared for and nurtured, pain free, until one passes.

Who can help you make these decisions? There are so many residential options to consider that it can be overwhelming (even if you have full-time flexibility) to go and scout out what works. Luckily, a whole industry has risen to help—from online to in-person help.

Web-based registration services offer help. They collect your information and needs through a questionnaire and soon after you will be getting calls and emails from facilities in the community you select with the benefits and services you've identified.

If you'd rather work with an individual, there are professionals in every market who can help you find the right place. They get paid by the venue, so there is typically no cost to you. They may go by the title of Lifestyle Consultant or Senior Referral Service or Senior Placement Counselor.

Before making a decision, you'll want to create a list of parameters; your "Must Have" and "Would Like" lists. To figure out your parameters, look at the daily life and lifestyle of the person who will be moving.

First, where do you want this new residence to be? Identify the most desirable neighborhoods (proximity to you, centered between family members, close to current doctors or medical/research centers, near a favored house of worship or volunteer work, near friends and support network). Make a circle on a map around that specific area and try to target a new residence within the optimal zone and then start to span out by five-mile increments to find something within a reasonable distance from optimal if the facility/residence comes with more benefits or better pricing.

Try asking yourself questions like these to fill out your criteria search list:

❖ Are there amenities that are important to your loved one? How about activities?

❖ Is transportation needed to bring your parent to doctors and to other appointments or do you need all medical services available in-house?

❖ What kind of medical services might be needed and do the places on your "visit" list have them available? How do those services get billed?

When I first started to search, my father needed to walk every day, preferably outside. A walking trail that is visible to staff (not going off campus) was therefore critical. My mother enjoys exercising in the pool. Thus, a pool was critical, preferably with aquatic classes. A fitness center with treadmills and exercise equipment was not going to be enough for either of them.

In comparison, my friend Rosemarie's mother loves to sing, so karaoke-style programming and entertainment are important to her.

Check the small print carefully. If you're looking to move in some place quickly, you might not take the time to read everything thoroughly. Make sure that the deposit you pay to hold an apartment or to be on the waiting list is credited properly. Find out about any move-in fees, premium apartment extras, non-refundable deposits, entertainment or social dues (not common), and/or security fees. Are there any other incidental charges or taxes added to the bill each month in a rental? Make sure you know every fee involved because that will be important in your budgeting process.

If You Think A Move Is Necessary

If you wait to do research until you desperately need a residential option for your parents, you might run into some issues, as explained to me by a Psychiatric Nurse Practitioner, Madeline, at the Green Memory Center in Boca Raton, Florida. Madeline said that she has had clients come to her frustrated that they couldn't get in where they wanted to because they waited so long that when they were ready, a room was not available and, rather than being able to wait for the right fit, they needed to find something immediately and had to settle elsewhere.

Some clients bemoaned having to move their loved one several times because they needed a new service (memory care, rehab, nursing care) that wasn't offered at the first residence. Or that they ran out of money at the private pay community and needed to move the loved one to a Medicaid facility.

One spouse found out that she couldn't live with her husband who needed memory care, so they had to find two separate spaces at different facilities, which made visiting much more difficult and expensive.

Tour Independent, Assisted, and Nursing care facilities before they are needed. Eliminate all the ones that don't meet your criteria and keep a list of the ones you like handy for if/when the time comes.

If you absolutely love a place and they have a waiting list, put your name on it. You can always politely decline if a spot opens before you need it, but you will remain at the top of the list for the next available slot until you are actually ready.

Make sure you discuss the expense and budget options with your financial planner before making a decision, so you have a realistic view of how long existing funds will last based on the costs of the facilities you are considering.

Considerations when comparing residences:

- Research the company's reputation in the community (and possibly nationwide if they are part of a large management group).
- Ask about staff turnover.
- Observe the staff—do they look overwhelmed, frustrated, annoyed? Or do they look engaged and happy, interacting with residents and each other?
- Observe the faces of the residents you see while on tour—do they look happy? Engaged? Or cranky?
- Do staff members greet you as you walk through the building? Do you observe staff talking to residents or brushing right by them? Does staff seem to know residents' names?
- Is the place clean? (Check the bathroom near the dining room and/or in the lobby.)
- Is the place going through construction or is construction planned in the near future?
- Try the food. Most residences will set up a complimentary dinner or lunch for you and the potential resident.
- What is included in the monthly fee? How often do the fees increase?
- Do they accept health insurance or long-term care plans? What happens when/if you run out of money?
- What additional services are offered that might be needed down the road? Are they in the same building, on the same campus, or linked via a relationship but located off campus?

COMPARING AND CHOOSING
RESIDENTIAL OPTIONS

If you search on the web, you will find many styles of checklists for taking tours of senior residence facilities. Compiled from several lists, aside from aesthetics and pricing, here are some of the most common things people compare from place to place:

Location: Do you need the facility to be close to you for visiting ease? Or does it need to be near existing doctors? Should it be near the water or up in the mountains? Is climate a concern? Is a view critical?

Food: What is the meal plan like? Dress code in dining room? Formal (jacket and slacks for men), semi-formal (long pants and collared shirts), casual (nice shorts and dressy tees okay), or no dress code (come in whatever)? What are the food service options (buffet, waitstaff, takeout, delivery, special needs attended to)? Sit anywhere or assigned seating? Sit on your own or be invited to join with another table? Set dining times, make a reservation, or open/any time dining (e.g., you can eat breakfast food at lunch or dinner, lunch at 3 p.m. if you want)?

Grounds: Do you want a view? Does the complex/building have lush gardens (well maintained), water areas (lakes, fountains, ponds, waterfalls), outdoor sitting areas, shaded gazebos, barbecue area, walking trails? Driveways and roadways clear of debris, no potholes or big cracks? Garbage areas well-hidden? Building paint fresh or old and tired/chipping? Evidence of mold, slime build up, or rot anywhere?

Security: Is there a guard gate? A receptionist to clear before entering the building? Locked doors (24 hours or night only)? Apartment keys coded to track entry to apartments? Windows on ground floor secure? Windows on upper floors locked or anti-fall protected? Windows and patio doors secure for storms (snow, hurricane, tornado)? Do residents wear a tracker? Is there a code to enter or leave the building or their apartment? Check-in required by residents, so staff know who's on the premises in an emergency?

Services: Laundry—weekly service (linens only or all laundry included) or washer/dryer for self-service in apartment or laundry room on the floor?

Transportation: Are there free shuttles and driver services to get your parent to shopping, doctors, recreation/entertainment activities (museums, theater, sports games), day trips, airport/train stations, religious services? What is the distance they will take you? What is the process for booking a time? Is there on-site parking? Assigned spaces? Is there valet service? Where do guests park? What are the charges if not free for any of these?

Utilities: What's included in the price? Cable/TV, phone, internet/Wi-Fi, electric, water, trash, sewer, gas, heat, etc.

Pets: Are pets allowed? Is there a size or weight restriction? Are there any fees related to having a pet? What are the rules? If you're allergic to animals, are pets allowed in common areas or dining halls?

Health Services: Is there a clinic, a nurse, a physical therapist, or doctor on-site or visiting? Is healthcare in the apartment available? How is this billed? What's included? How are emergency situations handled by the staff? What happens if you have your own doctor visiting? Are there regular visits from "house" specialists (e.g., podiatrist, dermatologist, allergist)?

Assistance Services: Can you bring in your own aide? Do they have aides to hire? Are there limits to the amount of time you can have an aide in your apartment or on the premises?

Accommodations: What are the sizes of apartments available? Apartment, house, villa, etc.? Single or with roommate? Can couples stay together? How many bathrooms? Bathtub or walk-in shower or both?

Safety Features: Do you have a speaker system to call for help? Can the staff notify residents in their apartments via speaker? Is there an emergency pull cord in the bathroom and near the bed? Emergency alert system for self and/or residence? Fall detection systems? Smoke detector serviced by building staff? Sprinklers? Hurricane or tornado pressure glass? Locked windows or doors? Fire or storm evacuation plan? Power outage plan? Back-up generator and food will last how long?

Activities: Crafts (needlework, quilting, papier-mâché, woodworking, model making), Arts Oriented (music, theater, painting, photography), Literary (library, book clubs, lectures), Outdoors (hiking, walking trails, cycling, gardening), Mechanical (auto, boat, tech toys), Social (discussions, holiday parties, celebrations for milestones, live entertainment, cards/games), Religious (services, chaplain, prayer or meditation space), Tech (internet café, computer center).

Convenience: On-site banking, sundries shop, mini grocery market, salon/barber shop, manicure/pedicures, massage/facials.

Fitness: Personal training, exercise classes, fitness supervision. Is there a pool with aqua exercise classes?

Guests: Guest apartments, guest passes for facilities, guest dining privileges and fees.

Energy/Comfort: Is light important? Exposure of apartment could be critical to mood. Number of windows/sliding doors? Is a breeze important? Do you need overhead fans in the apartment? Ability to open windows/doors? Would you want/need a terrace or big windows that open? Need to be near elevators?

Typically (but not always), the more services and staff required, the higher the cost will be. Not everyone needs everything offered, so finding a place with the majority of your "needs" and some of your "wants" within your budget is the goal.

Once you've created a way to eliminate a bunch of choices and target the right ones, you'll have the questions to ask the facilities when you tour or talk on the phone.

One suggestion: Make a list or a chart so you can look back later and compare apples to apples. If every facility provides the answers to the same questions, it's easier to see the differences. Plus, take it from my experience, after a while, they all start to blend in and you forget what one person said vs. another! A chart or a form you fill out for each venue will help you keep your facts straight. At the end of this chapter I've included my own comparison cheat sheet for your review as a sample.

Can I Afford to Move My Parent?

Set up a chart to compare what your parent is spending now to the savings and expenses that come with the new places you are considering.

* Factor in housekeeping, laundry, food, utilities, taxes, insurance, healthcare costs, maintenance services, fees for social activities, transportation, etc.
* Calculate with income from social security, pensions, interest income, plus IRA, stock portfolios, and all other investments and savings.
* If you sell the house, car, other property, etc., and invest that money, how long could your parent afford to live in the places you've selected?

This is where that financial planning professional can become extremely valuable! Plus, you might learn enough at a visit with an elder law attorney to help you plan correctly to make your assets last longer.

Don't forget to factor in the cost for you, as a caregiver, and how that impacts the financial picture. If taking care of your parent has caused you to lose income or required you to stop working altogether, then how does your being able to go back to work impact this picture?

If caregiving is wearing you down and your doctors or family think you're heading for a breakdown (emotional or physical), then what is the result of you being unable to take on a caregiving role going to look like? How much is the value of your own health?

If your parents cannot afford the full cost of a facility on their own, are there VA benefits available? Can you and your siblings contribute a little to supplement what your parents do have?

I spent a lot of time trying to figure out what made sense for my parents. I am not a financial wizard. I hate number crunching. I can do it, but it doesn't come easily to me. I finally figured out how to boil it down to some basics. On the most simplistic level, maybe this will help you get started with a rough number. Your financial planner will get you something far more accurate for your situation.

1: Annual fixed income (SSI, Pensions) + Annual IRA and dividend distribution + Annual salary/work income = Total cash/income per year
2: Savings available divided by the number of years you are estimated to live = Annual savings distribution
3: Taxes on your taxable income (15%, 25%, more?)

Total Income (1+2) − Taxes you have to pay (3) = Amount you can afford each year if you live the predicted amount of years for your profile

Go to ssa.gov/oact/population/longevity.html to calculate life expectancy based just on gender and birth year.

Try http://apps.goldensoncenter.uconn.edu/HLEC/ for a more complex formula based on lifestyle habits.

Once you know what you have to work with, then you have to factor in your expenses. Costs of monthly fee for a residence plus medical out of pocket expenses (prescriptions, aides, deductibles, supplemental insurance plan fees)+ monthly living expenses (utilities, phones, dry cleaning, housekeeping, repairs, transportation/auto, entertainment, groceries, etc.) = cost of living per month × 12 = annual amount needed to cover your lifestyle.

If these final numbers are not coming out equal or giving you enough leeway for emergencies, consider reducing expenses, reducing taxable income to cut tax costs, or increasing revenue/income options. Talk to your financial planner to help with this!

MY FACILITY COMPARISON CHART AS AN EXAMPLE:

Facility Name	Facility 1	Facility 2	Facility 3	Facility 4
Community	Delray Beach	Boynton Beach	Boynton Beach	Boca Raton
Address				
Contact				
Phone				
Email				
Website				
1 bdrm monthly	$4,411 for 2 people	$7,000 for 2 people	Single Rooms Only	$3,900 per person
2 bdrm monthly	$4,800	NA	NA	NA
Entrance fee	$185–250K	0	0	0
Toilets	1	1	1	1
Independent living	Yes	Yes	No	No
Assisted living	Stay in apartment	Yes—move to different wing	Yes—move to different wing	No
Nursing	Connected	Connected	Yes	No
Rehab	Connected	Connected	Bused	No
Memory	Connected	Connected	Yes	Yes
Mom/dad stay together	Yes	No	No	No
Monthly meals included per person	30 meals monthly	2 per day, per person	3 per day	3 per day
Dining room style	Informal	Formal for dinner	Informal	Informal
Bistro/café on-site	Yes	Yes	No/Snack area	No/Snack area

Facility Name	Facility 1	Facility 2	Facility 3	Facility 4
Take-out	Yes	No	No	No
Room service	No	No	No	No
Sabbath services on-site	Yes, weekly and holiday	No (bus will take you)	Once a month	No
Housekeeping	Weekly	Daily	Weekly	Daily
Laundry	Linens—weekly	All clothes—weekly	All clothes—weekly	Yes—machines available
Utilities (power, water)	Included	Included	Included	Included
Wi-fi	Included	Extra	Extra	No
Cable tv	Included	Included	Included	Not in room
Washer/dryer	In Apartment	Extra	No	No
Stove/oven	In apartment	No	No	No
Microwave	In apartment	In apartment	No	No
Refrigerator size	Full	Counter depth	No	None
Terrace	Screened area	Not really	No	No
View	Scenic available	Options available	Pond possible	No
Walking trail	Yes	No	No	Yes
Van/driver on call	Within 10 miles	Within 10 miles	No	No
Shopping trips per week	3	On demand	No	No
Day trips	Yes	Occasional	Yes	None
Pool (number)	1	None	None	None
Water classes	Yes	Bus to pool and aqua classes	No	No
Fitness center	Yes	Physical therapy	Physical therapy	No
Staff in fitness center	Yes	Yes	Yes	No
Exercise classes	Yes	Yes	Yes	Yes
Notes	Dad can't pass exam: on Namenda and Aricept		Single bed rooms	Memory care only; single bed rooms; shower in room.

MOVING OUT OF THE HOME

Every day, before moving my parents to an independent living community, I looked around at all the "stuff" in their condo. When I sold and closed down their New York condo apartment, it was so difficult to figure out what to keep and what to sell. And, if I wanted to sell anything, it would have taken time to find a buyer for their collections or furniture. Instead, to save time and running around, everything went to consignment and we received a tiny percentage of the real value. At a certain point, with a deadline looming, you are just happy to have any income from your "stuff" instead of paying someone to come and cart it away!

Real Estate Issues You May Face

- ❖ Selling home(s)
- ❖ Financial considerations in planning for future residential needs (long-term care insurance, Medicaid, VA, hospice) benefits and factors to include in decision-making
- ❖ Selling contents of home(s)
- ❖ Merging homes (seasonal residences into one residence)

In the real estate section [see page 225], there is more about selling a home and the options for processing household items in the most time efficient and/or financially rewarding ways. Truthfully, depending on your parents' tax situation, donating your home contents to nonprofit organizations might have more financial benefit than selling things.

Sometimes, you do things that make no logical sense at all, just to keep the peace and create an easier transition. There's a pallet of photographs in boxes sitting in a corner at my brother-in-law's production plant just waiting for my mother to suddenly decide she needs to see some of those images. She'll never look at them. But knowing they are available has made Mom feel secure.

- ❖ What do you have at your parents' place that you want to hang on to?
- ❖ What do your siblings want from the home?
- ❖ What can you do to start preparing for the future? Are your parents open to a discussion about this?

Here's a checklist I found for organizing a home when ready to move. This list comes from a recognized leader in relocating seniors, Moving Station. The Moving Made Easy Checklist includes questions to help you and your parents assess household inventory, what you need, and what you don't, how things function, their quality and condition, and then connects it all to feelings and emotions.

Rules of thumb:

- Get rid of multiples; keep the one that is your favorite and/or has the highest quality
- Take photos of sentimental items that you will be donating or gifting
- Start using your "good" china and crystal as your "everyday" dishes and glasses

Questions to consider:

- How many do I have?
- Have I used it in the last year?
- Can I acquire it again if I need to?
- Do I have enough space in my new home for it?
- How often will I be using it?
- How many would be enough?
- Is it in style and/or current?
- Is it good quality?
- Is it accurate?
- Does it work correctly?
- Is it reliable?
- What are my specific plans to use this item?
- Is this *really* important?
- Can something else perform the same function?
- Would I buy it again if I didn't already have it?
- Can I live without it?
- Do I really "care" about this item?
- Do I want it taking up valuable space in my new home?

Scanning Photos

To clear out tons of paper and save space, use the technology available to save memories and important information without clutter. Start scanning photos, old cards and letters plus legal, real estate, household, and financial papers. Discard originals and keep digital copies.

Scan to reduce clutter but keep important info.

A printer/scanner is not very expensive and would enable you to process a bunch of memories and important documents into a computer or onto a flash stick. A scanner with an OCR (Optical Character Recognition) function will enable you to search your computer by keyword to find all documents with that word. You could also rent a high-speed, high-quality, photo scanner for a few days to get the project done. Perhaps a young student in the family would do the project as part of a family tree homework assignment? Or, you can take the photos to a service that will transfer the photos to digital format in the highest resolution possible.

If money and/or deadlines are no object and spare time is in short supply, you can bring your boxes to a memory center or ship them to an online service. Either will scan your photos and give them back to you in digital format along with the originals. You'll pay a premium if you need quick turnaround (say for a 100th birthday party, family reunion, wedding, or something special).

I did this with about 10,000 slides that had been sitting in a never-opened, very large, tall box (under a designer sheet) in my parents' living room for about 25 years! I culled the collection down to family photos using a light board. I sent 2,500 slides to a service in the South that sent my collection off to India. It took eight weeks to come back, but the DVDs were amazing. I loaded them onto my mother's computer and my parents sat back and just watched a slide show for two hours! Then they said it was so nice, but they would never spend all that time watching again. URGH!! I curated a bunch of the photos from the bigger show (each slide had been converted into a unique jpg file) into a three-and-a-half-minute movie I created with a template in Microsoft. My parents watch that occasionally and I was able to share it on Facebook with other family members to celebrate my parents' 60th anniversary.

You could also play this as a screensaver on a household computer or in a moving picture frame that plays preloaded slide shows from a USB stick.

Photos are not just for hanging on the walls or displaying on the mantel or piano. They can be an integral part of keeping your parent vibrant and connected to love ones.

A social worker recommended that I take some old and current photographs of family and memorable events in our lives and put them into a book with the names of the people and locations. This is a great way to help someone with memory loss to remember names and connect with faces. It's a jumping-off point for your parent to relate stories, happy memories, and anecdotes about "the old days." Stimulating the brain is an important way to keep your parent engaged and healthier. Having a parent be able to tell the stories to children, grandchildren, nieces, and nephews is often a way to open that window into coherence and presence.

If you want to create such a book, there are several memory businesses locally that can take care of this for you. Online you can find Snapfish or Shutterfly (at this writing) or go to Costco or Walmart photo centers. It shouldn't cost that much. My 20-page booklet cost me $10. (I LOVE coupons and discount codes!)

There are professional photo organizers who can manage the whole project for you.[11] And there are some great books on the market that provide additional options for self-organizing. *Photo Organizing Made Easy: Going from Overwhelmed to Overjoyed* by Cathi Nelson is particularly helpful.

I took a family photo taken at my parents' 60th anniversary brunch and turned the photo into a jigsaw puzzle based on a conversation I had with my father's speech therapist. It turns out the pieces of the puzzle I ordered were way too tiny, but my dad was excited when he saw the box. (We worked with other puzzles later that helped him find patterns and colors and shapes to keep his brain working. Look in discount stores for great deals. Especially around holidays. Focus on the children's department.)

---

[11] APPO (Association of Professional Photo Organizers) has a list of certified members sorted by location. https://www.appo.org/search/custom.asp?id=1460

Memorabilia and Special Items

Put things that your parents might want to take with them wherever they go into stackable clear bins or boxes:

Clothing:

- Sort clothing by size, season, decade. Once boxed or hung this way, when you need to pare down for moving day, you'll be prepared.
- Keep most favorite and frequently worn clothing easily accessible.
- Discard anything torn, stained, or frayed.

Bathroom & Kitchen:

- Trash dated/expired products that have no use any longer.
- Reallocate samples collected and stored "in case we have guests" and donate them to a homeless shelter to be distributed to people who can make use of it all! (Especially those hotel mini sizes and cosmetic gift-with-purchase samples you keep saving!)
- Keep most frequently used items labeled and in convenient boxes, trays, drawers, and cabinets with easy access.

Awkward Discoveries

Sometimes the things we unearth during the excavation of our parents' space may bring revelations that are disquieting, to say the least! These discoveries may come when parents move or after our parents pass away. You may find unexpected surprises that bring on all sorts of emotions and "what do we do now" questions.

If your parents are still around do you bring up what you found? Do you keep or discard? Do you ask questions and investigate? What if your opinion of your parent changes because of what you found? Whatever could you be talking about, Fern?

Well, let's imagine all the storylines of Lifetime movies...

- ❖ Records that there's another family hidden somewhere else
- ❖ You're adopted but never knew
- ❖ Your mother or father has had a lover
- ❖ Illegal business dealings have funded your family
- ❖ There was a murder/death you didn't know about
- ❖ Someone had an abortion
- ❖ Your parents were in the witness relocation program
- ❖ There's cash in the wall from illegal drug dealing (okay—I took that one from *Breaking Bad*)
- ❖ You find a *Fifty Shades of Gray* closet/room/drawer
- ❖ There's a dress, heels, and a wig in Dad's closet

And then there's the PORN collection...

I flew to Florida to help my father close out his sister's home after my uncle, Dad's brother-in-law, passed away. My aunt and uncle were proud to be the "odd ducks" in the family—theater-type people with a very private lifestyle. Not seemingly with a lot of friends from what we could discern. And quirky. Way quirky! Loved them so much! Uncle was always sharing dirty jokes and stories. All in good fun.

Going through Uncle's computer was awkward. His porn collection was museum-quality extensive! Quite the connoisseur. Book cases were filled with DVDs, CD-ROMs, VHS tapes, and books. Many of them old and valuable classic porn. Then I found the photo collection. Remember the theater people reference? Imagine that put to good use in private photo sessions!

Going through their bedroom, I was absently wondering how the kitchen could be packed with so many tools for cooking, the extra bedroom had been converted into a survivalist storage locker, but the bedroom had sparse clothing for my aunt and uncle. Folding and packing and thinking, I suddenly jumped back, hands in the air. EWWW I found a rubber vibrating tongue that made a motion of licking. And that was the top of a pile of a lot of interesting devices and fuzzy, pointy, furry, clip-style things.

"Dad, why don't you leave the bedroom to me? I don't think you want to see the stuff your sister has in here!" Dad left the room. Good he did, because the other things I found in that room certainly explained a lot. The closed-off windows around the house? Uh huh, when you're a nudist, why would you want people peeking in!? The reason for their limited clothing options was now clear.

My uncle (in his mid-eighties) was without his wife for about a year before passing away. I found a box of 30 condoms in his nightstand. That's one optimistic old dude! (But at least he was being safe!)

Now this was all my relatives' but not my parents'. What do you do when the stuff you find IS your parents'?

Simon, a writer friend of mine, found erotic literature written by her father and started collecting it. He was famous! His work is valuable. She's writing a book about what it feels like to get into your parent's head and read what he thought about sex. She finds her father's voice and mannerisms in the characters and dialogue of the books he wrote. Questioning if the female characters were conjured up or real. And so on. She's venting her feelings on the written page.

You have to find your own way of processing what you learn. You have to look at how you feel about what you discover. Maybe it was something you just shake your head at and move on. Something you say, "Past is past," and forget about it. It becomes the family "funny story" you tell new friends.

But what if it was something that goes deeper than a porn collection? Something that shifts your thoughts about your family? I suggest that talking with a therapist is probably in order before speaking (or not speaking) with your parent. You're going to want to get your emotions in check, your thoughts fully explored, and think about the outcome of any discussions. What is the goal? If your parents' memory is disappearing and their ability to understand the discussion is diminished, then what do you really accomplish? However, sometimes there are questions that need to be answered and you want to get to that answer before your parents' ability to cognitively respond is gone.

AFTER THE MOVE

Congratulations! You found the place that would be awesome for your parents. Perhaps your parents even agreed that it's the right choice. You've finished the move and your parents are in the new place. Whoo hoo! Things are going to be much better now, right?

A few days later you hear, "I HATE it here. I want to go home!" And that message gets repeated. Often. And you want to cry. And you feel guilty. And you wonder where you went wrong. Perhaps you start feeling like crap and want to run away and hide and tell someone else to just take over and have everyone leave you alone!!! Okay—maybe that's interjecting a little too much of my personal experience here?—but it can happen. I've been assured this is a normal part of the process and we *all* go through this. Whew. It's not just me!

My dad, three weeks into his new apartment, told me the place was killing him. He couldn't take looking at all the old people. Even though Dad is 85, in his own mind, he's a young guy. Watching other people challenged with walking and talking and eating (even in Independent Living) was difficult for him. It didn't help that Mom convinced him to attend a lecture and one of the men had a cardiac event and nearly died right in front of my father!

I went home and cried for an hour. Did we make the right choice? Was I killing my father more quickly by moving him? Would my siblings hate me forever? The guilt was overwhelming. Luckily, I called upon the support network I had created and was able to simmer down and recognize that it takes time to acclimate and all new residents go through these transition pains.

It's only that everything feels more on the surface and bigger, more urgent, more devastating, when you're older. These old folks turn into drama queens and kings! Allowing Dad to express his feelings was important for him. I had to stay away from going into "my father must hate me" thought cycles.

In my quest to find resolutions to make the transition as easy as possible, I learned a bunch of tips and tricks. Some I wish I knew earlier, others I learned just in time. I share them with you…

Familiarity

Keep things as familiar as possible. "New" and "fresh" sound great to us and to college students and those moving into their first apartment or to the newly married, but when someone reaches their older years and you're moving them out of their day-to-day routine, they are not going to like it. Where they've been living is comfortable, instinctual, familiar. You can slowly change things over with them later—but not at first.

Property: As much as it's possible, set up your parents' furniture, art, mementos, clothing, bathroom supplies, night table contents, etc., in the same way they were at "home." Night table to the right or left of the bed. Lamp and clocks and pencil holders all in the same place. Pillows in the same order. Pictures that

219

were visible from the bed, dining table, or couch should be visible still. If the TV was in the bedroom before, put it in the bedroom in the new place. Your parent may tell you it's okay to move things around, and that's fine, but know that it will make the transition one click tougher.

Put clothing in the closets and drawers exactly as they were at "home." Don't follow your instinct to organize them by color or season or move them to where you think they would make more sense. You move Mom's bras to the former sock drawer and suddenly she's hanging out like a bra burning '60s hippie chick!

Let your parent reorganize things as they like, when they like. Your job is to get things out of boxes, put items in the rooms they belong in or on the furniture as it was, and to get rid of wrapping and moving supplies. (You don't want them secretly packing everything back up and moving out again!)

Bathroom: Lay things out on the sink and in the medicine chest and cabinets as they were at "home." Use the same towels, washed in the same detergents. Put existing products in the shower or bath. New products causing a rash or feeling differently on skin or creating an allergic reaction will set back transitioning. Skin or clothing smelling different could click a trigger to something unpleasant.

Tools/Tech: Here's where things get messy. You move your parent to a new place and suddenly there's a new phone system, new internet, or new television provider to learn. All the comfort that came with being able to manage technology is suddenly gone. Now everything is "stupid," "makes no sense," "impossible to use," doesn't work, etc. Frustration levels kick up a notch. Some millennial has designed the new place to be completely Wi-Fi- and Bluetooth-oriented so that everything can be managed from your smartphone! How wonderful…*IF* you're a person who is familiar with technology and you have good vision and can see the buttons and dials and you can hear the beeps and notifications and you don't have shaking hands or fingers that suddenly need to push tiny buttons and you own a smartphone and computer AND you understand technology and don't have any memory or cognitive loss and can easily absorb new instructions on how to work everything! That's a tall order!

Throw in the anxiety of having left a familiar place and you've got a recipe for depression, fretfulness, and anger. Not a great place to begin a new phase of life. And who gets blamed? You. *You* helped them move and now it's *all* your fault. Oh joy.

To reduce Senior Tech Anxiety (STA—I think that's a clinical term I just coined!) be proactive in getting your parents acclimated.

(a) Make simple instruction sheets with photos (maybe laminate) to help figure out how to use all the new "stuff" for the purpose your parent requires.

(b) Do a training session for each thing, one at a time—don't try this all in one day.

(c) Find someone in the complex or building who your parent can call to come and help when frustrated.

(d) Get yourself familiar with everything so you can be the "tech support hotline" if necessary.

I ordered my parents the phones with bigger keypad buttons and added name tags to the speed dial function buttons, had their old phone number forwarded to the cell phone (because Mom was good with her cell phone but not at pulling messages from the new automated message service), taught them to turn off the TV with the remote and leave the DirectTV box on in order to keep the captions on all the time, set up their Wi-Fi and Netflix accounts to just pop up on the screen when they turn on the computer, etc.

Routine: Following the same exact routine is challenging when you've moved to a new place. Whereas before your parent may have been responsible for meal preparation and supplying the home with groceries, now perhaps they don't have to worry about that. Well, what happens to all the time that was dedicated to sourcing, purchasing, storing foodstuffs, and then planning, prepping, cooking, serving meals, and then setting, clearing, and cleaning the table and dishes, pots, and pans? Try to arrange going down to meals in a dining room around the same time as mealtime was at "home." Perhaps go shopping for some small snacks—just to continue with the grocery thing. Or try substituting shopping for something else. Encourage your parent to try a new class to replace shopping and prepping.

Waking up; taking pills; dining; social and entertainment activities; getting and reading the newspaper; going for coffee, breakfast, or meals; shopping; laundry; bathing and grooming; dressing, exercise; and volunteering all need to get put into a daily and weekly schedule that mimics how it was at home. It may not be exactly the same, but the more familiar, the more comforting and less stressful.

People: Is it possible to bring some recognizable people to work with your parent in the new place? Can you set up appointments with the same manicurist, housekeeper, aides, delivery people, etc.? "See, Dad? We haven't changed that much about your life! Joey is still here to cut your hair."

Even if the same people can't be physically near, keep the energy of the old place close by bringing in the hometown newspaper, magazines from the organizations and places Mom and Dad used to go all the time, and photos of good friends. Host video calls with most valued people. Maybe a screensaver on a tablet, computer, or photo frame with memorable images of family and friends can help.

Bottom Line: Familiar = Comfort

The New Home Downward Spiral

Four weeks into his new residence, and Dad started sharing that he had been having dreams about suicide! He said he moved because I told him how great it would be for Mom, that it would be great for both of them, and that it was good to do it before he woke up one day and didn't know where he was. I was right, Dad admitted. But it's not what he expected, he complained.

Dad was out of sorts because when he was "home" everything was familiar and because he was not challenged or confused, he felt less sick, less like he was declining. He knew how and where everything was.

[Note: This is one reason why moving your parent earlier is better than waiting too long.]

So now, in an all-new setting, Dad was just more aware of how much brainpower he'd lost. And that was understandably quite scary to him. He doesn't remember that at "home" he was also unhappy, getting agitated, hating even his own cooking, and not wanting to go anywhere or talk to anyone.

Dad went to the physical therapist in his new building to work on cognitive skills. He used to be able to answer some of the memory questions, but now his decline had developed to the point where he could remember nothing asked of him only a moment later. It made him depressed. Luckily, he was able to verbalize his depression.

After consulting with my peer group, I asked his neurologist if a prescription antidepressant would help. It seemed that a lot of people used something to help lessen anxiety while going through this kind of major emotional and physical change.

I told the neurologist what my friends shared with me: Marcia's mother was depressed and ready to die after a major surgery about two years before she moved into assisted living. She said, "I think I am done." She was put on Lexapro in rehab and, in a few weeks, she was laughing and happy again. When she moved into a residence in Boynton Beach, Marcia's mom fell in love with all the fun programs.

Rachel's mother was suicidal after losing her husband and moving into assisted living. A few weeks on Ativan, and Rachel's mom was singing at karaoke night. The positive side of Alzheimer's for Rachel's mom was that she stopped feeling the lifelong pain she'd had in her wrists every time she tried to paint. Once she moved to the assisted living facility, she found herself painting—pain free—again.

CBD oil was recommended to me for my father as a natural alternative to pharmaceuticals. It takes the edge off. No "high" if you get the legal kind without the THC. However, CBD oil has been shown to affect people's INR results and, since my dad was taking Coumadin, that was not something we could risk. So the neurologist put him on Lexapro. Two weeks on Lexapro, and Dad began to feel a little better, less anxious, less stressed, and months later he was joking around again. On the new drug, Dad was able to rationalize that his happiness was now coming from the fact that my mother was ecstatic in her new home with all the activities and people to keep *her* brain and body active.

I wish my dad would go to counseling, but he refuses. So, I make sure to let him vent to me as often as he needs to. And every time Mom starts trashing something about their new home (other people, the food, the staff, the technology), I remind her that she needs to talk positively. If she keeps talking negatively, I tell her, she is going to push Dad into a depressive downward cycle.

Loneliness is another issue. Persuade your parent to find a table with other people at mealtime and to attend activities with an instructor or other residents. Take day trips, volunteer for local organizations or within the building/complex, attend religious services—find something that feels good. These options are the easiest ways to avoid feeling lonely—especially when a move may come as a result of spousal loss.

Nondrug alternatives to help a parent cope with negative emotions related to change:

- Psychological counseling
- Support groups
- Anger management tools
- Dietary changes (less sugar and carbs)
- Sleeping habits enforced
- TV-watching for feeling less alone
- Classes and educational activities
- Meditation
- Exercise (especially tai chi, Qi Gong, yoga)
- Coloring

REAL ESTATE

If your parents are going to move to a new place, then you're going to be dealing with real estate issues of some kind for the place they currently call home.

Whether your parent lives on an estate, in a house, a condominium or coop, or has a rental apartment, when signs of dementia creep in or physical issues arise (as typical aging brings on) that makes the physical strategies of daily living more challenging. As a result, real estate questions come to the forefront.

Issues are slightly different if you're looking out for two parents living together vs. a single person. More issues arise when your declining or ailing parent is living with a partner who is anywhere on the scale of simple roommate to spouse and unrelated to you. And discomforting questions arise when your parent is caring for an aging or ill partner and it's not someone who has even been in your life that much, isn't someone you know well at all, or is someone with whom you more often disagree than agree.

Selling Real Estate

When Mom or Dad (a) needs more money for care, (b) has to be moved to a caregiving facility or to a family member's residence, or (c) can no longer sustain the expenses and maintenance of their home, then you may find yourself having to find funds by selling property or real estate.

There are books and tons of online info on how to go about selling real estate. I am not an expert in this area. However, the difference for readers of this book is that, as caregivers, you're probably selling real estate that is not yours. You're selling it for a person or people who are perhaps still alive. And, potentially, you may be trying to sell your parents' property without their cognizant awareness because of mental decline.

Okay, no problem. Call a real estate agent, put the place on the market, get an offer, sell the property, take the money and apply it to your parents' care. Done. No problem, right? Whoa, Nelly! Not necessarily! You are managing this for someone else and you may have some issues that are not related to the run-of-the-mill process of selling the property:

❖   You may not have Power of Attorney or access to the trust that owns the title.

❖   Your parents may not understand why you need/want to sell their property and may object.

❖   You may not live in the area where the home is located.

❖   You may not have contacts in the area where you want to sell and perhaps no understanding of the market.

❖   Your parents may have been neglecting their property and repairs are necessary or liens may have been applied.

❖   Your parents may have been neglecting to pay the expenses related to their property, so there could be debt and/or creditors to manage.

❖   Your siblings may weigh in with their own thoughts about the idea of selling the family homestead or distribution of the contents therein.

Dana, a real estate agent in Boca Raton, Florida, with 30 years' experience recommends the following:

1)   Have the conversation with your parents early. Have them change the title before they get sick. Change the property title to a life estate or put the property in a trust with the children named as trustees. This will make it easier to sell if you should come to that place.

2)   If you can, talk to your parents while they're relatively healthy but aging and ask them to get rid of as much as they can on their own. This will help the children later when they're grieving to not have to manage getting rid of a house of memories. Pare down to what you NEED vs. the extras.

Once you sell the property, you want to be able to get out of there quickly.

Dana just lost her 95-year-old mother and, when she went to clear out the apartment, there was nothing even in the drawers! Her mother had cleared out everything in the home except for five outfits, two sets of sheets, two of each dish and utensils, and two towels and washcloths. Dana's mother had told Dana that she wanted to get rid of her furniture and live on lawn furniture and that she didn't want Dana to have to handle emptying her apartment. Dana thought it was so touching that her mother wanted to take care of this before she passed so her family wouldn't have to, but she wouldn't let her mother live on lawn furniture!

Dana recommended that you talk to your parents about scaling down. It makes it easier on you, the children, later. If your parents are not sick, they can do this. Over time, you and your siblings should help them downsize. It might actually bring up some nice memories and stories to share as you go through things not recently on view.

Clearing the Home

Lilly's mom is a hoarder. Lilly actually had to buy her mother a new condo to live in so Lilly could clear out the old home and prepare it to be sold! And, because her mother had become so neglectful and absent-minded as dementia set in, the town put liens against the empty property until the yard, windows, and inside of the home were brought up to code again. As you could imagine, selling a property with liens is a nightmare and, in this case, not possible because the liens totaled four times more than the value of the property!

My instinct would have been to just toss everything into a dumpster, right!? Not so much! Cleaning out the home became challenging because Lilly's mother informed Lilly that money was hidden in boxes and stashed away throughout the house. But Lilly's mother couldn't remember where she had put it. With thousands of dollars hidden away, getting a dumpster and tossing everything out was not an option. Not to mention unearthing a treasure trove of family photos and possibly valuable "old stuff" that *Antiques Roadshow* makes you feel might be the big-ticket item to solve all your financial problems!!

In order to get her parents to agree to move closer to where Tana lived and move into assisted living, Tana chose not to sell her parents' property. While simply packing to move some of the furniture and necessities, Tana found almost $4,000 in cash hidden throughout her mother's home. That money would be used to take care of her parents' home in Florida while the parents were living in Georgia, near Tana.

My grandmother had socked away her "egg money" over the 40 years she lived in Brooklyn. Without that money—because Grandpa was a gambler—Grandma and Grandpa could never have retired to Florida.

The lesson is, it's not always smart to just toss everything in a home into the trash!! If you can have your parents sort through stuff while they still can, chances of tossing away something valuable (like cash or jewelry) are much less likely.

What's the Real Estate Plan/Strategy for a Caregiver?

Start early and get all the paperwork lined up before your parents are unable to make decisions for themselves. With your name on the title and/or Power of Attorney in case of incapacitation, you can handle a multitude of issues.

If you didn't do that in advance, find an elder law attorney to help you navigate this process. If money for a lawyer is an issue, call your local Agency on Aging for local resources.

Online and in local papers, you should be able to find project managers to handle whatever needs to be done—organizing, clearing, selling items at a garage sale or online bulletin boards, dumping, cleaning, repairing, packing, or moving. (Detailed suggestions for clearing the house appear earlier in this book on pages 213–216.)

Look on any property sales website to see what properties in the area (with similar square footage, number of rooms, neighborhood, and amenities) are selling for.

Look at the listings for recent sales to see what agents or agencies seem to be prodigious in your desired neighborhood and contact a few of them to interview. Dana suggests that you find someone who "farms the area" and is familiar with the building, complex, or community. Find an agent with whom you develop a connection and have them walk you through the listing and sales process.

Dana recommends that you have your real estate agent do a CMA (Comparative Market Analysis) for the area in which you're looking to sell. And she advises you to be realistic about the price you want to set. The better the price, the faster the turnaround. The better the price, the more "as is" you can sell the property.

Be aware of possible peaks in selling seasons to be able to manage your schedule to be ready during the most profitable, quick turnaround times. For example, peak selling season in Florida and Arizona is during the winter, peak selling season in Vermont or Colorado could be during skiing season, better selling seasons in the northern Midwest (e.g., Illinois, Michigan, Wisconsin) would be during spring or summer or fall. Cape Cod, Long Island, and other beachfront areas are best right before, during, or right after summer breaks.

Selling Contents of Home(s)

It's been decided that you want or need to sell the home. What do you do now with everything inside that home?

Inventory—what do you have?
Research—what's it worth?

Will you sell off items individually or try to sell them as a package? Are you under a deadline? Do you need this done ASAP or can you spend time working on this? Do you have the time to work on this alone or do you need to bring in someone to help? Do you just need the contents removed and put somewhere for now because the place needs to be emptied? Do you need the contents moved to your neighborhood, so you can deal with it from there?

Some resources to help:

- Estate Sales Managers
- Antique Dealers
- Consignment Shops
- Relocation Experts
- Relocation Movers

Is it all junk and you just want it gone?

- Junk Haulers
- Charities

You might want to start with your local house of worship, soup kitchen, or homeless shelter to see if there's a need for what you're able to donate. Find people looking to get back on their feet. Or find a Habitat ReStore, where they sell your used items to families looking for an inexpensive way to set up or refurbish a home.

I was in a crunch situation and decided to just clear my energy of all the "old" stuff I'd been moving with me again and again. I called a charity I had done some fundraising for and found out a family of two parents and four children had been burned out of their home a few weeks before.

I was able to provide that family with all the things from my home that gave them a complete kitchen setup of dishes, pots and pans, serving pieces, utensils, gadgets for cooking and baking, and even decorative items. Plus, they got furniture, linens, air mattresses, storage cabinets, a couch, chairs, and a dining room set. Because my weight fluctuated so much, they had clothing for three different-size women! And, because I'm an event planner and former school teacher, they had party goods and holiday decorations and toys and craft stuff for the children to use. So, not only did I cleanse my clutter energy and stop paying for storage, but I also got a personal sense of pride that I was able to lend support to an entire family going through a horrible crisis, with all the stuff I'd accumulated over the years. Plus, I got a tax deduction because I had everything inventoried with photos as documentation.

Selling it Yourself?

Marketing/Advertising—Let people know what you have is available

Track and Sell/Donate

Check with your accountant. If your items are high value and you resell on consignment with a non-profit at a loss, there may be a tax benefit for charitable donations.

There are online calculators to tally the value of what you donate. While that list of every item is a pain to create, come tax time, you'll be glad you did. I used the charitable donation calculator built into Turbo Tax to calculate the value of the items we donated when clearing out my parents' New York apartment as we moved my parents full-time to Florida.

With help from some neighbors, friends, family and/or paid experts, you can handle this. It isn't difficult. Just time consuming. Get started early on sorting, inventorying, and boxing things up and, when it absolutely has to be done, you'll be ahead of the curve and ready!

PHASE IV

END OF LIFE

NOTES

HOSPICE

Hospice services are designed for end-of-life care. How do you know when to look into hospice? When a terminal diagnosis is given; when you're told that "it will be sooner rather than later" for a parent to pass; when your parent signals in some way to let you know they do not want resuscitation (ready to go); when there are frequent trips to the hospital and emergency rooms; uncontrolled weight loss, trouble breathing, hypoxia, persistent pain, or an altered mental state.

Hospice team members will sit with your parent, keep them company, offer support to keep your parent comfortable and, if needed, administer palliative care to keep your parent pain free and comfortable.

Hospice typically includes medical attention, comfort, emotional support, spiritual care, caregiver support, and then grief counseling. I have found the most wonderful people with patience and caring beyond measure who work and volunteer in hospice. You've got to be a special kind of angel here on Earth to help people gently transition to death.

Hospice services can reduce the need for readmissions to a hospital. You will find that hospice services will either send staff to your parents' home or your parent may be moved to a residential hospice center.

Some hospitals have programs to sit with patients (when you can't be there). I worked in a hospital with a program called "Nobody Dies Alone." Volunteers came to fulfill those companion duties. If nothing else, just holding a hand or reading a book to someone at the end of their life will help them feel less scared and alone.

Whether through your long-term care insurance, Medicare, health insurance, government programs, scholarships, nonprofits, crowdfunding sites, or the VA, you can find support to help pay for this care.

Once you've interviewed people, toured the locations, and selected your best options, make sure to have that info added to your key contacts list. If there are addresses to be added, include those in case an ambulance or driving service needs to move your parent.

Palliative Care

At any stage of illness, you can call in palliative care to focus on pain relief along with whatever treatment your parent is receiving. Hospice care is called in when treatment for the illness stops and it is clear the person will not survive. Both forms of care provide comfort to the patient and offer the caregiver some respite.

WHEN YOUR PARENT PASSES AWAY

Being prepared in advance so that this shutting down process is not overwhelming is the best way to get through this rough time. A binder or folder or envelope with everything you will need already prepared will make things less overwhelming when you are not likely to be in a clear-headed and focused frame of mind.

If you've completed the sections in this guidebook, you should have easy access to all the information you need to implement the following tasks. These are listed in typical order of priority:

Before the Funeral

- ❖ Notify your family and the closest friends of your deceased parent
- ❖ Call your parents' doctor to get a legal pronouncement of death
- ❖ Contact the Funeral Home to retrieve remains
- ❖ Take care of any animals (and/or dependents on the property)
- ❖ Manage any caregivers or hired staff still on the premises
- ❖ Contact organ donation organization (according to wishes of deceased)
- ❖ Contact officiator to plan and implement final wishes for burial/remains
- ❖ Notify community management where parent resided (nonresidents will be in the home, moving trucks coming, funeral, etc.)
- ❖ Locate Will, Trust, Insurance Policies
- ❖ Prepare an obituary
- ❖ Contact Social Security
- ❖ Contact Estate Attorney
- ❖ Contact Executor

After the Funeral:

- ❖ Contact Financial Planner/Advisor/Accountant
- ❖ Visit safe deposit box and/or vaults
- ❖ Apply for and get copies of death certificate
- ❖ Notify credit reporting agency
- ❖ Cancel credit cards, bank cards, etc.
- ❖ Cancel all accounts on auto pay and subscriptions
- ❖ Redirect mail
- ❖ File final tax return (check the box on form to indicate person has passed)

Death Certificate

When someone dies, the death must be registered with the local or state vital records office within a matter of days. The vital records office can then issue copies of the death certificate, which you will need to manage your parent's estate and burial arrangements.

The funeral home, cremation organization, or other person in charge of the deceased person's remains will typically prepare and file the death certificate. Preparing the certificate involves gathering personal information from family members and obtaining the signature of a doctor, medical examiner, or coroner.

There are three ways you can obtain certified copies of a death certificate:[12]

❖ The funeral home you're working with can get certified copies on your behalf.

❖ You can order certified copies from a third-party company.

❖ You can order the copies yourself from the state in which the person died.

Note: A notary is not authorized to notarize or certify a copy of a birth or death certificate, despite what you may have been told by an airline or travel agency. Only a custodian of vital records can properly certify an original or copy of a birth or death certificate.[13]

A certified copy is a copy (often a photocopy) of a primary document that has on it an endorsement or certificate that it is a true copy of the primary document. It does not certify that the primary document is genuine, only that it is a true copy of the primary document.[14]

Upon completion, the death certificate is transferred to the county vital statistics office where the certified copies are processed. On average, this usually takes 10 to 12 days (sometimes up to six weeks when there has been an investigation, autopsy, or a delay when the medical examiner is signing).[15]

You will find the death certificate number in the top right-hand corner. Most states put the deceased's Social Security number on the certificate to make it easier to apply for benefits and to close accounts. Sending this information to the government ensures that you can collect the Social Security death benefit for your parent.

There are two different types of death certificates. They are used for different purposes.

1. Certified copies of the death certificate WITH cause of death are needed for:
   ❖ Each life insurance company with whom the decedent has a policy
   ❖ Veteran's Administration
   ❖ Certain bank and savings accounts (that involve life insurance)
   ❖ Credit Unions
   ❖ Surrendering Military I.D.s

---

[12] Everplans.com
[13] Quickdocs.com
[14] Wikipedia.org
[15] Nationalcremation.com

- ❖ Credit life insurance on loans, credit card accounts, mortgages, etc.
- ❖ Stocks and bonds
- ❖ Annuities and retirement funds

2. Certified copies of death certificates WITHOUT cause of death are needed for:
   - ❖ Removing decedent's name from deeds of property, home, etc.
   - ❖ Vehicle registration changes
   - ❖ Filing a Will or probate administration at the county courthouse
   - ❖ Most other transactions of public record

BOLO: BE ON THE LOOKOUT FOR SCAMS RELATED TO DEATH

The Obituary

You may have perhaps heard stories of people who read the obituaries in big cities to get a jump on a new apartment that might have just come available. You may have heard about funeral homes that try to get as much money out of grieving families as possible and yet others are the most gracious and loving places to be when someone passes because they "get it." Perhaps you've watched crime dramas where you see burglars looking for homes that will be empty because everyone will be at the funeral. These are all real situations. There are horrible, opportunistic people who prey on grieving families. Don't let yourself be scammed or manipulated. Plan ahead. Be cautious in what you leak to the world. Not only your friends and family see what you post or display!

Sid Kirchheimer, author of *Scam-Proof Your Life*, published by AARP Books/Sterling, wrote an article in the AARP Bulletin in March 2018 titled "Death Notice Double-Cross: Be careful with obituaries—scam artists are reading." I hope you never have to deal with any of this, but just for your information:

When obituaries are published in newspapers, on websites, and in social media (so easy to get the word out to everyone now), be aware that this information can spoon feed scammers the precise nuggets they need to reach out to you in your time of emotional insecurity. All of the protocols you normally follow for identity safety and home security should be in place but watch out for these particular dangers. And be aware that crooks have time. They may not call right away, but will save this information for a few months and use it down the line. So today and tomorrow—be aware and on alert.

On the Day of Funeral

Don't post the address of the deceased's home unless someone is going to be there to watch the home while the funeral is in process.

Make sure neighbors have protection and someone watching their homes if they will be at the funeral, if you publish the address publicly.

Social Security Number

Crooks can purchase or figure out Social Security numbers from information and history you might post in the obituary or on social media. How old someone is, where he or she was born, where they lived, etc.

provides all the clues! Once the Social Security number is in hand, crooks can do all sorts of nefarious things like opening accounts, running up credit card charges, applying for loans, etc. To prevent this:

- ❖ Send notifications to the major credit reporting bureaus and the Social Security Administration as soon as possible after death to ensure nothing can be done with that Social Security number.
- ❖ Shut down social media for the deceased person.
- ❖ Keep an eye on all credit card and bank statements for any charges.

Note: You can preemptively put a credit freeze on someone's account when they reach a point of mental incapacity or when they become ill.

Grandparents Beware

If you post the names of the children and grandchildren—as in "survived by his wife Laura, daughter Susan Smith (giving her married name) and grandchildren Sammy and Rebecca"—that gives scammers enough info to make phone calls to survivors to claim they need help. You've perhaps gotten the spam email or calls about someone mugged and stuck in a foreign country or someone needing money to make bail and too embarrassed to call the parents? With info from the obituary, con men could say they are trying to make it back for the funeral or heard about the death and feel like they should be there for you. If your family is prone to getting into trouble or travels a lot, have a secret code word that the person needs to use, or ask for details that only that person will know. Click. Crook hangs up and you are saved!

You Owe Us Money!

If someone calls saying you have to pay off your dead family member's debts and they are calling to collect, hang up. Unless you cosigned on something, you are not legally responsible. If you're not sure, ask a lawyer. Don't ever send money over phone or via money gram, or meet these people anywhere. Tell whomever is on the phone that the executor will handle everything after probate and you will not be discussing this with any individual debtor.

NOTE: Legitimate companies will not ask for prepaid debit cards or wire transfers. Don't send payments to crooks.

Hidden Insurance Policies

Using names in the obituary or social media would provide enough information for a person impersonating an insurance agent or attorney to call a survivor to claim that your parent or relative took out a policy in secret that benefits YOU (oh wow!) and you just have to pay the last premium or some kind of transfer fee to get the realistic sounding money award. WATCH OUT!!!

Your Father Wants to Talk to You from Beyond

You will not be cursed if you don't pay money to a clairvoyant calling from around the globe claiming to be passing on a message from the dead person. Really? Want the message and believe that your loved one would try to communicate this way? Go to someone you trust locally. No one is calling you from around the globe for this! A Ouija board is much less expensive! (BTW—I do believe people communicate from beyond the earthly plane, but I don't think I'm getting a phone call from a stranger about this. That's a very Whoopie Goldberg in *Ghost*—the movie—thing.) Again, if you want to give it a try, have a question that only the deceased person would know the answer to—nothing that could be found in media or papers lifted from the trash from your home as you're cleaning things out.

Debts and Obligations

Some quick facts I picked up from various sources about paying a deceased person's debts:

The estate should pay for:

- ❖ Credit card balances
- ❖ Lease buyouts
- ❖ Loans
- ❖ Unpaid hospital or medical bills (check your state because, in some states, whatever balance is due after the parents' estate pays medical expenses from existing funds, for which you might be responsible)
- ❖ Unpaid residence fees
- ❖ Other legitimate debts (with paperwork to follow the trail)

Medicaid may try to recover money that was paid out by Medicaid to pay for your loved one's care from the estate.

Even if you had your parents' Power of Attorney (which ceases to be in effect after death), unless you or your siblings have cosigned on something with your parent, you all should not be liable for any debts incurred by your parents. Check with your lawyer to be sure that things are set up that way.

The proceeds of a life insurance policy cannot be diverted away from the named beneficiaries to pay for the debts of the deceased person, but if the beneficiary has outstanding debts, creditors can and will attempt to take some or all of the payout, depending on the amount of the debt.

Social Security

How to report a death to the government:

You should give the funeral home the deceased person's Social Security number if you want them to make the report. If you need to report a death or apply for benefits, call 1-800-772-1213 (TTY 1-800-325-0778).

You can speak to a Social Security representative between 7 a.m. and 7 p.m. Monday through Friday. View SSA.gov (Social Security Administration) for any questions you might have.

TURNING OFF SERVICES

Before I attempt to start listing all the different companies you need to contact to turn off services that are billed for the home, let me just say—check your local listings!!

The following services will continue to be billed to your deceased parent, even if the home is sitting empty or sold, until someone tells them that the account is cancelled.

Look around the home of the deceased person:

❖ Pull the bills from the mail (but understand that some things may not be billed in the mail but are paid on an auto-deduct plan or annual billing)
❖ Make a list of anything connected to a provider
❖ Make a list of what needs to be paid
❖ Provide that list to the executor of the estate to process

Standard accounts to look for:

❖ Wi-Fi
❖ Phones
❖ Water
❖ Trash
❖ Sewer
❖ Electric
❖ Messaging services
❖ Fuel delivery
❖ Newspapers and magazines
❖ Cable or Digital or Direct TV
❖ Netflix, Hulu, Amazon Prime, or other internet streaming accounts
❖ Landscapers
❖ Homeowners insurance
❖ Pool care

RETRIEVING PERSONAL INFORMATION FROM TECHNOLOGY

Earlier, we discussed the need to have the passwords and login information for your parents' devices and technology. Hopefully, you've gathered all of that in advance or your parents have left you a file with everything listed.

The basic instructions for how to gain access to information on the computer, phone messages, tablets, smartphone, etc., can be found on the web for the make and model of the device. Mostly you'll find you need to power on, enter the login then a password.

If you're trying to get rid of the content in order to donate or scrap the items from the home and you don't want anything personal to be accessed by potential crooks, just deleting files will not scrap them entirely from the system. Someone really talented can still pull the info. Data Forensics! You will want to pull the hard drive and/or SIM cards. Check the web for tips on how to do that on the model you are trying to clear. Or call your favorite IT person. Check local listings (or call) for police-sponsored Hard Drive Shred events.

To reset the system of a tablet, phone, or computer to allow someone else to use it, drag everything to the trash, clear the trash, and try going to settings to reset to manufacturers default settings. It may ask if you want reset all the content or erase all the content. I know when I inherited my Uncle's new Dell laptop I did not want his collection of erotica on my new work computer! Erase and delete I did, immediately!

GETTING INFO WHEN YOU DIDN'T COLLECT IT BEFORE DEATH

Oh my. Something happened unexpectedly, and you haven't even had time to gather all the info you need. Now you're trying to figure out who to pay, what to cancel, who to talk to, etc.

Here are some ways you might be able to find that information:

Go through the mail: Collect, sort, and respond with final payments and cancellation of accounts, which will require you to include a death certificate. If you're giving final bills to the executor to pay, make a note of everything that needs paying but you should still call and cancel the accounts.

Call each vendor or provider: Find out the exact cancellation process required by each vendor so that it can be noted on the file immediately. Note who you spoke to, on what date, at what time, and get a confirmation number.

Get the checkbook records: Find out who your parents paid for the last six months. If you have online access, you can just download previous statements. If you don't have access, bring the death certificate to the bank, they should be able to give you a complete list or copies of check images. Each bank has unique policies.

Organize the paperwork in the home: As you're cleaning out, set up files for utilities, merchandise, travel, auto, etc. All the same categories you use to itemize your tax receipts will be great folders to set up while you're going through the paperwork. Once it's sorted, you'll know what needs to be managed, what needs to be shredded, what to keep to complete a final tax return, and what should be scanned and then shredded!

Property documents: If you can't find the physical copies, you'll need to contact the bank or tax assessor's office or other government office in your city to get copies of the relevant documents so you can sell (or cancel the lease). Or the auto dealer (there should be a sticker on/in the car) for auto lease.

If you haven't already resolved issues surrounding your parents' home, check back to the chapter on Real Estate and what you can do to make disposing of property less harried.

NOTES

In Advance of Emergency

There are emergencies for medical reasons, of course. But no matter where you live, there could be other outside factor emergencies. In the Northeast and Midwest, there are snow storms; in the Southeast and central United States there are hurricanes and tornadoes; in the Southwest you might have sand/wind storms and droughts; on the West Coast there are earthquakes; to the Northwest, there are forest fires, mud slides, and snow. No matter where you are, the chances for a natural disaster exist. Never mind that a house fire, flash flood, or power outage can create a mini disaster on any given day. So, how can you be prepared to ensure your parents' safety in an evacuation situation? Advance preparation for all types of emergency occurrence will keep things calm at a frenetic time.

Steps to take:

❖ Keys: If someone needs emergency access to the house or apartment, make sure you have spare keys and your emergency contact info left with a trusted neighbor, the management/security office, the dog walker, etc.

❖ Learn CPR

❖ Locate AED [Automated External Defibrillator] (or buy one for house possibly)

❖ Keep critical information for emergency services near the phone: hospital of choice, primary care physician contact info, blood type, medications, hardware to note (e.g., pacemaker, titanium hips)

❖ Get your parent an ID bracelet or dog tag with important information engraved

❖ Consider enrolling parent in Alzheimer's Association Safe Return® Program with MedicAlert®. Helps people who get lost get found and returned home

❖ Sew ID tags in your parents' clothing in case your parent is unconscious or unable to speak

❖ Keep an item of clothing with parents' scent in Ziploc bag to aid recovery dogs

❖ Identify neighbors or friends who would be willing to help in a crisis

❖ Plan emergency evacuation routes out of town

If your parents have need for refrigeration for medicines, are immobile, or need electricity for oxygen or other life-sustaining equipment, or you have pets or other special situations, *please* call around in advance of an emergency and find out which shelter would be best in your area and what rules have to be followed.

If your parent has Dementia or Alzheimer's or is prone to wandering, consider giving local police a photo and profile of your parent so it can be circulated more quickly in an emergency if you get separated. Or, if your parent takes the car and doesn't return and you fear he/she is lost and confused, the police can use the file information for an immediate Silver Alert broadcast.

Emergency Preparedness

Prepare an Emergency Kit:

In the house, for peace of mind, keep copies of your most important papers and precious items in a waterproof and fireproof safe in case something happens when you're not home.

In an emergency evacuation situation, you can grab this box with important documents:

- ❖ Will
- ❖ Durable Power of Attorney/Healthcare Proxy
- ❖ Health Summary (laminated and one page if possible)
  - ❑ Blood type
  - ❑ Allergies
  - ❑ History of conditions, current status, previous surgeries
  - ❑ Doctor Contact List
- ❖ Advance Directives/DNR/Donor Form
- ❖ Insurance Information (policy numbers/contacts)

Evacuation Bag:

Plus, keep a bag prepared for an evacuation situation. If this bag could be waterproof and easy to carry (e.g., knapsack, bag with shoulder straps, wheels, etc.), you can get mobilized more easily.

- ❖ Extra medication (7-day supply with list of meds and dosage, copies of the Rx, and prescribing doctor contact info in Ziploc bags), oxygen or special supplies
- ❖ Hand sanitizer
- ❖ Picture ID (extra small IDs with your parents' info and caregiver info)
- ❖ Extra clothing for a few days (sleepwear, day wear, undies, comfy shoes, flip flops for showers, rain ponchos) [Hint: pack a few versions in zipper bags, one bag for each season]
- ❖ Personal hygiene items: Travel sizes of toothbrush, toothpaste, mouthwash, hair brush, razor/shaving cream, deodorant, etc.
- ❖ Incontinence products
- ❖ Identification and/or tracking ID products
- ❖ Flashlight (extra batteries)
- ❖ Bottled water (one gallon per person for at least 3 days)
- ❖ High-nutrient drinks and meal substitute bars
- ❖ Paper goods (toilet paper and paper towels; plus garbage bags)
- ❖ First aid kit (including medical-quality gloves)
- ❖ Hearing aid batteries and eyeglasses (with cases)
- ❖ Small sewing kit with extra safety pins

- ❖ Small toolkit or multi-purpose tool
- ❖ Water purification tablets
- ❖ List of emergency friends and family contact numbers (in case your phone is dead but you can use another) kept in waterproof, resealable bag
- ❖ Back-up power cords
- ❖ Headset, earphones/ear plugs
- ❖ Face mask to cover mouth and nose (in case of dust/allergens/flying dirt)
- ❖ Activities (books, puzzles, photo albums, recorded music, paper/pencils, etc.)
- ❖ Favorite familiar items (foods, pillows, blanket, etc.)
- ❖ Solar-powered charger for devices and/or radio (hand crank or solar)
- ❖ Insect repellant and sunscreen
- ❖ Emergency cash (travel purse to wear under clothing)
- ❖ Food/snacks (3-day supply of non-perishable, easy to eat food; bags for trash; manual can opener; paper cups; and straws)
- ❖ Pet supplies (collar, food, leash, carrier, bowls, water, plastic bags for waste, ID papers, vaccination proof)
- ❖ List of shelters in your area that can handle people with your medical or cognitive issues and/or pets

Sheltering Away from Home

In a shelter, take your parents to a quiet corner near the restrooms, away from windows, walking aisles, and exits.

When in a shelter or in transition during an emergency, it is essential for you to keep calm and try to hold hands with your parent, give reassuring hugs. Emotions can get really bent out of shape during these uprooting, off-schedule events.

TRAVELING WITH YOUR PARENT

Transportation Challenges

Sandra retired from work and wanted to move her mother to South Carolina, so Sandra could be closer to all of her siblings. This would enable Sandra to share the caregiving and nurturing of her mom with her family instead of being the sole person responsible for her mom. However, her mother had major cognitive impairment combined with incontinence issues, a strict medicine regime, and difficulty walking. There was no way Sandra was going to put her mom in the car to drive her from South Florida to South Carolina.

Perhaps there's a family event your parent should attend, or a specialist for your parents' condition requires transporting your parent to a far-away office or hospital, or you are rotating care between siblings who don't live right in the same neighborhood—transportation might become a challenge to manage.

The solution for Sandra and her mother was a medical transport company. For a flat, pre-determined fee plus tolls, the transport van will pick up the client and provide a driver and a qualified staff person to make the drive. The bathroom may or may not be in the transport vehicle.

Some people don't have physical issues and thus a car ride is not a huge physical challenge. However, the risk at a rest stop, restaurant, or gas station of a person with dementia walking off, or getting distracted; or someone older and frail getting injured, having a bowel incident, or becoming overwhelmed is quite possible.

An airplane, bus or train trip might be easier for you to stay with and focus only on your parent, but the amount of distractions and frenetic energy in large transportation hubs can bring different challenges.

Here are some tips for transporting or traveling with your loved one.

Pack:

* Copies of important documents (Durable Power of Attorney, health information, contact information, medication lists, doctor list, etc.)
* Trip itinerary and tickets
* Medications
* Plenty of water
* Some snacks
* Activities—simple games, puzzles, tablet with apps or movies, repetitive tasks (e.g., linking paper clips)
* Hat, in case of sun or rain
* Blanket and pillow
* Wet cloths or hand sanitizing gel and/or portable spray disinfectant

- ❖ Toilet paper (and/or baby wipes)
- ❖ Change of clothing
- ❖ Plastic seat covers or blankets (if incontinence may be an issue from stress or diet)
- ❖ Ear plugs or headset (noise cancelling) to reduce stress from outside noise
- ❖ Soothing music

General Travel Tips for Transporting Seniors:

- ❖ Before leaving, take photo of your parent on your phone to show people if you get separated "This is what my parent was wearing and how he/she looked today."
- ❖ Stick with familiar routes for as long as you can
- ❖ Make sure your parent is wearing something trackable in case of separation (e.g., alert bracelet, carrying GPS cell phone, ID necklace with GPS, smart watch, stick-on tracker)
- ❖ Call hotel, airline, train or bus line, or rental car company in advance to request specific needs
- ❖ Travel during a time of day that is optimal energy and attention for your parent
- ❖ Identify support contact information for stops along the route in case needed
- ❖ Set timer for medication times
- ❖ Avoid rush hour travel times to minimize congestion and crowds
- ❖ Consider requesting wheelchair assist to get your parent from place to place efficiently with minimum disruption
- ❖ Contact TSA (Transportation Security Administration) at least 72 hours in advance to get information about what to expect
- ❖ Carry business cards with information about your parents' situation to give/show to staff to reduce misunderstandings without embarrassing your parent
- ❖ Ask for assistance from crew when needed
- ❖ Carry small bills to tip people who help along the way
- ❖ Use family or companion restrooms so you won't have to leave parent unattended
- ❖ Mostly: STAY TOGETHER AT ALL TIMES.

The Wandering Parent

Wandering off is one of the most distressing things about a parent with dementia. The thought of a loved one out there, lost, with an inability to ask for help keeps me up at night. When a kind stranger or a public servant finds your parent wandering, will they be able to get your loved one back to you? There are ways for you to make that easier.

Jordana's husband was in an Adult Day Care center he went to several times a week. Jordana got a call more than an hour after her husband had opened the gate and simply walked off the property because someone was bringing in boxes and left the front door propped open.

The police found Jordana's husband three miles away, walking home. He was safe and fine, but that kind of incident nearly put Jordana in the hospital with stress and anger.

Suzanne's mother wandered out of the house naked while her aide was using the toilet. She was a few blocks away before they found her! Since she was naked, she didn't exactly have a phone in her pocket for anyone to help get her back home!

No venue or aide is perfect, so you need to have your strategies in place to make the recovery process more expeditious. We take our lessons on recovery strategies from parents protecting their children and people trying to recover lost animals. Think about how to help others help you:

In your parents' smartphone, label contact names with ICE (In Case of Emergency) and put those names in their phone Favorites list (for example: ICE, Jane, daughter). This makes it easy for your parent to find the number, speed dialing, and so EMS can find your contact info in an emergency situation.

Hang a printed list of ICE contacts for your parents in their home in a visible location (bathroom mirror, over the sink, on the fridge). This list could help an aide or caregiver put out an alert quickly if your parent wandered off. You and your siblings should keep copies. It's not a bad idea to keep your parents' ICE list in your phone contacts as well.

If you have family with dementia, Alzheimer's, or brain fog and this person is prone to wandering off, it could be hugely helpful to provide information for anyone finding your person to know who to contact.

* You could try a tattoo (henna, permanent, or temporary). Search the web for custom temporary tattoos for as little as 20 cents each in bulk. [e.g., "I'm {name}. Call 123.456.7890 if I'm lost."]
* A locked Medic Alert bracelet or dog tags/necklace (combines a Medic Alert notice with contact info "if found").
* Labels sewn into clothing (like a child has for camp) that have the person's name and a contact phone number. "Bob Smith. If I'm lost, please contact x at x.")
* Set up Find my Phone function on your parents' smartphone. Or order trackers and attach to wallet, shoes, or belt (anything worn every day).
* Go to https://ifineedhelp.org and order patches and ID tags that provide a QR scan code for anyone who finds your loved one to log in and find out who to contact and see urgent medical information (allergies, blood type, pacemaker, etc.). It also provides a GPS location of where to find your parent.

❖ Installing a driving tracker (such as those used for parents wanting to track new teenager driving safety) will allow you to see where the car is and how the driver is doing.

❖ Consider activating a Silver Alert call. When you know someone is missing, you can put out a Silver Alert (best if you've filled out this paperwork in advance with your local police department) to activate a community-/area-wide electric signboard posting advisory (like an Amber Alert) for people to look for style/year/color/plate of the missing car. They can text the location of your loved one's car to a code number.

❖ Consider a MyNotifi device (mynotifi.com/medical-alert/wristband) which is linked to a smart-phone. If your parent is wearing the device and happens to fall, your parent can request help. The app will notify YOU and then you choose if you want to notify emergency help. If it can't reach you (or the other two designated people on the list), the app will send emergency help. MyNotifi lets you know about the incident and where the incident occurred.

BOLO: BE ON THE LOOKOUT FOR ABUSE/NEGLECT

Always be on the lookout for signs that your loved one may be a victim of abuse or neglect. Unfortunately, there are people in this world who enter caregiving professions without the patience and temperament required for this very intensive, critical work. And there are family members pushed unwillingly into a caregiving role who would sooner wish their turn at caregiving was over.

Watch out for:

❖ Financial exploitation
❖ Physical abuse
❖ Neglect
❖ Sexual abuse
❖ Abandonment
❖ Emotional abuse

Have you noticed any of the following?

❖ Bruises
❖ Skin discoloration
❖ Scars
❖ Pressure marks
❖ Broken bones
❖ Burn marks
❖ Severe depression
❖ Bed sores
❖ Knotted hair
❖ Mouth sores
❖ Swollen gums
❖ Withdrawal or cowering
❖ Bruises around genital areas
❖ Broken skin abrasions cuts
❖ Sudden change in mood or emotional swings

If you feel there may be abuse, call your local Elder Abuse office or the National Center on Elder Abuse to find a resource in your area. ncea.gov or acl.gov.

Be aware that if the abuse is from a spouse or other family member, you may run into a situation where the abused person won't file a complaint or freely talk to someone who can help.

If the victim is cognitively impaired, there may be no conscious recognition of abuse, and thus it will be up to you to show evidence with photos and share stories of what you've witnessed.

Financial Scams

We also have to watch out for people who will try to take our parents' money. From outright theft to more subtle overcharging, to doing work that doesn't need to be done, to risky investments, opportunists abound; especially in retirement community areas.

The Department of Elder Affairs in Florida circulates a flyer with recommendations to minimize the risk of becoming a victim. Warn your parents about the following. Manage situations where you can intervene without causing your parents embarrassment. Recommendations include:

- Compare estimates
- Get proposal and pricing before beginning work, in writing. Provide a small deposit. Make sure contract says payment is for completed and satisfactory work only
- Get multiple bids
- Have contractor responsible for filing and showing permits
- Don't let anyone pressure your parents into making hasty decisions
- Don't open the door or take advantage of "free" estimates from people you didn't contact
- Never pay cash
- Do not pay for unfinished or undelivered work
- Use direct deposit for incoming payments
- Never give anyone a signed blank check
- Conceal valuables and cash
- Don't let someone pressure you to sign something if you don't understand it
- Control access to your funds—the bank can help
- You will never have to pay to get a prize—it's a scam
- Never share credit card or Social Security information with people on the phone—especially if you didn't contact them and they are not known to you
- Never share your PIN or access codes
- Review your monthly statements to be sure there's nothing unusual or unfamiliar
- Don't carry multiple credit cards or your Social Security card with you
- Don't pre-print or write your ID information on checks
- Remove mail from mailbox promptly
- Shred or cut up personal information on anything you're discarding
- Stop mail when away from home
- Keep a copy of everything in your wallet in a safe place
- Shop online only with secure websites where you should see a lock image in the browser bar and the address will be https vs. http
- Request a credit report annually from all three credit reporting agencies for free

If you suspect your parent has been victimized, close (or put a hold) all financial accounts immediately.

Keep a copy of anything that you send out, get contact names of people you speak with, write down dates and times of communication and results/next actions.

PART IV

CAREGIVER SUPPORT

NOTES

Help! I'm Overwhelmed!

The next critical area, which we tend to put off because other people always seem to take precedence over ourselves, is being good to ourselves. It is *not* selfish or narcissistic or self-indulgent to take recovery time, known as respite time, when caregiving because, if you don't do it, you will not be able to care for anyone else for very long.

The one thing I was told over and over again was "do not wait until you are about to collapse before calling in help." John, in my first caregiving group, was at the point where he had undeniable resentment and anger toward his mother because he had given up everything in his life to care for her. He did such a great job that his mom persisted on much longer than he thought she would have.

John had retired early from an extremely lucrative but stressful business and was anticipating playing golf and relaxing around the pool; having outings with new friends. Yet, his new job turned out to be caring for his mother. He hadn't played golf more than a few times in the years since he moved to Florida. He had not made any new friends, nor had he spent more than an occasional day at the pool. Of course, he was resentful.

Even after hiring aides to take care of his mom a few days a week, John never felt he could leave for more than a few hours. He only left his mother to work as a referee for basketball and softball games, which gave him great pleasure for a few hours a week. The reality is that when his sister came to stay with his mother, John didn't have a clue where to go or what to do with his time because his entire schedule focused on caregiving and his mother's routine. John worried his sister wouldn't be able to handle things and would need him. Luckily, John decided to go to Las Vegas, and he spent a few days indulging.

Caregiver.org has a wonderfully supportive website with a magazine for caregivers. The site warns that caregivers who dedicate themselves to caring for loved ones without taking care of themselves have been shown to demonstrate high levels of clinical depression and anxiety disorders, suffer from heart issues and other illnesses resulting from fatigue and stress, exhibit loss of self-esteem and self-identity and, quite often have difficulty sleeping at night.

Treatment for medical issues resulting from fatigue, relentless stress, and worry can become expensive and if, as often happens, the caregiver has left a job with health benefits in order to be a full-time caregiver, the financial toll can lead to long-term financial nightmares.

Our instinct is to be there all the time for our loved ones. If I go out and do something for me, then I feel guilty. "He's home and suffering...how can I take time for a manicure?" "Mom can't even eat without me feeding her, how can I go out to dinner with friends and enjoy myself?" "If I leave the house, my father will go nuts worrying about me."

A mental adjustment needs to happen here—where you get to a place of accepting that you need respite too. And there are agencies and resources to give you that time. So, once you've got someone lined up to give you a break, what can you do with that time?

Social Activities: Get together with existing friends or make new ones. Try Meet Up groups, Craigslist, or Facebook, or go to the library bulletin board, or peruse an Adult Education curriculum guide to find activities and people interested in the same things you are.

Non-Parent Related Friends: Getting together with the neighbor who checks in on your mother is not taking a break from caregiving. Find friends your own age, with similar interests or background and avoid talking about caregiving duties for a break period.

Physical Activities: Engage in physical activities to reduce stress, keep you healthy, and bring about an endorphin high. Endorphins are the body's "happy drug"—a critical component in getting quality sleep, maintaining a balanced mood, self-confidence, social engagement, and a healthy appetite. Release endorphins and you worry less and keep your brain sharp.

Passions: Continue or develop hobbies and activities that you love. Whatever it is, it should make you smile when you think about it—something that no one else needs to appreciate or even know about—but that makes you feel inner joy. It could be something artistic, something you build/construct, or a category of things you collect/sort/organize/research. Or it could be dancing in your underwear, planting an herb garden, singing karaoke, or whittling wood. Maybe it's baking, brewing a batch of bathtub beer or backyard wine, knitting a sweater, creating a meal for all the senses, or shopping in a farmer's market. Whatever it is, embrace it and throw yourself into it whenever you can!

Spiritual Connection: "I don't have time to sit and do nothing!!!" you protest. But, stopping the madness of your life for even five minutes to meditate, pray, journal, or find a way to be totally still—let your brain go blank for a brief time—is documented to keep you healthy and sane. Believing in something outside of your own body and self, pulling on those resources that seem intangible to some, you'll see benefits like slowing down aging, increasing happiness, improving concentration, and improving health. What's so intangible about that?

Caregiving Connections: It is *so* important to find other people going through the same thing you are. You need to vent. You need to dump. You need to be in a safe space where people understand and don't judge you when you start wondering when will this ever stop? Wondering if you can live up to your promise to keep Dad at home until he dies? Feeling guilty that you want to just run away and abandon your parents to your siblings? Find a caregiver support group *early* in the process or a therapist who works with caregivers. Don't wait until you're crying yourself to sleep every night or drinking/drugging/eating to numb your feelings.

Respite Care—Often & Early: Take advantage of local services, friends, your parents' friends, and anyone else who offers to help. When someone says, "What can I do to help?" or the more vague "Let me know if there's anything I can ever do to help" your answer should *not* be "Oh, nothing. You're so kind. I'm good." Your answer should be "Thank you! How wonderful. Yes, I can use your help. Could you stay with Mom/Dad for two hours so I can take care of a few personal things?" And then go get a massage/manicure/pedicure/shop/take a walk/play basketball, etc.! Embrace the help.

Earlier in the book, we discussed the people who should be on your call list for parental caregiving. Here's a slight variation on that list. These are people who are there for YOU as caregiver—people you need on your list to help you thrive during a very overwhelming time:

- ❖ Friends (the ones who don't drain you!)
- ❖ Relatives (the ones you like!)
- ❖ Caregivers for your parents

- Caregiving support group for you
- Spiritual/religious leaders and practitioners, friends from your house of worship
- Pet care (dog walkers, sitters, cat feeders, etc.)
- ICE contacts—your in-case-of-emergency contact list
- Food (caterers, food delivery, online ordering, etc.)
- Medicine (drug stores, delivery, online ordering, etc.)

When your parent has to be in the hospital, having a support group to relieve you from being on duty will make a world of difference. If you have people willing to help, assign people with different responsibilities. If you keep a list of what you need handy, when someone says, "Let me know what I can do to help," you have it ready!

Roles You Might Assign

Comfort—people to sit with your parent

Home manager and/or helpers—to take care of tasks at the home (bring in mail/newspaper, return phone calls, take care of pets, water plants, put out trash, etc.). Help with organizing closets, cabinets, garage. Handling lawn care, pulling hurricane shutters, running errands here or there, and so on.

Food—to bring snacks or meals to caregivers, comfort people or your parent (if permitted)

Computer/Communication—to update a health status website (like caringbridge.org or posthope. org), Instagram, Twitter, or Facebook with your parents' status to reduce the number of "how is he/she doing?" inquiries; to set up auto responder emails; to respond to emails or voicemails; and to activate (or create) a phone/email tree to communicate updates and needs.

SIBLINGS

Ahhhh—the siblings. If you are an only child, you might choose to just skip right ahead to the next section. Maybe there are no children and you're a niece or nephew, cousin, aunt, or uncle who is taking on caregiving. You may feel the world is on your shoulders and that this is all overwhelming to handle alone, but, from the stories I hear of people working with disobliging siblings (and other family members), you might want to count yourself fortunate! You might find...

- ❖ Siblings disappear and leave you to manage alone
- ❖ Siblings are over involved and second guessing everything (too many cooks)
- ❖ No one is taking responsibility (no one authorized to make decisions)
- ❖ Siblings are trying to get rid of your parents (collect parents' assets)
- ❖ You are fighting over money and possessions
- ❖ It's complicated (new spouses/extended and blended families, divorces, and second/third spouses)
- ❖ There is no money available for care

As many types of families as there are in the world, there are just as many different kinds of relationships people have with family. However, I have found that there are some overarching themes caregivers face when multiple voices get involved in managing parents' care:

There's the "I don't live nearby, so I trust you to handle it" long distance sibling, the "I'll tell you what to do and you do all the work" from the too busy to get their hands dirty sibling, the "Tell me how much money to send" from the emotionally disconnected relation. And then you have the "I live nearby, so I'm in charge" sibling, who makes you feel like your contributions don't matter, and the bossy sibling who is *always* right and everyone has to follow along, or else. There are the siblings who have disappeared from family life (for whatever reason) and you feel like you should let them know what is going on, but they never respond. And the situation where somehow, you've managed to pay all the expenses and manage all the details, but your siblings seem to be right there suddenly when it comes to determining whether to pull the plug, go into hospice, sell the house, or divide up the estate.

Sadly, I hear stories of the dutiful caregiver who shows up often and is totally involved and gets the brunt of the anger on bad days and yet the parent still raves about the favorite child who barely even calls.

And there's the "you're the daughter and thus expected to take on this role" whereas the Golden Boy son is allowed to dash in and out and still gets acclaim. Or the reverse...the daughter gets all the accolades. "Why can't you be more like your sister?" while you are standing there having traveled from around the globe to be there for a birthday celebration or you've been on the forefront of handling your parents' financial, legal, and real estate management but haven't been able to be there in person.

I am blessed with the rare situation of long-distance siblings who are totally involved and let me know that they appreciate what I go through in caring for our parents. They recognize what I've given up for this time in my life as I focus my energy on my parents instead of my own ambitions and goals. I am offered respite time with scheduled visits by sis and bro so I can get away without feeling guilty. But probably, my siblings would say I'm the "I'm local, so I've got it covered, and kinda bossy" type.

"What," people ask me, "is the key to keeping a good relationship with siblings during this challenging time that can last from two days to decades? "How do I get what I need from my siblings without them taking over my life and trivializing me into a schlepper and gofer?"

When my parents started getting affairs in order and I was asked to help with getting legal and financial documents arranged, selling and clearing a condo that was no longer needed, and attending doctor visits to make sure that proper follow-up was implemented at home, I created a family newsletter of sorts. Eventually, it evolved into a weekly email. Which has now evolved into a somewhat erratically scheduled email when there's news to report.

Communication is essential to creating a cooperative relationship. If siblings feel left out of the decision-making and are unaware of what is happening, then there's not much chance of contributing or feeling their contributions are invited.

When I told him about my news communication process with my siblings, Scott Solkoff, co-author of *Florida Elder Law*, (now in its 15th edition) and a nationally recognized leading expert in the field of elder and disability law, said "Fern, be sure to write that in your book!" Solkoff said, "The main cause of conflict and disagreements in caregiving situations is lack of communication. The biggest family fights in our conference room are because people feel like things are being done in secret and without recognizing the other players' roles in the process."

In my communications with my family, I break the updates down by category and try to keep the info brief and to the point—with more details available by phone as required. My reporting categories most often are: Financial, Legal, Health, Home, Tech, Social, Other. Your categories will vary based on what's happening with your family, of course.

Health is sub-categorized into Mom, Dad, and also Me as my health (I have Epstein-Barr Syndrome, which makes me fatigue easily) is critical to the caregiving of my parents. Reports for all of us include exercise (and frequency or lack thereof), doctor visits, symptoms and drug interactions, Rx add in/removals, tests needed or taken and the results, emotional well-being, stress, anxiety, and balance are also included.

The tech category appeared because my brother is an IT guy and my mother is a photographer who uses her iPhone and Mac and various editing software. My job is to communicate issues so that my brother can get back to Mom with resolutions and answers. Also, issues with installing a home camera, or a driving monitoring system when Mom was driving, or getting tracking onto bank information and so on, is right up my brother's ability to contribute to caregiving in this way.

Social information helps me keep my siblings up to date on who else is involved with our parents—who sees our parents regularly and what involvement do they have in any decision-making or in our parents' health and well-being.

Altogether, this information (which ranges from a few brief sentences to a few pages long depending on what's happening), ensures that if something happened to me as caregiver, my siblings could carry on and my parents' care would not be compromised.

I am blessed that my sister has the resources and flexibility to be able to jump on a plane and take over if something happens to me. She comes to visit as often as she can to spend time with my parents. Calls them every week; calls me to just check in. And when I told her I might get a sabbatical trip to Italy, she said, "Don't worry; we've got you covered! Enjoy!"

Additionally, my update emails ensure that when we have occasional family calls or when one of my siblings visits and we all go to dinner, there's not a lot of need for long catching up conversation. It creates connections and, I hope, transparency.

Because I am a writer, a newsletter-like communication is easiest for me. My siblings can read it at their leisure on the train while commuting, sitting at the pool, or in the bathroom (no offense taken) if they like!

Alternatives to written newsletters could be video phone conference calls, regularly scheduled meals or gatherings (if all siblings are in town), text messages/social media messages when each thing happens that needs to be communicated, or a shared wellness log online.

The biggest challenges I have seen to group caregiving (with multiple siblings or people involved) come when there's a money issue (not enough or who is managing it) and when major health, financial, or legal decisions have to be made. Setting expectations about who is responsible for what and how those decisions are made and communicated will help alleviate negativity. Allowing for questions, comments, and alternative suggestions opens up new potential efficiencies and allows people to feel engaged in the process. Having my parents complete their Five Wishes document made clear their intentions before much caregiving even began, so there shouldn't be any need to argue or assume what Mom or Dad would want.

Setting expectations of who wants to help, who can help, what each person is capable of contributing and when, will go a long way to creating harmony.

If one sibling has time but no money, can he or she do legwork and day-to-day things? If one has money but a family and business to run and limited time, can he or she contribute to provide more services or perks for the parent? If one sibling has a home with room for a parent, can the other siblings provide relief on a regular schedule, so the host family can get away to spend time recovering without feeling guilty? Can the non-host siblings make financial contributions to help cover the costs of aid and boarding? Go ahead and divide responsibilities along the way so no one feels left out and no one feels overburdened.

Reviewing the recommendations earlier in this book on creating legal and health documents in advance with your parents *and* siblings will go a long way to avoiding conflict over the desires and wishes of the parents once communication becomes challenging. Knowing in advance how your parents want to be treated while alive, while sick, during last days, and after dying makes things so much less stressful.

SO, YOU'RE LIVING IN YOUR PARENTS' HOME?

As I am sitting in my parents' condo while they live in independent living 20 minutes from here, writing this guidebook for you, I find myself feeling many things. First, I feel guilty working on this book when I "should" be checking in on my parents or I "should" be doing some kind of work that pays me. But I am driven by a force outside of me to share this information because every single day someone says to me, "Ya gotta write a book!"

I feel uncomfortable in my space. I am not alone. I have a lot of friends and acquaintances I've made in the last few years who are also going through this weird transition phase of being a caregiver. Somehow, we've melded our lives into our parents'. And maybe there's a little resentment that I'm not "me" anymore. I am of-service and on call and my life is not my own to schedule as I like. The emotional side of me is feeling way different than the logical, good-girl side. It's a battle and I'm getting pretty bruised up at this point now that I'm in my parents' apartment.

When I moved to Florida a few years ago, I moved into an apartment in my parents' building. That worked until the apartment had mold and I moved out. I moved into my own apartment across town and that was lovely. A little inconvenient, but it was *my* space and I had my own life over there. I saw my parents by appointment. That worked just fine.

Now I'm basically house-sitting. If Mom passes first, Dad wants to move back here. If we run out of money, they might need to move back here. If my sister and brother want to visit, they will stay here. My parents' mail and all the bills still come here.

All my parents' accumulated stuff is still here. Mom calls me weekly with a list of things she wants me to bring so I can't just dispose of everything here! I've merged my stuff in where I could, but as I write this, my parents' bedroom has been converted into a giant storage closet of stuff that needs to be sorted, scanned, and sold. I have no time to work on that right now!

I live in the den, on the mattress and box spring I brought with me. I've gotten rid of my parents' mattresses. But that didn't help. I got rid of my parents' dark blue carpet with the mystery crunch. (Who puts down thick pile carpet in Florida?) That didn't help. I held a yard sale with some of the stuff that could go. That didn't help; it wasn't nearly enough.

Even with my furniture in the living room and my own bed, it still feels like my parents' place. It feels like I'm house-sitting. Or that I should be on vacation. I'm not relaxed here. I'm not myself. Impermanence.

I use the community pool and swim every day. I enjoy the 35-foot terrace with a view of the intracoastal. Folks, I am not suffering! This is certainly not a bad place to be. But it isn't mine. Do I sound petulant? Greedy? I feel ridiculous being uncomfortable! I feel ungrateful when I have an affordable, lovely place to live! That's a lot of stuff to have going on inside of you when you're also caregiving and trying to earn a living and trying to have a life. There is some relief in knowing I am not alone!

Marcia lives in her mother's house too. Her mom lives in memory care about three miles up the road from the house. Marcia works full-time and also says she's not comfortable where she lives. She's been living in the house for about four years. She moved from New York to Florida to help her parents. Her dad passed. Her mom faded into needing more care. Marcia and her adorable tiny dog live in her mom's house. It's her parents' furniture. Her parents' taste. She also changed mattresses to try to feel comfortable but still does not. Marcia, with full buy-in from her siblings, had the whole place recently painted sunny yellow, gave away her parents' furniture, and cleared out closets. She now enjoys coming home each day. On the most recent family visit, Marcia overheard her brother tell someone on the phone "I'm at my sister's house," instead of "I'm at my parent's house!" Wow, did that feel good, she shared with me!

Rachel moved south to care for her parents. Same story. Dad passed. Lived with her mom. Mom moved into memory care. Now her mom has passed. It's a four-bedroom, three-bath house for one person. It's too much. And the house is not "hers." Her mother's energy is everywhere. But Rachel doesn't know where she wants to go, what she wants to do. She travels. She's on the road visiting people all the time so she doesn't have to be in the big house on her own.

Rachel is investigating new places and has decided that she will downsize and try apartment living for a while, maybe each year in a different community until she figures out where she wants to buy. Or maybe she'll just keep traveling!

If you are feeling like you're in the same boat, and you are feeling like nothing is yours and you can't relax, know that you are not alone. If I had a magic wand and a lot of money and I could fix things, I would, but I don't.

I've changed the chandelier in the dining room, reorganized all the closets so I know where things are (because we need eight bottles of glass cleaners and room deodorizers!!), got a new refrigerator, and replaced the broken laundry room equipment. I arranged my furniture so that my couch isn't just replacing their couch, my arm chair is not in the same space their chair was. I need to have things look and feel different. I plan to paint the space in the colors I prefer. It's a gorgeous apartment. It's just overwhelmingly my parents' energy. Slowly it's acquiring my energy.

Here's my plan so when I walk in, it feels like I'm home and not just visiting or house-sitting! Maybe you can try some of these:

- Paint
- Incorporate new furniture, accessories, and lighting and change the layout
- Burn candles/use aromatherapy to change the smells
- Invite friends over to enjoy the space
- Do an energetic cleansing by burning sage and reciting cleansing affirmations (find them online and use what you find that speaks to you or write your own)
- Read up on Feng Shui (the art of energy flow management via moving furniture, accessories and colors, textures, plants) and make some changes to help the chi in your space reflect you and your goals

Eventually, I will start downsizing my parents' things. Selling off, scanning and shredding, donating, a little at a time. Right now, Mom texts me with her list of needed items: the bronze handbag, two decks of cards, mat boards for the 16" × 20" frame along with framing tape, the red long sleeve shirt for Dad. "At your service, ma'am!" is what I think with a mental sarcastic salute, as "I'll be right there," are the words my mother hears.

COMPENSATION FOR CAREGIVING

Let's say you are saintly and you've become the chosen one to take care of your parents. What starts out as a couple of hours a week can gradually turn into a job. I just attended a Fearless Caregiver workshop, where I learned that caring for someone with cognitive decline (e.g., dementia) can take up to 25 hours a week. If they live with you, up to 40 hours a week. And this is on top of all the other responsibilities of your life. Spouses spend up to 60 hours a week caring for their partners with decline.

Often caregivers realize that they can't be a caregiver and maintain a job outside the home. So, out-the-window goes that revenue and all the financial benefits that come with a job (e.g., health insurance and retirement plans). Similar to deciding whether to hire a nanny, put a child in daycare, or become a stay-at-home parent, the decision may come down to whether you can afford to hire care so you can go to work, or is it more cost-effective for you to be the caregiver? Is it more cost-effective and efficient to have your parent live with you or for you to move in with your parent than to manage and pay for two households?

If you have siblings to help financially, that is huge. If your parents have long-term care insurance, that's a big help. Are there veterans or disability benefits coming in that can go to pay the bills for the household? What if your parents are able to cover all the expenses but you're living with them and not working? What about your personal stuff? Do you, an adult, want to ask for an allowance from your parents? What will your siblings say if you are getting money from your parents, but they aren't? How all things come together after a parent passes and any remaining funds get divided can sometimes be impacted by what was spent or received while the parents were living.

I was relieved to find out that there are programs that can provide compensation for the caregiver, even if that person is a family member. There are ways to structure your parents' funds, before they pass away, to cover living expenses and compensation for you. And there are services that are free that can provide you with a needed break and time away so you can do something that is just for yourself.

As with any advice, these are general information and you should consult with some of those experts mentioned throughout to get information based on your particular situation. Call the elder law attorney, the area Agency on Aging, your financial person, the legal aid people in your area. There's help out there to figure out what opportunities there are for you and what the limits, terms, and requirements might be. Compare the pros and cons. Some things to ask about:

Personal Services Contract/Agreement

Essentially this is a letter of agreement between you and your parents stating what you've agreed to do for them and how much they will compensate you for said services.

This kind of contract allows you to get paid. As a most simplistic explanation, the benefit of this is that since your parents are using their funds to pay for services they need, the funds are deducted from their net worth and won't be counted when and if they apply for Medicaid.

Siblings who see you getting money for specific services provided may not feel like you are unfairly getting something that they aren't receiving. You're putting in the time and doing the work and getting compensated. This isn't about who loves your parents more or who your parents love more.

On the other hand, you do have to claim this money as income on your tax return. It's not free money. Talk to your accountant about how this agreement affects you in the short and long run.

If your parents don't have money to pay you, their long-term insurance might be able to cover your services if you have a Personal Services Contract. Also, the Veterans Administration offers supportive funding in a program called Aid & Assistance, which allows the VA to pay for your services for your veteran parent. (FYI: This program could also pay for an outside person to come in and help your parent if you needed to go to a job.)

Expenses

You and your parents might set up a joint account that is in both your names or gives you access to an ATM debit card from their account so that you can pull out money to pay for expenses. This will help you cover costs for care that perhaps your spouse does not want to come out of your household joint account. Or maybe your siblings want to see an accounting of where funds have gone.

If you have used your own funds to cover your parents' expenses, keep a record. Writing up a statement with what is owed and keeping that current, getting reimbursed monthly perhaps, will provide the record keeping that may come in handy later when the estate is finally settled.

If you are fully caring for and funding your parents—ask your accountant if you can deduct your parents as dependents.

Income

Your parents' Social Security or pension funds may be paid directly into a checking or savings account that can be used to pay for household bills. You can pay the bills online through bill paying functions of the bank's website.

One friend of mine gave up her relationships and full-time job, volunteering to care for her father and husband. All the pensions, disability, and Social Security went into one account and she used that money to pay for the living expenses for the family. Another friend moved her father into her home and her dad's Social Security paid all the living expenses for both of them. Both friends still had part-time work and freelanced from home in order to pay for personal items and extras. The challenge is when the person you're caring for passes away and the money stops coming in, you now have no income until you can find a job. Finding a new job when you're over 55 is not an easy thing.

Gifts and Inheritances

Your accountant and lawyer will determine if gifting or setting up inheritance accounts will be the best way for you to receive money to compensate for the care you are providing. There are too many variables and I am not qualified to provide accurate information for your particular situation. There are tax implications for now and after your parent passes to discuss.

Social Security Benefits for the Spouse and/or Children

When a person who has paid into the Social Security system passes away, the spouse and/or children of that person may be eligible to receive benefits. Contact the Social Security Administration to see if you qualify: ssa.gov.

Typically, a person might be eligible to receive Social Security benefits of spouse/parent if:

- ❖ Widow or widower is taking care of deceased's child (under age 16 or disabled)
- ❖ Child is unmarried, under 18, and still attending high school full-time
- ❖ Disabled children, if disabled before the age of 22
- ❖ Widow or widower is at least 60 years of age
- ❖ Widow or widower is disabled and at least 50 years of age

FINDING EMOTIONAL SUPPORT AFTER YOUR PARENT PASSES AWAY

Whether you have invested one day, 1,000 days, or 10,000 days into caring for your aging or sick parent, you are connected simply by being born, raised, or adopted. On the day and in the weeks and months following your parents' passing away, you will most likely be feeling an assortment of emotions. Everyone will try to comfort you. You might attend services, read books, and listen to tapes to find something that helps. You might disconnect for a while. Hibernate. Or you may do the opposite and rush into a busy, busy life to keep yourself distracted—to embrace your freedom from caregiving responsibilities.

You may feel relieved to be done with caregiving, then lost with all the sudden time availability, then guilty at being happy to have the extra time, then angry that you feel guilty when you deserve this time to recover and take care of yourself. You might feel like you should be sad and maybe you are, but it doesn't look like what you think other people think sadness should look like. We judge ourselves and then we put ourselves in the shoes of others and judge ourselves again through what we perceive that person might feel. And suddenly, you can't sleep or you never want to get out of bed. Or you start traveling and exploring—locally or globally. Whatever you do, it's okay. It's about *you* now.

My friend Marcia thought she was doing okay after her dad passed away. She was busy taking care of her mom, the house, the details of getting things sorted out and transferred over and so on. But every time someone needed a copy of the death certificate, Marcia found herself brimming over with tears and waves of sadness. To this day, when Marcia finds copies of the death certificate, it brings on the same intense emotions.

Marcia also found herself feeling hurt and angry every time she felt she had to "prove" that her father really had died and his name really, truly, should legitimately be removed from whatever list, account, service that Marcia was talking with. As if Marcia would lie about such a thing!

Whatever your path, whenever something makes you stop in your tracks and brings on strong emotions that you wonder if you will ever stop intensely "feeling," you might be open to having some support.

You are amazing that you did this for your family!!! Take this time for yourself and find out who you want to be now. It's all YOU!

Most of these resources you probably already know about, but I'm listing them here anyway, just in case you need a reminder as you sort out and share your emotions:

Identify Your Needs

Take a journal or scrap paper, and start writing down what you want, what you need, what you dream about. Keep putting the list down and coming back repeatedly to update and revise. Once you've got a good list, sort the list into time frames and budget and rank each thing on importance. Think, "If I had only (blank) months to live, which of these would I want to have checked off?"

Or try writing your own eulogy. What do you want people to say about you when you're gone? That you were a hard worker? Is that it? That you were selfless and giving? What about the inner you? How about also adding some things that make you happy. "She was so happy when she was singing. We loved hearing her perform." Or "That girl could dance around the house like nobody's business!" Or "We were so proud to watch her finish [insert your vision!...her first marathon, triathlon, Tour de France, kayak the Colorado River, novel, rescue all those animals, clean the river in our hometown, or plant that garden for the homeless to eat from]."

With these in hand, you have the beginnings of a plan to get back to your own life. You've done your work for the universe, you've been a good person to your parents, now take a bit of time for yourself to accomplish something in your dreams. BE the vision of yourself you have had in the back of your mind. It's okay. Really.

Grief Support Network

Just like when you're caregiving, you need people to vent to and share your stories with, laugh with, and talk to—you need the same in grief. It would be easy to say that you want to keep going to your caregiver group because they know you and they are your friends, possibly. But they want to talk about their living parent. You need to process the grief and loss of your parent who passed. It's different. Socialize outside of group with your caregiving friends, but find yourself a grief/bereavement support group. Often the groups can be found within the same organizations. You can also find them where you worship, at community centers, and through various local nonprofits.

If you can, look for a group that is focused on children grieving for parents. Losing a spouse or a child is a different energy and a different kind of loss; different emotions. A group for adult children who have lost a parent will help you connect more quickly with people who "get it."

For many, there is no substitution for being in a place of worship where the connection to God feels strong. No matter your religious background, where you choose to worship and how you choose to pray and connect with the oneness outside of your single entity, you will feel heard if you can connect with others of the same beliefs. Check your house of worship (or others in your community if you don't have one yet) and see if there are bereavement support groups offered. If not, ask for a meeting with the clergy to discuss what you're feeling and see if support or advice is forthcoming.

Hotlines

A search on Google for "bereavement hotline" brought up 820,000 listings. There's a hotline out there for you!

If your parent had Alzheimer's, Parkinson's, diabetes, cancer, or just about anything else (even just getting old!), there are phone numbers to call for help. There are online chat groups, call-in counseling groups, and tons of local chapters to visit and find people who have gone through similar challenges.

If you are someone who needs to talk to a supportive ear at 3 a.m., or you're pacing and anxious in the middle of the day, there are support options out there for you to click or call into. Just do a search online or call your local Area Agency on Aging for referrals.

Neighbors/Friends/Family

Friends, family, and neighbors are a mixed bag of possible mine fields and support. Getting past gossip, way-too-personal questions, and morbid curiosity may allow you to find someone who you connect with to be there for you—unselfishly. Someone who knows you and your story is a wonderful thing in that you don't have to begin at the beginning. However, these people also have expectations of you, the super child who took on the caregiving role, and may want a little of that kind of attention coming their way. They may have opinions on things you did or didn't do and want to share them at this time. There may be some emotional baggage connected to the loss of your parent that is personal and not something you want to unpack at the moment with people who will continue to be in your life over time. Or, the neighbor, friend, or family member may have had issues with the person who passed away and all they want to do is vent. So, wade slowly into the neighbor/friend/family pool for support and make sure the waters are fine before immersing fully!

Tools (Journaling, Writing, Poetry, Music, Dancing, Gardening, Etc.)

As I previously discussed, finding your peace in a place of beauty or creativity or expression is another way to be supportive. Using tools to express yourself and examine your feelings is uplifting and will set you free in a way. Keep trying things until you find what works for you. No one else's opinion matters at this point. You have to process the way you process. There's no right or wrong way to do this.

A FEW TIPS FROM CAREGIVERS

"Ask questions. Just because someone says one thing can't be done, doesn't mean it couldn't be accomplished another way. Ask doctors, ask insurance companies, ask facilities...for alternatives."

—**Rachel**

"Get help early. Don't be afraid to ask for help before you are overwhelmed."

—**Lee**

"Just because it's natural, organic, or vegetarian, doesn't mean that it won't be harmful when mixed with other supplements or pharmaceuticals. Ask a holistic doctor and research side effects."

—**Brighter Day Health Store**, Savannah, Georgia

"Don't wait to get things in order just because everything is okay right now. One accident or a stroke and everything can change in a minute. Get affairs and information in order. Have the hard conversations early. You're NOT making your parents feel like you are pushing them into the grave; you are taking care of them and making sure things are easily handled for all concerned and you want to know what THEY want while they can still tell you."

—**Rachel**

"I wish someone would have told me to get long-term care insurance when I was younger. No one thinks they will need it. But Medicare, private health insurance, and supplemental or gap insurance programs don't cover full-time residential nursing or rehab care. Some of the medical expenses are covered for a certain

amount of time, but not the facility. With the cost of nursing care at over $10,000 a month in many places, and the cost of full care aides in the home running $40,000 to $80,000 a year, long-term care insurance makes sense when you can start younger and pay low premiums every month."

—**Fern**

"Find what someone needs at that particular point in their life and try to make that better."

—**Dr. Juan Pretell**, Orthopedic Oncologist, University of Miami Hospital

---

AT THE END OF THE DAY

At the end of the day, caregiving is enriching and fulfilling and difficult and gut wrenching.

You can laugh because your mother calls you to ask you where she put her ointment (how would you know?) and cry because of the same thing. You can feel love and still be resentful. You might feel guilty about everything—helping too much, not helping enough; wanting to be there to support your parent, but wanting to run away and let them figure it out alone or pass the baton to a sibling. You might love the aide who's helping but be jealous that the aide is adored by your father because the aide is there all the time. You cry when your parent remembers your name but can't recognize your brother when he comes on his quarterly visit, but at the same time be secretly happy that you are finally being recognized and not pushed out of the way or ignored in favor of your "famous" or "talented" sibling.

Millions of people around the world are stepping up to take care of their parents. It's a challenge fraught with emotional roller coasters, financial overwhelm, legal problem solving, and day-to-day minutia that needs to be managed. It ain't easy, folks. So, give yourself some credit. You are amazing. There is support out there if you want it.

Guilt is a useless emotion. Feel it, process it, and let it go. It is what it is.

Accept that we are on high alert all the time and that it will wear us down unless we consciously decide to honor ourselves along with honoring our parents.

You are not alone! Reach out—we'll hear you. The resources are in your community and on your computer. Just ask for help! PLEASE ask.

People tell me that I'm an amazing advocate for my parents. I'm there at every doctor meeting and test. I keep their calendar and remind them of things they need to do, take, find, etc. I worked with my sister to research, then toured and then found my parents a place to live to get the help they need so they won't be left hanging in case I have an emergency! I question everything and everyone if I'm not comfortable with what I'm hearing. I review every contract and every paper they sign. I visit my parents, take them where they need to go, bring them their mail and the extra things they want that are located in my current/their former apartment. I watch out for their money and make sure they are legally protected by finding the best team to advise me.

I am not asking for praise, but sure appreciate a little recognition of the efforts I'm making when I get it. I'm sure you too are in this situation. You know the right thing to do, you are a good person, or you wouldn't have stepped into this role to begin with! You are there to advocate for your parents too. Hang in there! The universe will reward you for your efforts. I'm confident of that.

Pay attention to what you're seeing in your parent. Notice the differences and changes that might mean something and speak up. This bracelet is too tight and cutting off her circulation! You can't add another drug to the regimen, it will cause her blood to clot too much when mixed with the others. Can you please check for shingles? She's had this rash too many times and they just keep putting cream on it. Before you diagnose him with Alzheimer's, did you check for a pituitary infection or cancer that can be causing Alzheimer's-like symptoms? Let's check for a UTI before we put Mom in a dementia ward; this isn't normal behavior for her! Could he have hospital delirium and not really be getting worse?

As I said earlier in this book, we, the child of an adult who needs care, become the parent and take on a thousand specialties. We become mini-experts in a full range of topics. Give yourself credit for what you learn, what you share, what you do! You are versed in medical, legal, financial topics. You fix the things that break. You are a driver, a nurse, a fortune teller! You keep the calendar and run the household. You, my friend, are a marvel! Embrace your super powers!

Thank you for letting me share with you. If you now know what you didn't know you needed to know, then I am happy!

Treasure the time you have with your parents while you can. (And remember that you're modeling so your children know what to do for you!!! LOL)

Wishing you many blessings on your journey down the river. See you at the party on the shoreline when you get there!

Fern

To Contact Me:
Fern Pessin
222 Yamato Rd.
Suite 106-257
Boca Raton, FL 33431

info@IllBeRightThere.com
561.757.8237
IllBeRightThere.com

RESOURCES

NOTES

When I entered this phase of my life, I didn't know where to turn. I found terrific resources for people at all stages of the caregiving journey and I started to share them with others. You may be able to cut weeks, months, or even years off the learning curve on how to do everything by taking advantage of those already in the know. Let them help to make things easier for you!

Note: The contact info included below was current at writing of this book. Web addresses, links, and phone numbers may have since changed. Current information can be found by doing a topic or name search in your browser.

Assessment

The Alzheimer's Association has a terrific self-assessment you can do online. I think it offers something for anyone in the caregiver role, whether the person they're caring for has dementia/Alzheimer's or not. The Caregiver Self-Assessment Tool can be found in the Alzheimer's Navigator section of the Alzheimer's Association website at alz.org.

Topics include: Driving, Home Safety, Knowledge of Alzheimer's, Working with Your Doctors and Healthcare Professionals, Activities of Daily Living, Financial Planning, Symptoms and Behaviors, Care Options, Caregiver Support, and Legal Planning.

I'm sure that if you complete the surveys in some or all of the topic areas and print out your to-do lists, you will likely also receive information about local resources to help you.

Alzheimer's and Dementia

❖ Alzheimer's Association 24-hour help line—the care consultants here are compassionate, patient, and knowledgeable: alz.org; 1.800.272.3900
❖ Local Alzheimer's Association for classes and educational materials: alz.org/findus
❖ Alzheimer's Foundation of America: alzfdn.org; 866.AFA.8484; info@alzfdn.org
❖ Alzheimer's Disease Education and Referral (ADEAR) Center: 1.800.438.4380; nia.nih.gov/health/Alzheimers
❖ Alzheimer's Research and Treatment Center: 561.209.2400; researchalz.com
❖ Brain Matters Research: doing research on Alzheimer's and Dementia solutions; 561.374.8461; brainmattersresearch.com

Driving

- ❖ American Occupational Therapy Association (AOTA) provides a nationwide database of driving programs and specialists. If you cannot find a resource here, contact your local rehabilitation hospital's occupational therapy department for assistance. aota.org
- ❖ AAA (Automobile Association of America) self-assessment for driving competency for seniors: https://seniordriving.aaa.com/evaluate-your-driving-ability/professional-assessment/
- ❖ Driving services: App-based on smartphone: Uber (uber.com)/Lyft (lyft.com)
- ❖ Driving services: Search local taxis and other on-call resources for local transportation under keywords: medical transport, medical taxi
- ❖ Silver Alert Program: Affiliated with local law enforcement, the silver alert (like an amber alert for children) posts the vehicle model, color, and license tag on highway signs, and via emails and text alerts to engage the community in reporting and finding a senior who has taken the car and hasn't returned home and is likely lost. Contact your local police department for program details.

Heart and Brain

- ❖ American Heart Association: 1.800.AHA.USA.1 or 1.800.242.8721 or Outside US: +1.214.570.5978; heart.org
- ❖ American Stroke Association: 1.888.4.STROKE (1.888.478.7653); http://strokeassociation.org

Emergency

- ❖ Red Cross: Local classes in First Aid, CPR, and AED: redcross.org
- ❖ FEMA: Federal Emergency Management Agency: fema.gov

Medical: Physical Body, Mobility

- ❖ Administration for Community Living: created around the fundamental principle that older adults and people with disabilities of all ages should be able to live where they choose, with the people they choose, and with the ability to participate fully in their communities. acl.gov/
- ❖ Clinical Trials: clinicaltrials.gov/ Offers nationwide searchable listings of local physicians, drug companies, and hospitals offering clinical trials. Trials offer free medical care and drugs. Get started here, but there are likely many trials that are not in this database.
- ❖ Cancer Center information: cancer.gov or 1.800.4.CANCER (1.800.422.6237)
- ❖ Medline Plus—reliable health information: medlineplus.gov

❖ NIA: National Institute on Aging; nia.nih.gov

❖ Centers for Disease Control (CDC)—cdc.gov/vaccines/adults/index.html for more information on adult vaccines.

❖ Johns Hopkins Medicine on Prevention Guidelines: hopkinsmedicine.org/healthlibrary/conditions

Caregiver Support

❖ AARP Membership: Magazine, website, discounts, many resources on latest research and tools; AARP.org; 1.888.OUR.AARP

❖ AARP Foundation: 1.800.775.6776; aarpgift.org—Information on estate planning and legacy issues

❖ Alzheimer's Care Resource Center: Resources for caregivers; based in Florida. 561.588.4545; info@alzpb.org; alzheimerscareresourcecenter.com

❖ Caregiver.com: They host local conferences and events that are free to caregivers and there's a free webzine with great info

❖ Fearless Caregiver events: caregiver.com/conference

❖ Home Health Aide Schools: Search by city and state on the web

❖ National Alliance for Caregiving (NAC): A wonderful resource group that offers many programs; caregiving.org/

❖ Powerful Tools for Caregivers workshops offered nationally; 503.719.6980; mail@powerfultoolsforcaregivers.org; powerfultoolsforcaregivers.org

Services

❖ Adult Day Care Centers: Caring.com: caring.com/senior-living/adult-day-care to find local adult day centers—often nonprofits have sliding scale fees

❖ Caring.com directory of Area Agency for Aging or Elder Advisory Agency in your area caring.com/local/area-agency-on-aging. Talk to a Family Advisor toll-free: 1.800.973.1540

❖ Discussion groups: Foreign Policy Association fpa.org or Socrates Club: Local Socrates Clubs—people meet to discuss current events (usually at a library or book stores). No national organizing body.

❖ Eldercare Locator: 1.800.677.1116; eldercare.acl.gov/Public/Index.aspx

❖ Family Caregiver Alliance: 1.800.445.8106; caregiver.org

❖ Legal Aid Society of your community: Legal aid provides legal assistance to people unable to afford legal representation and access to the court system.

❖ Louis and Anne Green Memory & Wellness Center; Boca Raton, FL; 561.297.0502; nursing.fau.edu/outreach/memory-and-wellness-center/

❖ National Family Caregivers Association: 202.454.3970; thefamilycaregiver.org

❖ Search local JCC and YM/YWCA for classes and resources for mind and body, pools, day trips.

❖ Senior Community Centers: National Council on Aging offers a national directory of accredited senior day programs. These programs offer activities during the day to keep active seniors engaged to keep mind working, social skills intact, avoid boredom and depression.

❖ Senior Exercise Classes: See Senior Community Centers and/or search for local area senior exercise classes/programs.

❖ Veterans Administration (VA): va.gov; facebook.com/VeteransAffairs; 1.844.698.2311

Abuse and Fraud

❖ Report suspected elder abuse: 1.800.96.ABUSE (1.800.962.2873)

❖ Credit Card Fraud alert on all accounts: Equifax: 1.800.525.6285/ Experian: 888.397.3742/ TransUnion: 1.800.680.7289

❖ Federal Trade Commission [FTC] (for financial fraud): 877.438.4338 or 877.FTC.HELP (877.382.4357)

❖ Get annual credit report updates: annualcreditreport.com/index.action

❖ Food and Drug Administration [FDA] (for drug, vitamins, and medical device information/ fraud): fda.gov or 888.463.6332

❖ Social Security: If you need to report a death or apply for benefits, call 1.800.772.1213 (TTY 1.800.325.0778). View SSA.gov (Social Security Administration) for any questions you might have.

❖ WikiHow has a description of how to do a criminal background check: wikihow.com/ Do-a-Criminal-Background-Check.

Helpful Websites

Resources quoted or mentioned within the text:

❖ AgingWithDignity.org—articles and resources for people aging

❖ AllLaw.com—information about legal issues

❖ APlaceForMom.com—the nation's largest free senior care referral service; 866.518.0936

(To help you find local assistance: *There are many names used to describe Assisted Living **Referral Services** such as: **Senior** Housing Advisors, Assisted Living Locators, and Placement Management **Services**.*)

❖ Care.com—information and resources for caring for someone and for self

❖ Caregiver.com—information and resources on being a caregiver

❖ Caregiving.org—information and resources on being a caregiver

- Caringbridge.com—website for friends and family to check on the health status of someone without having to intrude on busy caregivers
- Craigslist.com—promote garage sales, sell household items, find help with innumerable tasks, hire people
- DailyCaring.com—website for friends and family to check on the health status of someone without having to intrude on busy caregivers
- Etsy.com—purchase business cards to communicate your parent's status, sell household items, earn income by selling craft items while caring for parents
- Everplans.com—funeral and death information
- FindLaw.com—information about legal issues
- FreeConferenceCall.com—group video and phone call service to bring in multiple people
- GoGoGrandparent.com—concierge service that manages Uber/Lyft rides for non-tech seniors and hangs with them through the whole ride; communicates with family.
- iPhone FaceTime (https://support.apple.com/en-us/HT209022)—group video and phone call service to bring in multiple people using Apple phones
- JustAnswer.com—ask questions and experts offer answers
- LawDepot.com—find legal forms
- Legalzoom.com—lawyers available to answer questions or review legal documents for modest fees
- MotleyFool.com—advisory information for investments
- NerdWallet.com—help with tech questions
- NoLo.com—legal articles and information, legal forms and software purchases, search for local lawyers
- Posthope.org—websites for connecting people in times of need, patient websites to post updates
- RocketLawyer.com—lawyers on call for a fee to review documents or answer questions
- Snapfish.com—group photo sharing and printing service, creating commemoratives and photo albums
- Shutterfly.com—image publishing service, transferring images to digital medium, creating commemoratives and photo albums
- Vistaprint.com—design and order custom printed marketing materials, signage, and photo commemoratives (calendars, mugs, car magnets, etc.); create business cards describing your parent's health status
- Webmd.com—ask medical questions, research medical symptoms, read articles on medical conditions
- WikiHow.com—ask how to do anything, articles on practical do-it-yourself projects
- WongBakerFaces.org—Wong Baker Faces Foundation: resources for helping and tracking issues around pain management; 405.608.8083; info@WongBakerFACES.org
- Zazzle.com—create (or purchase pre-designed) custom business cards to describe parent's health status
- Zoom.us—video conferencing for groups

Tools and Devices

Medical alert and fall detection:

- ADT Health: 1.800.276.0890
- Apple Watch: apple.com
- Medical Alert: 1.800.906.0872; medicalalert.com
- Medical Guardian: 877.638.4622
- MyNotifi.com: 1.800.541.1420
- Search for Medical Alert system and you'll find many comparison charts and links to websites

Apps:

- Apple Pay
- mSecure (password keeper)
- PayPal
- RememberItNow.com—an online and mobile app personal health journal to share with health-care providers and track daily health status
- TimeMaster—time tracker to track how many hours of caregiving you are providing or a paid worker is completing
- Wallet—secure information for paying at checkout (credit cards, ATM cards, frequent user program numbers, etc.)

Recommended Books and Materials

- *The Alzheimer's Health Care Handbook: How to Get the Best Medical Care for Your Relative with Alzheimer's Disease, In and Out of the Hospital* (2003) by Mary Mittleman and Cynthia Epstein.
- *Behaviors (How to Respond When Dementia Causes Unpredictable Behaviors)* Alzheimer's Association.
- *The Caregiver Helpbook: Powerful Tools for Caregiving* (2000) by Vicki L Schmall
- *The Family Caregiver's Manual: A Practical Planning Guide to Managing the Care of Your Loved One* (2016) by David Levy.
- *The Fearless Caregiver: How to Get the Best Care for Your Loved One and Still Have a Life of Your Own* (2001) by Gary Barg.
- *The Good Caregiver: A One-of-a-Kind Compassionate Resource for Anyone Caring for an Aging Loved One* (2011) by Robert L. Kane, M.D. and Jeannine Ouellette.
- *Helping Yourself Help Others: A Book for Caregivers* (1994 and 2013) by Rosalynn Carter and Susan K. Golant.

- *Home Accessibility: 300 Tips For Making Life Easier* (2011) by Shelley Peterman Schwarz.
- *Hospitalization Happens* brochure by NIH: Distributed by Alzheimer's Disease Education and Referral Center: Email adear@nia.nih.gov to request one.
- *How to Be Smart, Successful and Organized with Your Money: For a Better Today and Tomorrow* (2016) by Judith Heft.
- *How to Care for Aging Parents, 3rd Edition: A One-Stop Resource for All Your Medical, Financial, Housing, and Emotional Issues* (2014) by Virginia Morris.
- *Is It Time to Stop Driving?* And *Is Driving Your Best Choice?* Florida Atlantic University (Louis and Anne Green Memory & Wellness Center)
- *Multiple Sclerosis: Tips and Strategies for Making Life Easier, Third Edition* (Volume 3) by Shelley Peterman Schwarz
- *Oh My God, I'm Getting Older (and So Is My Mom)* (2014) by Scott Greenberg.
- *Parkinson's Disease: 300 Tips for Making Life Easier, 2nd Edition* by Shelley Peterman Schwarz
- *Photo Organizing Made Easy: Going from Overwhelmed to Overjoyed* (2017) by Cathi Nelson.
- *Scam-Proof Your Life* (2007) by Sid Kirchheimer *(published by AARP Books/Sterling).*
- *Staying Safe brochure* from Alzheimer's Association has many great tips and advice. Free. Order one, read online, or pick one up at any Alzheimer's Association local office or event.

ACKNOWLEDGMENTS

As my mother tells me, when I was two years old, I started taking care of my infant brother, Mitchell. And, at four years old, I took on caring for our baby sister, Dawn. My mother put me in a caregiver role from the very beginning, so it seems only natural that I was destined to find myself in this role again as an adult.

Watching my dad, Artie, look after his mother and then watching my mother, Hedda, deeply mourn the loss of her mother, I learned that this is what family does. I thank my parents for modeling caregiving skills and compassionate behaviors. I am grateful to them for all the support they've given me over the years to enable me to do work that makes my heart soar.

My siblings, though they live 1,200 miles away, have been advocates, champions, and defenders, offering help in any way they can. It's not easy for them to be disconnected by distance and unable to share in the minutia of managing our parents' health and home. I thank them for giving me the flexibility, trust, and recognition to let me get done what needs to get done for our parents day to day. I also appreciate my siblings' spouses and children for being there to support Dawn and Mitch through this very emotional and sometimes challenging time in all our lives.

Members of my caregiver support groups are mentioned throughout this book. I would never have learned and could not have written anything here without them. Special thanks to the Boca Raton caregiver groups at the Volen Center and the Louis and Anne Green Memory & Wellness Center. The group leaders and participants provided me with insights, tips, contacts, and recommendations every week since I started this journey in 2016. Group leaders Michelle Cooper and Patricia Ordonez have been particularly supportive.

Most special thanks go to several women from my caregiver groups who have become my personal support network: Jodi Cantor, Jordana McCarthy, and Lilly Mayhew have been there to listen and share. Marcia Sachs and Rosemarie Falcone, I would have spent a lot more time in therapy and crying instead of laughing if it wasn't for our talks and time together!

To Rachel Paskow, Tana Flagg, Mary McCormack, and Anne Greenberg: It is amazing how you care for and love your parents and family, friends, and pets, and steer me. Thanks for sharing, listening, talking, and being my cheering section!

To the experts who offered me counsel: I am blown away by your kindness, knowledge, and patience. Judy Simon, Judy Heft, Marie Duquette, Ruthlyn Rubin, Steven Brill, and Scott M. Solkoff—keep on doing the amazing work you're doing! You make a huge difference!

To Sandra Grace Brooks, you are my heart and soul. Without your insights and foresight, and our late-night healing sessions, I would not have made it through some of the rougher times. Helping me to heal myself is allowing me to reach out into the world and help others. You are a blessing!

Special thanks to the publishing team at Publish Your Purpose Press. Niki Garcia and Karen Ang are marvelous (and patient!). Mark Gibson gets me pumped up and dreaming big! Jenn T. Grace, publisher, and Heather B. Habelka, editor, you have provided the encouragement, motivation, and guidance to birth this book baby into the world, and I could never have done this without you! Your vision for the world inspires me daily.

I am truly blessed! I thank the universe for providing guidance to lead me onto this path.

CPSIA information can be obtained
at www.ICGtesting.com
Printed in the USA
BVHW021444220719
554058BV00014B/819/P

9 781946 384690